CW00539618

BEFORE THE HARVEST

August 1914

A Novel
by
Antony Bird

Antony Bird

To A.W. Bird, who was awarded the '1914 Star'

ANTONY BIRD PUBLICATIONS
Strettington House, Strettington, Chichester, West Sussex, PO18 0LA

First published in 2012

British Library Cataloguing in Publication Data
A catalogue record of this book is available from the British Library

ISBN : 978-0-907319-10-8

Published by Antony Bird Publications in association with:
Bonner Publications
The Old Wash House, King Street, Arundel, West Sussex, BN18 9BW
www.bonnerpublications.com

Printed and bound in the UK by CPI Group (UK) Ltd.

Contents

Acknowledgements

I have drawn heavily on Lieutenant-General Sir Tom Bridges' Memoir, *Alarms and Excursions*, (Longmans, 1938), and Frank Richards' *Old Soldiers Never Die*, (Faber and Faber, 1933). *The Great War Diaries of Brigadier General Alexander Johnstone,* Astill (ed) (Pen and Sword, 2007), has been the main source for Captain Henry Johnson. I have used *Le Cateau 26 August 1914* by Cave and Sheldon, (Pen and Sword 2008) as a source as well as my own *Gentlemen, We Will stand and Fight, Le Cateau, August 26 1914* (Crowood, 2008). Captain J.C. Dunn's book *The War the Infantry Knew* (King Ltd, 1938) remains to my mind the best book on the infantry fighting of the Great War and is a primary source for this novel. *The War Diary of Captain Penrose*, published in the Petworth Society Magazine in June 2004, pointed out to me by Mr. Brian Rich, and *The Churcherian*, the magazine of Churchers College, published throughout the war, have been useful as a source for Lieutenant Penfold. Nigel Hamilton's *Monty, The Making of a General* (London, 1981) is invaluable, but surprisingly sketchy on the events of August 1914.

I am also indebted, for various and separate reasons, to Dr. Philip Robson; Colonel JC Richardson RAMC; Susie Richardson; my wife Judie; my eldest daughter Dr. Lucy Bird; my brother Nick Bird RUSI; my father Tom Bird DSO, MC and Bar, Chevalier de Legion d'Honeur; Ms. Rosie Apponyi; Rachel Timlick; Mr. John Dennis and Mr. Simon Brett.

Antony Bird

Joint editor, *Eyewitness to War*, (Summersdale Press, 2006)
Author, *Gentlemen, We Will Stand and Fight. Le Cateau 1914*.
(Crowood, 2008)

Chapter 1

24th August: Lieutenant Penfold

The train was moving at no more than a fast walking pace and four young officers of the 1st Battalion the Royal Warwickshire Regiment, all subalterns, were playing a desultory game of bridge, using a valise as a makeshift table. Their Burberrys, their caps and their swords, which among other accoutrements marked them out as officers, lay on the overhead luggage racks. It had been the sharpening of the swords by the armourers at Shorncliffe two days ago that had brought home to the officers the stark fact that they were going off to war.

At least it was more comfortable in their carriage up by the engine than in the twenty-five wagons behind, the men forty to a wagon, a stencilled sign on each wagon - 'Hommes 40/ Chevaux 8' - that the men for some reason had found excessively droll. The train had just pulled out of St. Quentin station and was heading for Le Cateau. It was the 24th August 1914. They had landed at Boulogne only the day before, although the excitement and novelty of their passage from Southampton made it seem to them longer ago. Although they did not know it, they had landed on the day that British troops were going into action on the continent of Europe for the first time since the battle of Waterloo nearly a hundred years before.

The train clanked to a stop. Grey steam hissed from the engine's boiler.

Stephen Penfold was, at twenty-four, the oldest of the four card players, the other three being not long out of Sandhurst. He said, to no-one in particular,

'Do you think we should try and find out what's going on?'

'What, and get left behind when the train starts up again?' This was

Stephenson, who had actually been to France before, with his parents, which seemed to give him an advantage as far as knowledge of French customs were concerned. It was rumoured in the Mess that he had 'done things' with a mademoiselle, but exactly what was never clear. He had been to Rugby School which also gave him a certain cachet and he encouraged the rumour that Rupert Brooke was not unknown to him. He got out his pipe and filled it with Raven Mixture, as smoked by Caruthers of the FO. His nickname in the Mess, 'Puffing Billy', was partly due to his pipe smoking habit and partly due to the eponymous Rocket. Christian names were not normally used in the Mess between officers of the same rank; it was a sort of quirk of the Regiment. Penfold didn't have a nick-name. He wasn't the physical type to attract names like Tubby and the name Penfold didn't lend itself to semi-humorous monikers. No-one called him 'Nibs' as far as he knew.

'If you ask me it is all because the French railway company gets paid by the hour and they are taking their time to suit themselves'. The voice this time was that of Lieutenant Bernard Montgomery, not one of the card players. For 'Monty' this counted as some sort of joke. He had been reading a manual of military law in the corner of the compartment. Penfold was going to tease him about the way he said 'Fwench wailways', but couldn't be bothered. It was too hot. He knew that Monty's middle name was Law, but jokes about names were not the done thing. Monty was twenty-seven years old, like Penfold the son of a clergyman, whose family name had Norman origins. Monty took the view that people with Norman names made better soldiers than those with Saxon names, although he was prepared to make an exception for the Highlander.

'I'll tell you one thing though', went on Montgomery addressing the carriage as a whole, 'something that's been bothering me for some time now. And that's the number of military wagons carrying supplies like tents, bicycles, RAMC field kit, all going south. I mean, aren't we meant to be pushing north?' It was typical of him to be precise about the type of kit. 'No doubt we will find out what's going on when we get to Le Cateau. But I wonder what those men are doing digging in that stubble-field over there.' He buried his beaky nose back in his manual. He would have liked to stretch out and do some press-ups, but there was no room between the seats. The train started up again with a jolt.

Watkins, looking down at his cards, announced 'Two no trumps', but the other players had lost interest in the game. He folded up the valise and put the cards away.

Penfold looked out of the open window, the glass having been lowered and held by its leather belt fixed to a brass stud. The countryside was not unlike the downland around Petworth where he had grown up, large fields with stooks of corn piled ready for the thresher. What few cattle he could see were tethered or hobbled and kept close to the farms. There were fields of root crops, sugar-beet by the look of it, still in leaf. Penfold had applied to the Royal Warwickshire Regiment after Sandhurst partly to escape the stifling familiarity of Sussex life, but he had made them his new home. They were almost his family now, Stephenson and 'Monty' and, another of the card-players, Watkins. Watkins had only joined the Battalion from Sandhurst two months ago and was still a bit of an enigma. He was from neither an Army family nor a recognisable social type. His father was rumoured to be 'something in phosphates', whatever that meant. He seemed to have no trouble paying his Mess bills, unlike Penfold who dreaded the monthly account. Monty didn't have any trouble paying his bills since he neither smoked nor drank; perhaps because he lacked these outlets, and didn't hunt, at Sandhurst he had been more than exuberant at the end of term indoor rugby game played with the Mess silver. Even by the standards of the other subalterns Monty's tackling was considered a bit on the rough side. On night exercises his night vision was considered exceptional and was put down to his habit of eating raw vegetables.

At Sandhurst Penfold had been impressed with the Warwick's cap badge, an antelope, which reminded him of the deer in Petworth Park. The fact that as the 6th Foot they were among the oldest of the line regiments, formed in 1674, was a bonus. The six of Diamonds at cards was called a Warwick, another of those old Regular Army little jokes which appealed to him. When they used the term playing Bridge it gave Penfold the feeling of belonging to a secret society. So the Warwicks it had to be.

Riding to hounds with the Leconfield Hunt, sometimes as far as Charlton and East Dean from the meet at Petworth, gave him a keen eye for country. Looking out of the train window now at the Picardy landscape he found himself wondering about the military possibilities of the landscape, as if on a tactical exercise. That copse over there could provide shelter for a platoon, with good fields of fire to the north. That hill could provide a useful reverse slope. That sunken lane could provide useful shelter from artillery.

At Le Cateau all was bustle and whistles, the shouting of orders and the banging of carriage doors and men eagerly jumping down from their open-sided wagons, where they had sat with their legs dangling over the sides. They carried their rifles slung over their shoulders and helped each other with their packs, handing them down from the wagons, each one marked with the number of its owner. Staff officers appeared with map cases, some of which contained maps of Belgium but none of France, at least not south of Le Cateau. The adjutant sent an officer off to Brigade in search of maps of Le Cateau and Picardy. Clearly, there were those in England who had foreseen the Battalion detraining in Belgium; it was Belgium after all that the BEF was supposed to be liberating.

The train was too long for the platform which threw the staff officers into a frenzy, trying to get the railway staff to organise ramps to get the horses off safely. The men were formed up in their four companies and ordered to parade out in front of the station. An airplane, a Taube, appeared overhead, the black crosses on the undersides of its wings clearly visible even though it must have been at least at 6000 feet. Penfold's platoon, thirty-five men in B Company, who he was glad to see were all present and correct, loosed off a few rounds at it, without permission. It was their first shots of the war and it all seemed harmless enough. Penfold told Sergeant Fox to stand the men easy and wait for orders. He found Stephenson.

Stephenson was puffed up with self-importance. His little rather immature moustache held a few drops of moisture, which glistened in the afternoon sun, and his pipe was clamped in his teeth.

'I say Penfold, I've just found out from the MO, who's got it from the Colonel, that there's been the most terrific battle up in Belgium at a place called Mons and our whole army is retiring, the froggies are running away on our right and we're to go up, stop the rot and let the Mons troops through. At a place called Solesmes. And that a guardian angel appeared in the sky above Mons who saved our army. As soon as the wagons are loaded up and the horses hitched we're off. Orders from Sir John himself.'

Just then Penfold's groom, Private Lumley, appeared with Charlie, the mare Penfold had brought out with him from Sussex, the army paying his father, the Vicar of Petworth, £70. Good money and the vet had passed her as fit for a campaign in France. He had entered her two years running in the annual point-to point at Cowdray Park and had finished both times, although not in the first four. Penfold was a rarity among his fellow subalterns in having his own mount. He swelled up with pride. He was going to mount up, booted and spurred, with his sword at his side in its scabbard, and led his platoon through the streets of this town out towards the enemy, to the cheering of the local people who would be so impressed with the military efficiency of his battalion. He would show these froggies how it's done! All his life had been leading up to this moment.

The French infantry might look impressive in their red trousers and their cavalry in their breastplates and plumage, but for real soldiers you can't beat a British Tommy and a Warwickshireman at that. The men will march to the band, that'll put a jaunt to their step. But firing at the Taube? Shouldn't the men have asked permission to fire?

He noticed a civilian of about his age by the entrance to the station, a notebook in his hand and a Panama on his head. A spy wouldn't make himself so obvious, surely? Hang on, he's coming this way. 'Moore of *The Times*' he announced, 'Can I have a word?'

'I'm afraid I can't tell you anything; I've only just got here. But I can tell your readers that when we get to the boche we're going to stop them, not just the Warwicks I mean, we've got the whole of General Snow's 4th Division here to do the job'. Moore just nodded and made a note in his reporter's notebook.

The Battalion was now forming up, all one thousand of them, give or take, at full strength now that the Reservists were back with the colours. The men were loaded up with full packs, entrenching tools, rifles at the slope and full pouches on their webbing; a 60lb burden, including their great-coats. The sergeants bustled about inspecting the men's' kit, adjusting the webbing, almost fatherly towards the young soldiers. Sergeant Fox announced to Lieutenant Penfold's platoon, 'Kitchener wants his next hundred thousand, but he's already got you lovely lot, so look sharp and we'll show these good French people what we're made of. Attention on parade for the Company Commander! ATTEN-SHUN!'

Penfold's Company Commander, Major Haddow, rode up and issued orders to the subalterns that the Battalion would march in four columns, by companies, north-west towards Solesmes and rest after one hour; the Battalion to shelter the 3rd Division troops as they came through to the new line to the west of Le Cateau. They were to find billets in Solesmes tonight if they were lucky. So that was what Monty was seeing out of the train window: the trenches for the new line being dug. Penfold had faith in the top brass; no doubt they were leading the Germans into a trap. Haddow then spoke to the Company, leaning forward in his saddle:

'We have come here to fight, and for no other reason. We shall meet the enemy very soon. We will fight him with our guns, our rifles and if need be with our fists. There will be no surrender.'

Orders for the march barked out and the whole Battalion set off, the four companies separated by their mounted majors, the junior officers taking up station on the flanks, the transport bringing up the rear; the whole column taking up the best part of a mile of road-space.

As they left the town on the Roman road, which lay in a cutting, Penfold noticed old men and young boys walking back from the fields with shovels over their shoulders, led by a mounted British staff officer with red tabs on his collar; Monty's trench-diggers. Penfold, riding alongside his platoon, acknowledged the staff officer with a salute of his gloved hand. They crossed the St. Quentin road, a meeting point of two Roman roads.

They were marching now on the cobbles of the Roman road to Cambrai, although it was easier to let Charlie walk on the soft verge, easier on her feet that is. Charlie seemed glad to be out again, after the confines of the sea crossing and the seven hour train journey. The poplars were forming shadows across the road and the men beginning to sing something to the tune of *The Girl I Left Behind Me*. Penfold made out the words:

'Oh we don't give a fuck
For old von Kluck
An' all his fucking army'.

They repeated it endlessly, marching in time to the rhythm of the tune.

He wondered what his father would think of it. It was not exactly Gilbert and Sullivan. Penfold didn't of course sing along himself.

Officers didn't. Did the men think of him as a prude, because his father was a vicar? To be truthful, he didn't really know what the men thought of him, which if he admitted it to himself, gave him moments of queasiness. Before the army he had known working people, but most of them were servants on the vast Petworth estate belonging to the Egremont family. And at Churchers College in Petersfield there had been gardeners and the like. But his men were mostly Birmingham men, men who had known the grime of a workshop. Penfold prided himself on being a Gentleman, which could always count in the great scheme of things, even if, as he had to admit, Churchers was a very minor Public School. He would write some letters when he had the time, to his father and Bondie his old headmaster. He would tell them that the important thing was to play the game and play fair, unlike the boche, as the French call them, who don't know cricket and who have no sense of right and wrong and no sense of honour. No sense of humour either when you thought about it. But he was a card, that Kaiser, no doubt about it. They ought to put him in the music halls when the war is over; it would be sure to get a laugh. And then he could be pelted with rotten apples - except that would be too good for him.

The Major's talk about fighting the Hun with our fists; presumably he was not talking literally? Did he just mean to encourage an aggressive spirit among the men?

They were getting in to the outskirts of Neuvilly, having turned off the Roman road two miles back. The Battalion was now spread out over a mile of road, march discipline already getting a bit loose, the pack-straps already now rubbing flesh off shoulders. Old ladies dressed in black seemed to be the main inhabitants, to the obvious disappointment of the men. An old man in work clothes shouted 'Vive l'Angleterre!' One of the old crones wanted to give Sergeant Fox a rosary. Fox was a good Methodist. Penfold watched him accept the beads and put them round his neck. For Fox, a Methodist abstainer from the demon drink, to accept a

Roman Catholic symbol was a sight that wouldn't have been seen at home.

Penfold was fascinated in all around him and found that he was talking to himself. If that farmer chap over there offers wine, I'm going to order the men to leave it alone. I mean, the men are not used to it, and it's only four o'clock. Will they hold it against me? Anyway, the cookers will be up at Solesmes before long and there will be tea and bully and biscuit and jam.

Penfold watched some of his men break ranks and move towards a gaggle of girls at the water-pump. Some of the girls wore clogs and bonnets like their mothers but others were bare-headed and sported pretty lace around their collars. They had a basket of apples. Sergeant Fox came up to Penfold, grinning:

'Sir, the men would like to know how to say 'give us a kiss' in French.

Penfold didn't know. He wondered whether the question amounted to insubordination. Stephenson might know that sort of thing. He merely said,

'Just tell the men to march on, Sarn't; but let them have five minutes for a smoke.'

So they could sing along to the word 'fuck' but they couldn't say 'kiss' in French. He wondered whether German soldiers marched along singing ribald songs about Sir John French. Penfold remembered Kitchener's Message to the Troops in which he had enjoined them to 'resist temptations, both in wine and women'. But Penfold feared the men's scorn if he should lecture them on matters of decorum. Such things were better left to sergeants to deal with. He wasn't quite sure whether the Message had the status of an order to the troops of the BEF, or was merely advice on how to deport themselves.

Sergeant Fox wanted to ask another question. 'Mr. Penfold, the men have asked whether it is proper to march at Eyes Right when they pass a statue of Christ on the Cross.' Penfold again suspected insubordination, but merely said,' I don't think that will be necessary, Sarn't.'

The march was resumed, the men got back into formation with the easy familiarity born of years of drill; this is what they were used to, this is after all what an army did: march. But this time they were part, a small part, of a division going to war, Kitchener having decided that he could spare the 4th Division from its home defence duties.

A plane was flying over them, going north, this time with RFC markings, and the men gave a cheer, one of the more knowledgeable ones saying that it was a two-seater Avro scout plane made in Birmingham, where his father worked. To Penfold it looked a frail and vulnerable little machine but he envied the pilot his god-like status, inhabiting the heavens rather than the earth. No bullets could touch him there.

Solesmes, a town about the size of Petworth, turned out to be a scene of confusion to say the least, with what must have been the entire population thronging the streets to welcome the new arrivals. A young girl reached up to Penfold with a flower in her hand; he made out the words 'sale Boches', but urged Charlie on towards the centre of town where he knew they would form up, all one thousand of the Warwickshire. There was no sign of the Mons troops yet, but then they would be still coming down from the north, probably somewhere around Bavai by now. What there was, was French troops, and far too many of them. They were Territorials, that much he could tell, and a pretty poor show they made, just sort of milling about in the side streets with no sign of any officers. And that troop of French cavalry, Cuirassiers he supposed from their breastplates, the shiny metal covered with a sort of brown gauze, what direction were they going in?

A fine sight though with their plumed helmets, but what use are they going to be when the German machine guns get into action, got up like peacocks as they are? Their breast-plates made useful frying pans in the Peninsula, so it was said. And Saint Joan fought without the plumage, dressed severely, like a man-child, her young breasts flattened and squashed by the breast-plate of righteousness, her unsullied loins dressed in young goat leather. Kid-clad. And put to death for her dress-choice. But dressed to kill. She would fight for Lorraine now by God. Smite the Hun with the sword of honour. Perhaps it was her as the Angel of Mons, now on the side of the English, with her burnished sword held aloft. Or Queen Bess, another virgin iron-clad warrior with the heart and stomach of a King. Queen Bess with the bowmen of Old England by her side.

How are we going to get our lot through here with these Frenchies blocking the road? And here comes a convoy of refugee wagons led by a priest in an open Renault. Curious how the men at the reins seem to be dressed in their Sunday suits, as if going to mass or trying to make a good impression. Impress the Germans? With their dress-choice? The boche will be more impressed by the way they clog up our lines of communication, probably a fiendish Hunnish plot. And they've brought a cow with them, tethered to the back. Get them out to the road south, that's all we can do. But they're having a good look round at all our equipment. How many are Flemish with their dubious Germanic antecedents?

The Battalion was now filling up a large open space, with a statue of a mounted knight in the middle of it. A small boy had climbed up on to the horse and was sitting astride it, holding his arms around the armoured body of the unknown knight. Penfold wondered how he had managed to get up there. The noise of two thousand boots and a hundred horse-shoes on the cobbled surface was like thunder. The townspeople were cheering like a football crowd, with cries of ''ip, 'ip, 'oorah' audible above the din. Union Jacks were hanging out of the windows on the upper floors of the buildings. Penfold thought of how these flags, so hastily assembled from God knows where, would have to be equally quickly hidden under floor-boards when the Hun arrived the day after tomorrow. It was clear that these people had not yet grasped that the BEF was hell-bent on getting away to the south.

Major Haddow rode up. His face was brick-red.

'Mr. Penfold, if you please, the billeting officers will be round shortly, keep your men fell in. The cookers will be here soon. 12 Brigade are to go up on picket duty, or rather three Battalions, we and the whole of 10 Brigade are to stay as town troops. Get these civilians to move on as quickly as possible. When the Mons troops are safely through tomorrow we are to go south-west and take up positions near Haucourt before dawn on the 26th, at the latest. That will mean a night-march. Consult your map. Please inform Mr. Stephenson, Mr. Montgomery and Mr. Watkins. Parade here at 5.30 a.m. Carry on.'

Major Haddow, conscientious to a fault, who always had his copy of the Manual of Infantry Training within reach, was no barrack–room lawyer; he had publicly told his fellow-officers on the boat coming across the channel that it was his greatest wish to shoot, with his own weapon, a German officer. All the officers had been quite shocked. The prospect of being killed or killing the enemy, while it was in the forefront of everyone's mind, especially in the last three weeks, was never actually referred to in so many words in the Mess.

'Yes, Gerald, Sir'. He omitted to say that he didn't actually have a map. Platoon commanders didn't have maps; wasn't the Major meant to know this? Should he find the adjutant and put in a request for one?

Penfold still had a difficulty with the Regimental forms of address. No Christian names between officers of the same rank, but he was to call the Major 'Gerald'. The Colonel was 'Colonel' or 'Sir' but he was 'Mr. Penfold'.

'Oh, and Mr. Penfold, one more thing. This talk among the men of guardian angels. Smacks of superstition. The way to deal with the boche is with a well-sited Vickers and a platoon of infantry with full magazines, not angels in the sky. Watch out for any defeatism in the ranks. And remember: the word is 'Retirement' not 'Retreat'.

'Yes, Gerald,'

The Major rode off. The crowd of townspeople began to drift off, presumably back to their homes, now that darkness was falling.

Penfold called out to the ever-present Sergeant. Fox, 'Sarn't!'

He repeated the orders, adding an unnecessary rider that the men were not free to explore the town and its dubious attractions. The platoon fell out; most of them sat down on the cobbles, got out their cigarettes and pipes, pushed back their caps, leant against their packs, passed round their water bottles and looked around. The cookers would arrive soon. The place was a sea of khaki, wreathed in tobacco smoke. Sergeant Fox said, as if in a parody of a stage sergeant-major,

'Mr. Penfold, Sir, I shall see that the young uns are tucked up nice and cosy in their billet, a nice comfy barn next to the corn exchange. The cookers might even manage a nice cup of cocoa. But it's some of the Reservists I'm worried about; it's the new boots that are hard on their feet. But I won't be talking to them of any angels, unless I have it on good authority from Sir John himself, angels not being mentioned in the Manual of Infantry Training as far as I can recollect, Mr. Penfold. All present and correct at any rate, except for one man, name of Prescott, who is not fit for marching and not for much else. A Reservist and a barman in civilian life.'

'Very good, Sarn't, carry on. Tell Prescott we can't make exceptions. But try and get the MO to have a look at him.'

Penfold passed the order on to his fellow subalterns. They parted company with a 'good night, old chap', before they turned in for the last good sleep they were going to get for many a night, confident that the sergeants and NCOs were more than capable of getting the men back on parade by dawn tomorrow.

It was now 10.00 p.m. Lumley took Charlie off to wherever grooms go in search of fodder, always a mystery to Penfold. Not a bad first day in

France all told; at least they had marched toward the enemy who must be fairly close now. None of the men in his platoon had fallen out on the march. He must remember to inspect the men's' feet before tomorrow's start. And to make sure that they didn't dump their hated entrenching tools when no-one was looking. The men hate digging and they must be watched over. Parade in the square at 05.30 hours tomorrow.

Penfold found his billet, a terraced house, the door marked with chalk with his billet number, and opening at once when he turned the handle. In the front room the good people had put out a pitcher of drinking water, a ewer, a towel, a glass and some cheese. He assumed that his hosts were upstairs, and even now not wanting to alter their bed-time. A candle was burning in the fire-grate, in front of which a piss-pot had been decorously placed. Will have to find the lavatory in the morning. He had a nibble of the cheese, a sort of cheddar, and then remembered his mother's words about cheese and nightmares. He removed his Sam Browne, his tunic, boots and britches and folded them neatly on the only chair. He removed his socks and bathed his feet, using the towel as a face-cloth. He placed his gloves in his cap, took the loaded Webley from its holster and arranged it and the sword neatly on the floor by the cot-bed. Then he remembered that his valise, with all his personal kit, was on one of the wagons with the transport. So, no toothbrush and tooth-powder, and no chance of a shave. Damn. Must have a word about this with Lumley in the morning. He rinsed his mouth out with the water from the jug. He blew out the candle and got straight into the makeshift bed and drifted into sleep….

The main thing when we do come up against the Hun is not to show fear in front of the men. An Englishman does not run away. He didn't run away at Waterloo and he didn't run away at Agincourt.

And he realised that it was not so much fear itself that was his enemy but rather the fear of fear; and that was a different thing altogether, although not a subject that had ever come up for discussion among his fellow-officers. There was much that remained unspoken in the Mess.

Penfold knew enough history to know that both those battles were fought in this part of France. Old Bondie had taught them well at Churchers. Penfold knew the dates of the Kings and Queens of England; he could ride to hounds across country; he could even quote large chunks of Mr. Sponge's Sporting Tour; he could play a decent game of Auction Bridge; he was familiar with 'Infantry Training 1914'; he knew that the British Empire would triumph over its enemies and he knew that his Redeemer liveth. He was heartily glad to be a part of the Expeditionary Force, but there was a nagging doubt in his mind whether or not he should have been issued with a map. He didn't really know where the Belgian/French border lay. But then he thought it didn't matter much anyway; he would be on his way south tomorrow night and the next occupant of this little room would be German.

As Penfold lay in the cot-bed in the front room of the terrace house, knowing that Lumley, his batman as well as his groom, would wake him with a cup of tea well before 5.00 a.m., the occupants still upstairs, he could hear intermittent small arms fire in the north. That'll be 12 Brigade, he thought. *Where ignorant armies clash by night*, he could remember that bit of poetry by Arnold from Bondie's English lessons. Perhaps Lumley would remember to bring his toothbrush with the tea. And maybe his shaving kit as well. His lips mouthed the words 'Oh God make me brave', as he went to sleep.

Chapter 2

25th August: Private Edwards

Private Frank Edwards of the 2nd Royal Welch Fusiliers, 19 Brigade, was hot, tired, thirsty and his feet hurt. He knew when they were at Amiens as Line of Communication (LOC) troops with the rest of 19 Brigade that it was too good to last. That was a cushy number and no mistake; hanging around the station, trying to look useful as trains passed through on the way up to Mauberge. Plenty of opportunities for a drink of vin blanc at the bars around the main Place. There had been a big to-do when Lieutenant-General Grierson died in his railway carriage just out of Amiens. He was on his way up to Le Cateau when he had a heart attack. Edwards could see right away when he got a look at him that he wasn't a fit man, especially when his ADC had to help him and his twenty stone bulk into the train. The old boy could hardly fit himself through the carriage door.

The French girls weren't all that different from girls in Gibraltar or Jhansi for that matter. There were always girls of an easy virtue to be had near the barracks. The thing was not to get them het up; easy does it, a couple of drinks, or a few annas to the nigger pimp in the case of Jhansi, and Bob's your uncle, except that the corporals would get the first bite of the cherry when the men stood in line. The funny thing was that the froggie for lie together sounded like his favourite word 'cushy'. Would you 'cushy' with me seemed to get the message across. There was Arlene in the back of that bar in the Place des Armes who wore nothing under her dress. Did all froggie girls do that? Once he'd got in there there was no stopping her, perched on the edge of a table and both of them grinding away like troopers, she knew just how to tilt her perky little mid-riff for easy access to the lovely busy pink mousehole. Talk about the Entente Cordiale, this was a red-hot cordiale all right.

But now they'd been up to Valenciennes, had seen a bit of shelling on the canal, but ever since then it had been go like hell with bayonets fixed down through Solesmes, the full FMO, and now on the road for Le Cateau; no sleep for the last three days and nights to speak of. The other side of Solesmes his mate Buffy started jabbering away in Hindustani as he staggered along, making no sense at all, gabbing on about pahni, wandered off into a farmyard, lay down in the shit, refused to get up and had to be put onto a wagon. The doctor, Captain Dunn, was even called over to have a look at him. Well, everyone knows about the Angel of Mons and Buffy was seeing angels or something but he wasn't seeing sense that's for sure. He was marked down as a casualty but he was as right as rain after a couple of hours riding on a wagon. It was a case of 'soldier on, chum,' but he was allowed to leave his pack on a wagon. A staff officer, a major, had then come riding up, not far north of Solesmes, and told Edwards and the rest of his platoon, addressing the officer, the one they called Four Eyes on account of his specs, but whose name was actually Bosanquet, to take his platoon up that slope, take up a position in the trees and form an outpost. And do what exactly? Stop old von Kluck himself if he should happen to ride by? Well, they stayed there a couple of hours and then scarpered, with nothing more to worry them than the sound of firing to the northeast, field guns and musketry mixed up which must mean a fight of some sort. As it was they had had a fuck of a job catching up with their Battalion in the line of retreating men, coming across the Battalion as if by chance in the square in Solesmes, where they had got held up by the crowds and the crush of refugees.

The trouble was that they were in double-trouble; couldn't go anywhere but away from the fritzes and couldn't leave anything behind to lighten the load because if you did that you'd never see it again. They even had to carry their great-coats, rolled up of course, and the officers could inspect the kit at any time. No time to stop for anything more than a piss or a quick shit, and if you were lucky and the officer wasn't looking, an apple from a nearby orchard. When the Battalion did halt for a ten minute rest it was a devil of a job to get the men moving again, the sergeants having to kick the men back into life.

You weren't meant to take apples, the army called it looting, but the sergeants turned a blind eye, it was a daft order, of course it was. All the time carrying a full pack and digger, many lost a fair bit of kit on the side of the road. And you could be on a charge for that as well, on a charge being something I know about, usually I have to admit after drink was taken. And as for taking wine from the local people, who often thrust great jugs of the stuff at us, well, you could get a court martial for that. Kitchener's personal order, so they say.

Why we weren't issued with tropical kit like we were in India I'll never know, it's that hot. Mind you, we'd look a bit daft wearing the pith helmet here in France. Some of the men, the youngsters mostly, lost their caps or gave them away to the jeunes filles and they suffered until told to tie their handkerchiefs with knots at the corners and use them as head covering. Didn't make for a soldierly appearance exactly, but the sun baked them like apples without their headgear. There was a rumour that some other Battalion had orders from their colonel to hand in all white handkerchiefs, in case the men should be tempted to use them to surrender. Another rumour, which Buffy had heard from a man in the Scottish Rifles, was that that the fritzes tried out the old fake surrender trick yesterday, and then took up their rifles again when our officer stepped forward, and shot him down.

Bless them, the local froggies were coming up trumps with the manger as we went along. Thought we were going to save them from the fritzes, poor buggers. Never mind that we were going the wrong way, they were still pleased to see us. Or perhaps the back of us, you never know with the frogs. Just give me the vin blanc and the jeunes filles and I'll fight for them. But then fighting is what I do and what I'm paid for. I've fought the niggers on the north-west frontier and I've fought the bearded Dutchmen in the Transvaal and now I'll fight the fritzes who're going to be the toughest of the lot. And I'll fight as a swaddy, corporal be damned, even though Four Eyes wants to make me one.

Edwards' platoon was getting near Le Cateau now. A smart car swept past, with two high-ranking officers in the back and a driver with leather gloves and a full corporal's stripes. A Rolls-Royce, no less, flying a pennant on the front right wheel guard. It stopped just ahead of the platoon.

Edwards lifted his eyes from the pavé. Lieutenant Bosanquet brought the platoon to a halt.

'Eyes right'. Stand at attention for the Corps Commander, Lieutenant General Smith-Dorrien!'

The platoon saluted, slapping their arms across their rifles. The General got down from the car, all gleaming boots and well-pressed tunic.

You wouldn't know he had been in a battle, well I suppose Generals don't get dusty and tired and thirsty like the rest of us. But I noticed that two of the campaign ribbons on his chest were the same as mine; the North-West Frontier and the South African War, so we had something in common. Hang on, here comes a pep-talk.

'Stand easy…now I know all you chaps must be getting awfully tired and eager to have your chance to have a bash at the enemy. Your time will come, sooner than you might think. We want to make sure that when we do this, we do it on our terms and on ground of our choosing. I have a great admiration for the Royal Welch and I wish you all good luck and good huntin''. The general got back into the Rolls with the staff officer and signalled to the driver to move off.

And at that, at the urging of old Four Eyes, They gave him three Hip

Hip Hoorays.

Buffy said, 'That general knows his stuff, and no mistake. Reminds me of old Roberts in South Africa. A kindly looking old boy but you knew he wouldn't stand any nonsense from brother Boer.'

We pressed on, thinking less of our thirst and the fact that our serge shirts were sticking to our backs and our pack-straps were digging in to our shoulders and our feet were sore and our rifles were less of a friend than a burden, but what infantryman wants to be separated from his rifle? A few of the Welsh speakers even broke into song, but I left them to it, not being Welsh myself but a Shrewsbury man. We were bucked up by the General, but it always gives me an uneasy feeling when Generals talk to us, they never give you the bad news. I know that we are not paid to think, because a shilling a day does not leave enough left over for much in the way of thinking, but even so a man can't help wondering about what it would mean for us, the general's words about 'good hunting'.

A troop of Dragoon Guards rode past us then, going through our ranks from right to left, the men parting to let them go through, their harnesses jangling as they leapt the ditch on the left of the road. The officer acknowledged Four Eyes with a wave of his stick. A fine sight they made too with their rifles, the trusty short Lee-Enfields in their leather buckets and the leather gleaming in the late afternoon sun, and we all thought that with the cavalry watching out for us and Smith-Dorrien's words still ringing in our ears, well, we forgot for a moment that we were actually an army running away. We may well be an army marching toward a rendezvous with death, but it was going to be death for the enemy who was marching into our trap. 'Good hunting' means fighting and not running away, at least in my book.

And then we could see the church tower of Le Cateau, which we called Le Catoo, when we saw the sign by the road. Now the refugees are going both ways which makes it impossible for us to keep to the road, their carts not being able to travel on the fields, even though they are hard-baked and in stubble. Some of them must have thought the best way to go was west and some thought south. It's easier for us walking on the edge of the fields anyway, French cobbles and new English boots not being a good combination. It's mostly women and children and old men in the wagons, some with their beds on board, with cooking pots and kitchen utensils strapped on with rope and a dog sometimes padding along on a lead. But all I know is, you can't fight a battle with civilians all over the shop, the two of us just don't work together. I've heard that the fritzes up at Mons used a gaggle of civilians, children as well, as shields to stop our fire, well that doesn't surprise me, they can rape nuns they say, although nuns wouldn't be my first choice. But once a Hun, always a Hun.

The Battalion marched into Le Cateau from the north-west, over the Selle River in its steep valley and then up the wide main street towards the central square, which was not in fact square but more of a long oblong shape with the medieval town hall half way down its left side. The coming of the railway to this part of the Franco-Belgian border had brought new jobs and housing, but a surprising number of people still worked in the old trades such as lace-making. Lace-work adorned the bonnets and cuffs of even the less well-to-do women.

At least they've got some regimental police out directing the traffic now that we're almost in the town. Never thought I'd be glad to see the Red Caps. Christ, there's going to be the whole 5th Division here soon and then all the fritzes have to do is round us up like cowboys at a rodeo. Trap us in the town like rats. But Smith-Dorrien will sort things out. They say he was at Isandhlwana, if he can get out of that disaster he can get out from here.

Buffy said, 'I reckon it'll be every man for himself in this town. Like the Titanic. Our best move is to find the cookers, get a quiet spot and keep out of the way until we get our orders to move out.'

Me, I had other ideas. Buffy, the old soldier that he is, quite rightly is always one for a quiet life. Never volunteer for anything is a good motto to have in the Army, but there are times when a man has to go forth and this is one of them. Especially as it looked like there would be many of us who were not going to see the sun go down tomorrow, what with fritz just over the hill and everything all akimbo in the town. Eat, drink and be merry for tomorrow we die, well, whoever said that was some kind of a joker, but maybe he was an old soldier who knew what he was talking about.

'You might be right, Buffy, but I'm going to find myself a mademoiselle before we leave this town. They are going to be swarming all over the place and there's no better hunting ground than a town under siege. Just watch out for the Red Caps.'

The Battalion halted just off the main square. We took off our packs with relief and some men, the younger ones mostly, took off their boots, but I knew that this was a bad idea, if your feet swelled up you could have a devil of a job getting them on again. The first rule in the Army is look after your feet. The MO started to fuss over some of the worst foot cases, many of them like me reservists from Civvy Street, who found the new boots as unyielding as a Welsh teetotaller. A few of the men had even gashed the uppers with their bayonets, in an attempt to let the air in. We stowed our great-coats on the wagons and were glad of it even though us old Reservists know that once out of our sight our kit will be gone forever.

The church clock tower stood at the top of the square, it must be a regular beacon for miles around. We were told off into our platoons and ordered to wait for billeting instructions. We drank from the water trough as though we were cattle, and then filled up our bottles. Some of the local people stared at us, but some brought out baskets of cherries and plums. There was every kind of vehicle to be seen: automobiles, bakers' delivery carts, limbers, ammunition wagons, even a couple of requisitioned commercial motor lorries, one with the sign Waring and

Gillow, going nowhere with a broken axle. Waring and Gillow, that'll strike fear into the Hun, I say to Buffy. Everywhere there were piles of steaming horse-shit, an RFA battery must have been this way. It would be dark in half an hour, but the shops and cafes were doing good business and weren't going to shut up now. The Hotel de Commerce, that would be for officers no doubt, but the Café de Paris looked a good bet. There were staff cars lined up outside the Town Hall, the drivers wiping off the dust of the road. Buffy said the Town Hall was called a Hotel in France, and I said how do you know, but there it was in stone 'Hotel de Ville'.

A civilian was approaching, a gentleman by the look of him, with a suit of English cut and a Panama at an angle. 'Moore of *The Times*', he said, and produced an official looking card. Old Four Eyes got all officious and on his high horse and started to go on about how we were retiring according to a plan worked out by the Corps Commander and French himself, and this journalist wallah wrote it all down as if was gospel, even the bit about how we were going to have another bash at the Hun shortly. It was all good stuff, but looking around it was hard to see how this lot, a bedraggled mix of Battalions and a traffic-jam of guns and assorted infantry was going to be organised into a fighting force. But then I'm only a private soldier, what do I know. And I've got other things on my mind. Let the brass worry about sorting out this lot and I'll worry about sorting out a mademoiselle and a drink.

A major from the East Surreys approached Four Eyes and asked him whether he had seen any of his mob; he seems to have lost half of his Company somewhere on the road from Solesmes. And then a Captain from the Worcesters, from the look of his shoulder flashes, strolled up to Four Eyes and said, within my hearing, that he was looking for the Engineers, something to do with signalling equipment. How his 3rd Division signalling gear was all over the place and the newly arrived 4th Division gear was down the line beyond St Quentin and did Four Eyes have anything useful to contribute, like the location of somebody from

GHQ who could help him. Why Four Eyes could help was beyond me and beyond Four Eyes too, and the journalist chap heard all this as well, writing it down the way they do. And just then the Battalion cookers came up and we fell in and had a bit of a needy scoff. While we were scoffing a nice bit of Welsh cheese, what the cockney soldiers from the London Rifles call 'Stand at Ease', the billeting officer came up and said that there was no accommodation and we were just going to have to make do as best we could, which was all right by me because it gave me a free run of the town.

It was now almost dark with a blood-red sky in the west, which Buffy said was a bad omen, although he was always seeing bad luck in everything, from tea leaves to black cats. Time for a vin blanc at the Café de Paris I said to Buffy, we'll have a bon time with boko mangay if we're lucky. And just as we were about to give the place a shufti a commotion broke out at the bottom of the square three hundred yards out, there was a clatter of hooves and sparks flew up as iron horse shoes struck the cobbles. Christ it's cavalry and by the look of the helmets it's not ours and it's certainly not French. Our platoon instantly formed into two ranks, the front rank kneeling and me standing with the rest and we waited for Four Eyes to give the order to open fire which he did by shouting in a high-pitched voice like an excited schoolgirl, 'Target cavalry 300 yards south, five rounds rapid'. The Uhlans had their carbines out, there was no mistaking them and we fired in the gloom and we knocked at least one of them over and then they were gone but it was the first blood to us in the war. Why Uhlans should be so feared is a mystery to me, they're only men on horses with silly spikes in their helmets, but try telling that to a froggie, they strike fear into their hearts. But the fact that they are here at all is not good, they have no business being here. Like our cavalry they go before the main army and are a sign of bad tidings, like a single magpie.

Then orders came down that we were to stow our packs on the wagons and just pack a few items of personal kit, mess tins and hard rations in our haversacks. The hard tack not to be opened without permission from an officer. I had a good slab of bread tucked away in my tunic, being enough of an old soldier to know that tomorrow rations were unlikely to be forthcoming. We were issued with an extra 200 rounds of ammunition which we stowed in our pouches in the clips and then we knew that there was some serious business afoot and that morning stand-to was 0400 in the square, well before dawn. I suppose some men were told off for picket duty but it was not us, we were told just to go not too far from the square, which gave me a little bit of lee-way. I made sure my pack was on a wagon with the officers' valises, thinking there was a better chance of it being taken care of. Buffy's pack was already stowed away, out of sight and out of mind.

And then Buffy and me were ready for the Café, Buffy whose name was actually Bough, a married man who wrote long letters to his wife every week, although to me he was as good as married to the Army. He always ended these letters with the words 'I hope this finds you as it leaves me, in the pink'. He calls me 'Eddie', by the way. Anyway, off we went with some sous in our pockets, our rifles slung, but weighed down with all the extra rounds. The place was packed to the ceiling with men from at least six different regiments, everyone from the Duke of Cornwalls to the West Kents to the kilted Argylls, who still called themselves the 93rd, and what was surprising to an old soldier like me was that there were officers in there as well. I thought I saw the captain from the Worcesters who had talked to Four Eyes earlier. What is he doing here, he's not in our division, must be up to no good but you can't tell with officers. Officers are officers and men are men and you don't ever see them drinking together, in fact there are probably King's Regulations against it, but perhaps it was just the absence of available drinking establishments to account for it; that combined with the desperate straits we were now in. If you get too familiar with an officer you can be up on a charge for insubordination, as I know to my cost.

Whatever the reason, as I said, the crush of sweaty men from so many different units, the officers trying to look nonchalant, the few waiters in overalls carrying trays of beer, the smoke from a hundred cigarettes, a piano playing somewhere, and some local men and women by the look of it, well I've knocked around in cantonments from Delhi to Durban and I've never seen the like. If you could imagine a race crowd at the Derby in a room not far from being the Black Hole of Calcutta you might get an idea of the place. It was not a place of jollity with the singing you might expect in a public house in Blighty; you could hardly expect that when there was going to be shot and shell flying around in a few hours' time, although I did spot a few men around a Crown and Anchor board in a corner. There was quite a crush of men by the door, but they were buglers and only boys and it occurred to me that perhaps the frogs wouldn't let them in because of their youth. But not too young to die. . .

'How are we going to get a drink in here?' says Buffy, although he might have used another word as well, and I answered with the confidence of a bit more experience than Buffy, 'Just leave it to me'. Because in the gloom of the flickering gas lights I saw a place at the bar and strike me pink if there weren't a couple of jeunes filles not far from the vacant spot, standing together. It was just a matter of finding a way through the crowd. Buffy stayed at the door while I made my way through, clutching my rifle with my left hand and my cap at a jaunty angle. One of the jeunes filles was prettier than her friend, with reddish hair and sort of blue eyes, so I said 'Vin blanc, mamselle?' as bold as brass, and damn me if she didn't say 'Merci'. Well, I managed to get three glasses of vin, one for me and one for each of them and Buffy was going to have to shift for himself. I just sort of looked at the red-head and she stared back at me, in a hello-what-are-we-going-to-do-about-all-this-then sort of way. She wasn't exactly young but not over thirty either and tray bon in anyone's language. And I'm thirty-two, with fifteen years in the colours, the last five as a Reservist.

We sipped the vin for a bit. And went on looking at each other. I wasn't even aware of her friend, let alone Buffy. She then said in a just audible voice, and surprisingly in English, 'You will fight'. How was I to take that? But before I could think of a reply she said 'And you will go away'. Now these two statements could be taken as matters of fact, meaning that she knew we were going to scarper and leave her to the fritzes, but at least she thought I was a fighter. I couldn't exactly say 'why don't you come with me', which was what I had a crazy urge to say, the Army not being too keen on camp followers any more, not like in the Peninsula if stories of the old days are to be believed. I said 'I will fight the sale boche', the last two words being pretty familiar by now.

'How did you learn English?' I said

'I am a teacher, and it is required'

And I don't know what came over me, but then I found myself saying 'Well then it is required that you come outside with me so that we can talk in the fresh air', which is the oldest trick in the book but I hadn't got time for any fancy stuff. To my further amazement this is what she did, just nodded to her friend whose name I didn't know, I didn't know the red-head's name either come to that, but she put down her glass and she followed me towards the door to the street through the crush of soldiers. I took hold of her hand, which was warm and surprisingly dry. Buffy was still at the entrance to the café, but seemed to be happy enough talking to some East Surreys. He had got himself a drink so I didn't have to worry about him. We knew the time to be in the Square for morning stand-to.

The girl and I were standing by a limber piled with great-coats and I still had her hand in mine and I said, 'What is your name?'

'Suzanne.'

I told her my name, Frank Edwards, giving her both my names in a formal way.

The church clock at the top of the square struck eleven o'clock and I had never had such a feeling of time running through my fingers and wanting to do things with this girl before I reported for duty in five hour's time so I just said

'Let's go somewhere quiet'

'My parents live just over there; I live with them. They have already left for Reims. They think the boche will be here tomorrow and you will be gone. And then the boche will do what they want with us. And if they have to fight for the town they will be faché, annoyed, and they will do bad things.'

I was that desperate for this girl that I wanted to have her in the limber under the great-coats but I said, 'Let's go to your house', and again she surprised me by leading me off down toward the river on the west side of the town where we had come in. Her house was a non-descript single-fronted house in a terrace, not unlike my mother's house in Shrewsbury. I then had a picture in my head, of horrible clarity, of German soldiers, Uhlans, this time with their heads bare and taking this girl roughly by the arms and telling her to do what they said or she would suffer and then fucking her one after the other. It is the fucking that they will do, not the fighting, that makes the Uhlans so feared.

When we were in the house Suzanne at once unbuttoned her blouse and took off her smock-dress over her head but left on her shift. I tried not to look at the image of the Virgin over the mantel but in Catholic countries it's just part of the furniture. She told me not to just stand there like an idiot, she said 'Idio', but do likewise, which I did readily enough, but keeping my socks on so as not show her my bruised and swollen feet. She said 'Avence' which was a word I could hardly fail to understand and took hold of me and led me by my hard cock to a settee and settled herself on her haunches and she was not wearing any knickers and told me to enter her by kneeling on the floor, not that I needed telling to put one up the spout. I pushed in and she put her head back and all her throat was exposed which is the best bit of a girl to look at. I came in a rush and again the image of the Uhlans was in my head and I hoped that I would have another chance of getting one in the sights of my rifle. One for me and one for Suzanne.

I said, because it was worrying me, 'Will you stay here?'

'My parents wanted me to go with them; there was a disagreement. In any case I did not have the necessary, how do you say, permit from the Mairie, because I am a teacher. But I will not let the boche drive me from my home'.

'I will be back Suzanne.'

We lay together on the settee for some while but I was frightened of missing the four o'clock stand-to and I said I must go but that I would never forget her and would be back when we had driven off the sale boche. I put my uniform back on and my boots and wound on my puttees and strapped on my webbing with all the extra ammunition and picked up my haversack and rifle and I was a soldier again and ready to fight. I put my cap on. Now to fight, not just for the King, which I had signed up for, but for Suzanne and the people of this town who were going to suffer a long night of darkness if we left them, which we were surely going to do. He came back to the limber piled with great-coats and saw that there were sleeping soldiers under the coats so he took a coat and laid it on the hard ground and fell asleep on it, knowing that the men above him would wake him in time for stand-to. His rifle lay beside him and he had his arm across the stock. He had not even taken off his webbing.

It had started to rain before Edwards lay down, but he never even heard the thunder when it came at 2.00 a.m.

Chapter 3

25th August, Afternoon: Lieutenant-General Smith-Dorrien

Sir Horace Smith-Dorrien, Second Corps commander, had been in France for only six days, following the death from a heart attack of his predecessor Lieutenant-General Grierson. Sitting in the back of the Rolls-Royce with Brigadier-General George Forrestier-Walker, his Chief of Staff, he let his mind wander. He had not slept more than four hours a night since the 22nd and it was now the afternoon of the 25th.

His first meeting with the Army commander Sir John French on the 21st had gone as well as could be expected, considering the man was a fool and not to be trusted with a man's wife. Christ, French didn't even understand the role of cavalry - thought he was still on the African veldt. It is always infantry that does the real fighting. The important thing was to get into ground of our choosing, not like at Mons, that was a scratch affair but the men were wonderfully brave. How we got away is still a mystery and no thanks to French, or Haig for that matter, who will never look anywhere but his own self-interest. French took a devil of a time making up his mind what to do, it just depends on who he's last been talking to and if it's Wilson he'll take his orders direct from Joffre. He won't listen to me that's for sure, only yesterday he had the nerve to say I could 'do as I like', which was a calculated insult. He should be still at Le Cateau when we get there in half an hour and at least we can get some answers, like where is Haig, is he pushing on to join us at Le Cateau or what. And what GHQ is doing with the 4th Division. And what's happening with the French 5th Army to the east and west of us. And exactly where is this retreat leading us. At least we know now that von Kluck has got at least nine infantry divisions plus three cavalry, although it is how they are handled which is what counts. And if von Kluck's performance at Mons is anything to go by, he's not adept at handling large bodies of men or co-ordinating his arms.

Sir Horace came out of his reverie. He ordered the driver to stop so that he could have a word with these troops, Royal Welch by the look of them, noticing the flash of black ribbons on the mens' collars.

The old 23rd of Foot, if I remember rightly. Always think of themselves as the last in and last out boys. I'll tell them quite frankly that we'll give the enemy a blow soon and see how it goes down with the men. If you've been around British infantry as long as I have you get a feel for what the troops are thinking. Give it to them straight and no flannel about King and Country, they don't want to hear that.

*

'Well, George, did that go down well?'

'Splendidly, General, splendid'.

Getting in to Le Cateau was not easy with all the refugee carts but the driver made his way to the Hotel de Ville, where a few cars were parked, including what looked like Westminster's Rolls-Royce, with a liveried chauffeur standing nearby. We might have a use for him soon. Ah, the very man himself;

'Bendor, where is the chief? '

'He's gone off to see Snow of the 4th and then down to St. Quentin to make his new HQ there. You might find General Wilson or General Murray, but go easy on Murray, he's a bit fragile. Wilson is croaking as usual. Johnny Gough from Haig's HQ is here somewhere abouts and he might be able to help with news from First Corps, although my advice would be don't count on it. But I warn you everyone is a bit jumpy and keen to be away out of here. I'm just off to see poor old Grenfell of the 9th Lancers who's in hospital with a nasty leg wound. Silly chap would charge straight at the boche field guns outside Mons, not to mention a whole Battalion of boche infantry, although I hear he did rescue our gunners from a sticky position. You know what these cavalry chaps are like.'

Sir Horace and Forrestier-Walker went up to the Town Hall, the Private of the Artist Rifles coming smartly to attention as they entered. They found no-one of any use to them, just a few clerks packing up the remaining files and maps. There was a French officer, a major by the look of him, although it was hard to tell with froggies, who was asleep in a corner. He was quite clearly drunk and had been abandoned to stew by himself. They did find a junior RTO who told them that the HQ Guard, all one hundred of them, had left on one of the last trains out of the station. The civilian railway staff were refusing to work, with the enemy expected to be within artillery range within hours; most of them were plainly eager to flee south in the last train still standing on the down platform. The RTO made plain his opinion of the railway staff but they were nonetheless essential personnel. As the General and his chief-of-staff left the Hotel de Ville, Horace brushed past a civilian in a Panama hat who was eager to talk to him. No time for that now.

'George, the best thing we can do now is motor out towards Cambrai and have a recce at the lie of the land and have a look at the trench-lines which have been dug. Make sure we've got all the right maps and good binoculars; a pair of Zeiss would be useful.'

They left the town by the cutting on the Roman road, where they came in, Forestier-Walker assuring Smith-Dorrien that he had, of course, got hold of good six-inch FS maps. Horace said, as if to himself,

'This looks like a concealed exit if ever I saw one. And the river valley going south there, that needs troops on both sides of it. First Corps Battalions should be over there to the south of Le Cateau by first light.

Troops on the hill should have a good overview and the gunners can draw up on the other side and use the reverse slope. Would need observers forward on the hill-top. But we'll have to surrender the town, there's no time to prepare it for defence and what would be the point? Besides, our men don't know how to fight in towns, it's just not in their nature or their training. It's not the British way, it's what made me so nervous about being in Mons.'

George Forrestier-Walker cut in,

'I'd be happier if I could see some trench lines. Oh, yes, look, let's go over there, down that farm track.'

Between the track and the Cambrai road, where a rail-line lay alongside, were trenches, freshly dug, forward lines and support lines a couple of hundred yards back, just to the west of the Roman road to St. Quentin. It made military sense, they had good fields of fire to the north across the fields of stubble which came down to the road, poplar-lined at this point. And behind the trench-lines, to the west, the farm track went into a natural cutting, again very useful for defence. Someone here had known their business. There was a lone tree on the edge of the lane visible for miles and both generals agreed that it should be cut down, acting as it did as an aiming point for enemy guns. Forrestier-Walker was marking up his six inch map. But the Brigadiers and Lieutenant Colonels didn't need to be told to cut down trees by generals.

'Press on driver', said George, 'we've got three hours till night-fall to get out to Cambrai and back and I would dearly love to see some French cavalry out there somewhere.' The driver had a name like Cragg he remembered.

'That's what's worrying me, George. If we fight here tomorrow we've got a shorter front than at Mons, by a long way. But a shorter front is only of use if you've got friends on both flanks. We've got the 4th Division now, and I'm sure Snow will fight under my orders, but someone has got to look after his flank with his own cavalry stuck God knows where and it's going to have to be the French and that means cavalry and you know as well as I do what they can do and can't do.'

'Can't do, more like', said George. 'They would win first prize in a fancy dress competition, but I'd rather have our 4th Dragoons with a battery of 13-pounders any day than a whole division of Cuirassiers. I've heard that French cavalry like to stop at one o'clock for a vin rouge and a slice of paté, even if there are more pressing engagements. And they can't do much damage with their carbines. They'd look good in a tuppenny opera, but that's as far as it goes.'

The Rolls motored along, all six cylinders going nicely, now back on the Cambrai road, going north-west, with the sun in their faces. They got out to the north of Caudry and Horace repeated his misgivings about defending towns. 'We'd be better off letting the enemy in and then shelling him rather than fight in the streets. But Hamilton will be out here and he can work out a scheme.'

'Remember Horace, that at Waterloo Wellington had to worry about his allies, the Dutch-Belgians. He could never be sure how they would react under fire. But we've got nearly forty thousand of the finest infantry in Europe, which is ten thousand more than the Duke ever had, and by tomorrow morning they will be fully deployed'.

Smith-Dorrien made no comment. He was not given much to reading, not even military history, but he had a collection of books on the breeding of polo ponies. He thought of the men marching in the heat and wondered how they were bearing up. But the question was, would they be fully deployed by dawn or would some of them be still on the march, thrashing about in the dark and unfamiliar country? He had to assume that the great bulk of the Corps would be in position by dawn.

They turned off the Roman road to Cattenieres. Again, good fields of fire toward Cambrai, where French Territorials were said to be, under General d'Amade. But no sign of any troops of any sort. A flight of BEF scout planes was flying over, heading south, probably moving from one temporary base to another. It did just occur to Horace to wonder what he would do if some adventurous enemy cavalry should appear; try and outrun them probably. He went back to studying the landscape with the binoculars: an old manor house, a sugar-beet factory, some farms that could be used for defence, and a railway that lay in a deep ravine south of Fontaine and Cattanieres, these were the main features west of Caudry. A few small woods, beet-fields. It was all not unlike the sort of training ground the men were familiar with at home. It reminded Horace of his own county of Hertfordshire. He had parted from his wife only six days ago. While they were stopped by the road two small boys, about six years old, came out from a cottage and stood looking at the car, nervously keeping a respectful distance. They were the same age as his own sons.

They started to head back towards Le Cateau via Ligny, the driver using the claxon to clear the road, using his skill in dodging the carts and wagons of the refugees, most of whom were trying to get out to the west.

'This is the key, here,' said Horace, when they halted at Ligny, his eye for the ground recognising its importance right away. 'Guns here and machine guns facing east and west. We could hold off a whole division'.

His large chin pointed at the church tower. He jabbed his finger at the map folded up on the right square on Forrestier-Walker's knee. They pushed on to Bertry. 'Here is where I'll have my HQ, get the Engineers to rig up the lines as soon as we get back. But, George, we are going to have to do something very difficult and that is break off the battle at some point. Let them come on, let the gunners do their business and then break off. And if we are lucky von Kluck will commit his infantry too soon and we will be able to catch them in the open with our guns, which we were never able to do at Mons, in the close country there. And then we will stop them and deal them a blow. At Mons it was all infantry work. I'm becoming more and more convinced that we're going to have to fight tomorrow. And if our riflemen get a chance to hit them in the open they could kill a good number of the Hun. That church tower at Ligny could be an observation point for the RFA.'

Back at the town of Le Cateau at 8.00 p.m. the scene was of growing congestion, with the best part of an RFA brigade, the XV, watering their horses from the water troughs in the square. 5th Division troops were filling up the streets. Horace had a few words with the RFA brigadier, Headlam, definitely a man of the old school, born as he was in an era when smooth-bore, muzzle-loading artillery still ruled the battle-field. It was not Horace's job to tell him his business and in any case the orders for the morning were going to have to wait a bit. Headlam was preparing to move out to the edge of town and bivouac. From there he would be in position to move off south if the retreat was to be resumed, or take up battle positions if they should fight. He did admit to some anxiety about the lack of decent maps and not being acquainted with the local topography. Everything depended on the Corps Commander's decision in the next few hours. For the moment the standing order from GHQ was Retirement. But Retirement is only a word for retreat and an army can retreat and fight; a fighting retreat is a recognised act of war and Headlam didn't need a lecture on military strategy, or the need for guns and infantry to work together. Both men knew that the right of the line was going to be a key focus in any coming action, but it was not in Smith-Dorrien's nature to indulge in spurious exhortations to military prowess. Headlam was eager to get his guns into action, that much was clear. No more need be said. Horace turned to his chief-of-staff,

'George, there is no good work we can do here. We will go to Bertry.'

'Horace, all the necessary arrangements are in hand. We have already requisitioned the Mairie and we can use the telephone at the station until the Engineers rig up the lines to the divisions. There are French telephone operators standing by. A line is being kept open to GHQ in St Quentin'

'Very good, George. Please request Generals Hamilton of 3rd Division and Fergusson of 5th to come to Bertry by 2.00 a.m. at the latest. And Allenby of the Cavalry Division. That is the latest to ensure that we have time to get orders out to the brigades by dawn. I leave the method of despatch to you. Knowing what I do of von Kluck he will want to make his move soon after dawn. There might well be mist in the morning but it will not last long and will not mask our movements. And try and find out where Haig is, it's a simple request and one that nobody in this army can give me an answer to. Christ, the man can't be more than a few miles away, but he might as well be on the far side of the moon. Track down Johnnie Gough, he's the man to get hold of. And try and get hold of Macdonough at GHQ, the Intelligence chief, he's the only one there who seems to know what he's talking about. And now let's go.'

Corporal Clegg, the ASC driver, was generous in his use of the claxon in getting clear of the town, the General acknowledging the salute of a passing column of East Surreys with a wave of his stick. His silvery moustache caught the last rays of the sun as it went down over Cambrai, but he was in no mood to comment on the beauty of the sunset.

Chapter 4

25th August: Captain Johnson

Captain Henry Johnson of the 3rd Worcesters, 7 Brigade, 3rd Division was having a frustrating time. The fighting at Mons on the 23rd, where he was attached to 7 Brigade as Signals Officer, was, as far as he was concerned, all part of the same fight on the 24th. That is to say, the enemy resumed their attack at dawn on the 24th with waves of infantry attacking his 7 Brigade's position near Cipley, and he was lucky to get away in one piece, the 1st Gordons, 8 Brigade putting up a fine rearguard. For the first time the gunners with the 18-pounders had been able to fire at the attacking waves of grey-clad infantry, catching them in the open and doing good work, the shrapnel shells exploding in white bursts over their lines, the Gordon's machine guns adding to the killing. But still they came on. Johnson rode back and forth across the battlefield on his piebald mare, taking messages from Brigade to the 3rd Worcesters and 1st Wiltshires, and was lucky to survive, thanks largely to a good stout pair of wire-cutters by means of which he was able to get through the many wire fences on his horse, wire-cutters he had purchased himself from the Army and Navy Stores. He must have dismounted a dozen times. Major-General Hamilton was everywhere on horse-back and a nightmare from the point of view of a signals officer. The second-line Mons defence, which had existed in name only, was soon abandoned following the retreat order received by Smith-Dorrien at 3.00 a.m. on the 24th. But at Bavai where the Division was able to reorganise itself somewhat, Johnson found that his signals section was scattered to the winds and as a signals officer he was next to useless. His sergeant, Sergeant Rouse, was nowhere to be found. He had four hours sleep in a barn near Wargnies, just inside the Belgian border, with what remained of a company of the 2nd Irish Rifles.

Thirty years old, a superb cricketer, an old Wykehamist from an army family (his father had been Colonel of the regiment), Johnson did not have difficulty in choosing the Army as a career, although at Winchester the Army was not considered a natural home for those of its brighter alumni, which Johnson undoubtedly was. Possessed of a small private income, but with a family without land or an established business, the Army offered a haven but also a challenge. Comfortable with a signals manual as easily as Horace's *Odes*, the recent Clifford Moore edition tucked up in his valise along with *A Shropshire Lad*, he took the profession of arms extremely seriously. To him it encompassed a fascinating mix of scientific and technical endeavours, acquired skills and manly virtues. He had read Clauzevitz and Creasy and of course Caesar's *Gallic Wars* at Winchester College and was familiar with Wellington's campaign in the Peninsular War, or at least the Oman history. Unusually for an Army officer, he had read a fair bit of modern literature, Thomas Hardy being a particular favourite of his, as well as more popular books like G. A. Henty's. Housman's bucolic poetry ('What are those blue remembered hills?') he found appealing while being wholly unaware of any homoerotic content. Erskine Childers and William Le Queux had convinced him, if he needed convincing, that the Hun was a slippery customer whose machinations must be thwarted at every turn. Or as Housman had written,

> *Where the standing line wears thinner, and the dropping dead lie thick;*
> *And the enemies of England they shall see me and be sick.*

This particular deathless couplet of crashing rhyme didn't worry the Captain at all. He applauded its sentiment.

Just too young for the South African War, after Sandhurst he was gazetted to the Worcester Regiment in 1904 and posted to the 3rd Battalion, delighting in being addressed as ‘His Majesty the King’s trusty and well beloved’, the expression used by the Commission. Service in India in the days of Edwardian peace was not too strenuous and the young Henry Johnson found time to shoot ibex in Kashmir, play polo, but also study Urdu and Pushtu, the language of the North-West Frontier. He achieved the standard needed in Pushtu to qualify for the bonus payment of £45, which was sufficient to purchase a pony and enable him to hunt with the Peshawar Vale Hounds, who would meet at dawn on a Sunday. Johnson would return home by 10.00 a.m. to a breakfast of porridge and devilled kidneys when the heat of the day would destroy the scent. The pony doubled up as both hunter and Polo pony.

He was not married, thinking it not fair on a woman to demand the sometimes Spartan rigours of Army life on a captain’s pay. His life was contained by the Battalion, all the extant photographs of him showing him in a group, either in an officers’ line-up, or in a cricket team, the younger smiling schoolboy-cricketer with a hairless upper lip giving way to the sterner, moustached subaltern of the 3rd Worcesters but with the young Johnson always in the centre of his group. Sex was largely a matter of deferment, although there had been episodes of a sexual nature, so to speak, in ‘establishments’ in Cairo, Gibralter and other outposts of Empire. These episodes had on the whole been less than satisfactory. He had not recorded these episodes in the diary he had kept, the leather-bound volume itself acquired at considerable expense in Jermyn St, and that he was keeping now, albeit surreptitiously. There was however an ‘understanding’ with the sister of one of his fellow officers, Lieutenant Simon Brett, that she would one day be his wife, although there was no official engagement. She was called Phoebe and it was this enchanting name that had formed part of her initial attraction for him; that and her exquisite breasts with their surprisingly dark nipples which she had permitted him to play with in the summer house of his parents' house near Broadway, the house which had been in the Johnson family since the late eighteenth century, when a Jeremiah Johnson had become a successful brewer. It was the portrait of this Johnson, an early Thomas Lawrence, that hung in the hall. It was Phoebe's breasts he was thinking of now, cupped in his hands while they had sought shelter in the summer house, during a sudden shower. He had kissed each nipple briefly after which she had put them back into her blouse, a foretaste or aperitif of delights to come. He had quoted the line from *A Shropshire Lad*, 'My love is true and all for you', while she had refrained from quoting the rejoinder, 'Perhaps, young man, perhaps'. She had merely smiled, showing her even, pearly white teeth, her dark hair coiled up under the straw hat.

Phoebe had once come to watch him play cricket for the Old Wykehamists against a Hampshire XI at the ground he knew so well, Lords at Winchester, while Henry was home on leave. He had gone in at no 4, his usual position, and had made a quick 43 before getting himself foolishly run out. Batting at number 3 was Harry Altham, a chubby all-rounder with a habit of quoting Latin verse and odd bits of unconsidered trifles. 'Et in arcadia ego, eh Henry?' he would say as they ran between the wickets. Johnson called him Harry Arcadia, which then became Arcade and then Burlington and then Bertie in the roundabout way that in-bred institutions like Winchester College seem to find amusing. Calling him Bertie Altham had become an in-joke, but its origins were already misty. Altham was now serving in a junior capacity on the staff of 3rd Division, having attended the Staff College at Camberley, a beneficiary of Lord Esher's formation of a General Staff, a creation modelled shamelessly on German lines.

Phoebe had been watching the game with her brother Simon, then, like Henry, a 1st Lieutenant in the 3rd Battalion. It must have been in August '12. Phoebe was wearing the same straw hat she had worn in the summer house and she had a ribbon in Henry's house colours around the brim which he had given her. She was sitting with Simon on a tartan rug under the evergreen oak and Henry joined them after he had walked back to the pavilion. Henry noticed some boys from his old house paying much more attention to her than the match, which was in fact finely balanced. She said,

'What rotten luck Henry, come and have a glass of lemonade'.

'Henry, old chap, that extra cover was a bit too quick for you'.

That's what he liked about Simon, in a perverse sort of way. He could always be relied on to do or say something obvious. Not one of the brightest but the most dependable of friends, his boon companion at Peshawar and in Kashmir. And Arthur de Salis, a platoon commander in C Company, popular with the men and easy going, made up what he liked to call the Triumvirate. The days when the three of them had gone out rough shooting on the de Salis mixed farm near Redditch were among the most memorable of his life, the small bag of a couple of brace of English partridge and a few pigeons making just enough for the table. De Salis was also from an Army family, a great uncle having charged, and survived, with Cardigan at Balaclava. Johnson was now the senior of the three of them, by virtue of being a Brigade Signals officer.

Looking back now, he knew at that moment at Winchester that Phoebe was going to be his wife and Simon would do duty as best man at their wedding. Perhaps it was just his old house colours in her hat, the red and the brown, that made him so certain, although he couldn't of course say that to Phoebe. He knew when to tread carefully when it came to women's sensitivities, although thank goodness Phoebe hadn't filled her head with any of this women's suffrage nonsense.

At Mons he had found his first experience of being shot at by artillery and infantry not as unnerving as he had expected, and like everyone he had of course given the matter some thought. The first crack and high whistle of the rounds passing just over his head made him think that he was going to survive this battle after all, that bullets miss their targets, that the enemy was not on a rifle range, that really this is not as bad as one had expected. Not profound thoughts but he had a feeling, which he immediately quashed for superstitious reasons, that he might even survive this war. Of the necessity for this war he had no doubts. The Hun was bent on expansion by brutal and at the same time devious manoeuvering and must be stopped on the field of battle. The trouble was that one had to admit that he was a very determined and resourceful enemy and it was going to take a long time to do this. He also didn't play with a straight bat; Henry had heard alarming reports of German tricks such as using human shields in getting across the canal at Mons. He found that his conviction that we were in for a long war, at least till the far side of winter, was not a universal view amongst his fellow officers, who seemed to assume that the enemy would somehow collapse after the reality of war had penetrated to the chancelleries and bourses of their capitals. His understanding of history told him that this would not happen, at least for a while yet. After all, it had taken seven years from Wellington's first landing in Portugal to the final triumph of the battle of Waterloo, the last time there was a general European war as opposed to the Franco-Prussian War of 1870-1871. It takes longer to end a war than start it.

Early on the 25th he was summoned to Brigadier McCracken's 7 Brigade H.Q. in a farmhouse near Bavai. He went in to the kitchen, which doubled as a parlour, where extraordinarily there was the woman of the house at the sink, making a clatter with the dishes. McCracken ignored her. Johnson had the curious thought that in another place, if this was a Hun officer, the woman would not be allowed to continue her domestic duties.

'Ah, Johnson, good of you to come. We are now going off south via Solesmes for God knows how far, but I gather there is a line being got ready west of Le Cateau. But with the signals up the swanee as you know I can't get a clear picture. Sir John would like to get at least a big river between us and the Hun and that means pushing on down across the Somme where we can blow the bridges. And hope that the French will fight on our right. What signals equipment we have is simply not going to be deployed while we are on the march. I'm getting reports that a good number of stragglers are coming in all the time and our losses are not as bad as I first feared, although I hear that the Gordons in 8 Brigade have lost quite a lot of men. Anyway as I say I can spare you for a time.'

He paused for a moment while the bonne femme banged her pots and pans.

'Can you rejoin your Battalion, report to your company commander Major Crawford, but first push on with all speed to Le Cateau and see what you can find out about the situation from GHQ. Talk to someone who knows what's what and then come back to me and give me a report. I shall be somewhere in Caudry, the town hall I suppose. With any luck I shall be able to get on and have a scout around. Get the picture on 4th Div., which should be arriving at Le Cateau at any moment and who will be on our right, extending our line to the west. Liaise with your opposite numbers in Signals. Without signals we're in the dark, as you know. Have you got that? Right? Carry on.'

Johnson's diary entry was forming itself in his head:

I was dismissed. I re-mounted and set off back to the 3rd Battalion, which I knew was still just outside Bavai. Stragglers were still coming in, as McCracken had said. He was amazingly well-informed and wanted to stay that way, taking an interest beyond his own Brigade, the 7th, which was unusual in a brigadier. I managed to track down Major Crawford and informed him of my mission. I set off on the road to Solesmes.

What I came across on the road quite simply alarmed me. To begin with I came across horse cavalry with two 13-pounders and very relieved they made me with their thoroughly professional appearance. Not just a bunch of socially well-connected Hyde Park show-offs, but men and officers who knew their business and worked well together. I watched the two gun-crews under the command of a captain of my own age gallop off to take up a position covering our left flank. But after that things got very worrying. A retreat does something to troops. Granted they were now getting very tired and granted it was uncommonly hot and it would be a time for the cookers to catch up with them, but there was a slackness and a poor march discipline that was worrying. There was a marked difference between the battalions, the 1st Wiltshires as I passed them seeming to be in good order but men of the South Lancs and the Royal Irish Rifles were falling out of the ranks to lie down or forage, without their officers exercising control. All this while the enemy were surely in hot pursuit. A commander must ask the impossible and all those who fall out must be left behind, whether in attack or retreat, it's all in the Field Service Regulations, although I must admit I cannot recollect anything in the Regulations about the proper procedures in a retreat. Still, the Army has done it before, in 1808 in the Peninsula.

Johnson rode on, the heat most unlike a late summer in northern Europe, it felt more like being back in Gib with the Battalion, or even Quetta, and his thoughts went back again to his time at Winchester.

A battalion is like a school or one's House at school. It's quite simple. When you've got a firm grip on discipline, when the whole House is pulling together to win the Jacker Cup, when boys don't report sick because they know they will miss the fun, then you've got what we call good morale. That's why I come down hard on anything looking like feigned sickness, it's a symptom of poor moral quality. You can't hope to win a battle with poor material in the moral department. It's devilish tricky putting your finger on it, but you know when you've got it and you know when you haven't. It's all in Kipling: 'Strong heart....Beat strongly...something something The Empire round - in us thy sons, Who distant from the Seven Hills...require Thee, The Imperial Fire!' The

Roman Empire, Britain now, love and service, a constant thread. You can't defend the Empire with weak hearts. And goodly is our heritage and fair is our lot.

Johnson stopped to talk to a South Lancs subaltern in charge of a transport column. The young officer was agitated.

'I've got horses who can go no further and my orders are to shoot them. And I have no orders to commandeer French draught horses which I have passed in the farms along the way. I tell you, Sir, this is no way to go to war.'

Johnson did no more than acknowledge the subaltern's salute but pushed the piebald mare on, the sweat glistening on her flanks, past food dumps obviously left by the quartermasters for the benefit of the men following behind, hoping that these valuable stores would not fall into enemy hands. But how would the men be able to cope with these 7-pound tins of bully while on the march? And would they not be taken by local people who although generous with their own food to our men and kindness itself surely could not resist this manna from heaven? It looked like Robertson the QMG is trying to feed all the refugees from Belgium as well as the BEF. The stores were unguarded. But a quartermaster generous with his stores? Next it'll be seaside landladies giving out free beer.

A mile or so north of Solesmes, at a small cross-roads, there was a rudimentary road-block, manned by French Territorials, consisting of farm carts pulled across the road and lashed together. One cart, unlashed, served as a gate. The ill-dressed soldiers had ancient rifles, the sort used by British troops in the Crimea, but they brandished them in a threatening way in Johnson's direction as he approached. It became clear that an officer riding alone drew their suspicion. The Frenchmen, bearded and unkempt, demanded what was his unit, what papers did he have, where was he going? Johnson was not going to stand for this nonsense and luckily his school-boy French was good enough and the uniform enough, to convince them of his credentials. ('Je suis officier de l'armée Britannique. Je suis commissioné capitaine. Laissez passer s'il vous plait.') Quite what these ill-disciplined half-trained men hope to achieve except holding people up is not clear; the chances of them arresting a genuine spy is remote. He restrained himself and was allowed to ride on. Our Territorials are a model of military efficiency compared to this rabble.

He trotted past an 18-pounder battery, the RFA Major riding at its head, all six guns with their limbers and ammunition wagons taking up the best part of half a mile of road, each gun pulled by six horses, the brakemen ready for the descent to Solesmes. The Major, covered in dust, acknowledged Johnson with a wave of his riding crop, turning in his saddle to look behind him at the convoy. Once again Johnson was impressed with the bearing of these gunners who without doubt knew their business and had the guns to do it; altogether a most impressive sight, one hundred and seventy horses all told, with the riding horses and the draught horses combined.

He was approaching Solesmes, which lay in a hollow as does Le Cateau. He continued to write his diary in his head. In the town all was bustle, to put it politely. In fact it was like any town in the rear of an army which was about to be engulfed in war. It reminded him of Oman's description of Salamanca in the Peninsula and of Goya's sketches, some of which he had seen in the British Museum only two years ago. He came across a mounted officer of the Warwicks, a subaltern, newly arrived, which at least told him something of the progress of 4th Division. The subaltern said he was to stay put until all the 3rd Div. Mons troops passed through and then go down to new positions to the west of Caudry, where a line was to be formed. He was not looking forward to a night-march.

'Then you will be on our flank. I don't envy you your job when it comes to getting clear of this shambles'.

The subaltern, whose name was Penfold, then said,

'Are the Germans far behind, Sir? I have heard only distant firing. I can't get a word out of anybody. The townspeople are nervous and the refugees are spreading a good deal of alarm, not to say despondency.'

He chose to ignore this last remark. Troops should not listen to civilians in the matter of military necessities.

'The enemy will be here by nightfall if not earlier. But they will probably stop short of the town and shell it, regardless of civilians. They are coming on strong and seem almost to disregard our gunfire. I don't want to alarm you, but you should look sharp. Get the refugees on their way.'

And with that not very encouraging piece of probably superfluous advice Johnson went on, thinking it a shame to abandon all this good high ground without a fight. The subaltern looked a bit worried, as well he might. The two officers saluted each other.

At Le Cateau, it was the same scene as at Solesmes, if anything more chaotic. But Johnson had seen enough soldiering to know that the old phrase 'military precision' was an oxymoron, unless it was applied to a Guards' battalion on parade. There was no precision here: fighting units and rear echelon units were all mingled up. Part of the trouble which faced the BEF troops at both towns was that the British had no authority over either the civilians or the French Territorials. The MPs were doing their best, but they were busy with the BEF columns, never mind the French ones. The Territorials all seemed to be bearded, which gave them a piratical appearance. He soon discovered that GHQ had shifted down to St Quentin, which put paid to his contacting anyone who could put him in the overall picture. He decided to find out what he could and be sure to be in Caudry by soon after dawn tomorrow to report to McCracken and the 3rd Worcesters. It had always been a belief of his that one can learn just as much from an intelligent and alert junior officer as a bloated staff officer of senior rank, so he made it his business to do just that, to speak to officers who could provide him with information of use to the Brigadier.

He hitched the piebald mare to a rail by the Hotel de Ville, after watering her and himself for that matter, at the cattle troughs in the square. He noticed a smart white racing car parked in a side street, with a sporting rifle fixed to the bonnet. A liveried chauffeur, a civilian, was guarding the car and buffing up the paintwork.

A bespectacled lieutenant in the Royal Welch was as helpful as he could be and confirmed that he was to move out to what he confidently expected to be the battlefield before dawn. As the Royal Welch were in the independent 19 Brigade he expected to be in reserve but to play their part in the battle to come. Johnson then had the good fortune to speak to a man from *The Times* who told him that all the 4th Divisional equipment, including signals, was stuck down the line below St Quentin. Curious that one can learn more from a newspaperman than from the proper authorities. They had a brief discussion about the prospects for the morrow. The journalist, (his name was Moore he noted, which reminded him of the Peninsula), said Colonel Repington knew all the gen from the top brass, it was his job to get the view from the ranks and the junior officers. Johnson gave him the benefit of his views of the morale of the men as he witnessed it on the road to Solesmes. Some battalions do better than others; it has always been like this in the British army and always will be. Not all regiments can be like the Guards. It's hardly a military secret.

He then had a useful chat with a major in XV RFA Brigade, who told him he was trying to get his battery out to the west of the town, where there was a good supply of water for his horses in the Selle. He looked harassed but seemed to have the situation under control.

I looked in at the Café de Paris which was crammed with khaki, then managed to get something to eat at the Hotel de Commerce, sharing a table, an omelette and a bottle of Beaujolais with a Belgian bourgeois couple from Liege, whose de Dion was parked outside. Their hatred of the boche knew no bounds. They were to sleep in their car and leave at dawn. The husband wanted to talk about his escape from Belgium:

'Always it was the troops marching, marching, in their grey uniforms. And always the dust thrown up by the endless columns. And then the singing, of their frauleins in their heimat, but sometimes only of their wurst. They want our land and our coal and they want their wurst. They want everything these Germans. And with all these numbers of them it is impossible that they go home until they get what they want. What could our small Belgian army do against such multitudes? They will not stop until they get to the Pyrenees. We came by night to Charleroi and it is a miracle that we are here. We have left our furniture business; all is lost. And now I don't know how I am going to get enough *essence* to get down to Bordeaux where we have some cousins.'

When Johnson pressed him on the subject of hostage-taking the man became even more agitated.

'The first thing they do when they come to a town is to take the town burghers into their custody. And then if there is any shooting or killing of Germans the poor bughers are killed by firing squad. And I know that at Liege when a German officer was shot it was by their own troops who were drunk. We have done nothing to have deserved this cruelty.' The Belgian clicked his fingers at the waiter in a way that no Englishman would have done.

And was that the Duke of Westminster having a drink with some other gilded personage? I thought I recognised him from the pages of the Bystander and remembered that he was here with the RAC Corps of Volunteer Motor Drivers. It must be his racing car by the Town Hall.

Johnson watched as the Duke signalled to the waiter. Johnson could hear him ordering another bottle of Montrachet and the waiter shaking his head. Poor Duke, he'll have to manage with an ordinary Beaujolais like the rest of us.

Two 5th Division staff officers at the next table were talking in loud voices - they were slightly drunk - in that confident way that officers do when they consider themselves to be at the centre of events. One of them - a lieutenant looking barely twenty years old - was going on about his hamper that Mummy had sent out six days ago and God knows where it was now and wasn't it awful and probably those ASC men had helped themselves to his favourite marmalade.

While we were at the table there was an outbreak of musketry from the square, but then just the sounds of men shouting to each other ('Get that fucking wagon moved!.....where to Corp?......just fucking move it!...'), the clatter of horses and gun-carriages on the cobbles, all the sounds of a division sorting itself out into its various components, the last of the ASC wagons quitting the town. As I was paying the waiter for my dinner, the Belgian turned to me and said;

'Mon capitaine, will your army fight here at Le Cateau tomorrow?'

'That is not for me to decide, monsieur'.

I then found a quiet corner of the Hotel de Ville and planned to be on my way before dawn. I checked on the mare, still tethered by the water troughs, along with another dozen or so riding-horses. I gave her some apples which I had helped myself to from the café; they were going to be her last feed for some time. My thoughts as I went to sleep were of Brussels on June 16th 1815, when the British battalions marched out to do battle with a tyrant bent on our destruction. I was still very worried about our battalions on the march to Caudry, after what I had seen of their discipline earlier, or rather lack of it. I had faith in the 3rd Worcesters to maintain march discipline, with Brett and de Salis with them, but I hadn't liked the look of the 2nd Royal Irish Rifles.

It had rained heavily on the night of the 17th June 1815; some things never change. But the days were long gone when you could find a duchess to lay on a ball before a battle. The crash of thunder at midnight made him reach for his Webley, but he realised it was only a storm and he went back to sleep.

Chapter 5

Major Tom Bridges, 4th Dragoons, 2nd Brigade, Cavalry Division

The 4th Dragoons had crossed to France on Sunday August 9th, landing at Boulogne and being briefly fired upon by a battery of .75's, the French commander having been told that a hostile landing was taking place. They were the first British troops to land. All was soon sorted out amidst much back-slapping and hand-shaking and the Dragoons went up to Mauberge and Mons, riding forward to reconnoitre the Brussels road on the 22nd, down which the RFC had reported the Germands advancing. The officers and troopers were armed with the new pattern cavalry sword and the Lee-Enfield. Tom Bridges, aged forty-three, was a squadron commander in the 4th Dragoons, whose commanding officer, Brigadier de Lisle, had announced before leaving England that the first officer to kill a German with the new sword would receive an immediate DSO. That honour fell to Lieutenant Hornby on the 22nd who ran an Uhlan through in a melée in the village of Soignies, the Uhlans finding themselves hampered by their lances, many of them throwing them away in the fight. It was the first action of the war and one of the very few occasions when the *arme blanche* was used.

Major Bridges' war very nearly ended on the 24th. The whole Cavalry Division, four brigades with three regiments per brigade and nine batteries of 13-pounder guns and twelve new Vickers machine guns, had been shifted to the south-west of Mons and was looking for a fight with von Marwitz's cavalry divisons. In the words of Brigadier de Lisle, Bridges' commanding officer, it was 'trailing its coat'. It was confident of its ability to outfight any German cavalry force of equal size, with its long experience in colonial warfare. What nearly did for Tom Bridges on the 24th was a failure in the one area in which the cavalry prided themselves on being expert: reconnaissance. The Cavalry Division, a wartime creation, was tasked with both fighting and reconnaissance duties. As a fighting force, its natural sphere of operations was on the flanks of the moving Army, where it fully expected to chase away enemy cavalry patrols; indeed the officers and troopers were burning with the desire to use the *arme blanche* for which they had trained so long. The squadrons very definitely were not expected to charge enemy infantry or guns or indeed a combination of both, unless they were seen to be in disarray or actually running away. On the morning of the 24th August, the day after Mons, Bridges charged into the village of Andregnies, near Elouges, at the head of his squadron, sword drawn and eagerly expecting to clear whatever scattered enemy could be found round the village. His horse, Umslopogass, fell down with a broken leg and the rest of the Squadron rode over the Major, breaking one of his cheek-bones. The Major lost consciousness and was taken into a cottage. The fall may have saved his life because the rest of the squadron rode straight into a mass of German infantry who would have shot them all down were it not for the fact that the Germans were poor shots at a moving target, but the presence of the enemy infantry came as a complete surprise to the Dragoons.

The Major recovered to find himself in the cottage together with the two elderly owners, a man and his wife, two Red Cross orderlies and some wounded troopers. There were now at least a battalion of German infantry within two hundred yards and bullets were striking the walls and shuttered windows of the cottage. In the vegetable garden at the back the Major spied a broken down horse in the gooseberry patch. He jumped through the window, as far as his shattered face and his height of six foot four inches enabled him to, crawled onto the back of the horse, got into a maze of cottage gardens, and found an exit from the village which took him to a hill where the remains of the 4th Dragoons and 9th Lancers were rallying. By this time the horse could go on no more and the Major shot it with his Webley. Francis Grenfell of the 9th Lancers, already wounded in the hand but full of the exhilaration of a successful rescue of some guns, for which he was to be awarded the VC, told him to hang on since help would surely come. It came in the shape of a silver-coloured sports car, the private property of Captain Sadlier-Jackson, a Cavalry Signals officer. Grenfell was himself rescued, after being wounded again, by the Duke of Westminster in his Rolls-Royce, driven by his chauffeur. Grenfell was taken to Bavai, while the intrepid Major was taken to a big farm which was being used as an advanced dressing-station. He was pronounced whole, except for a splintered cheek-bone and slight concussion, although his Regiment had already posted him as 'wounded and missing'.

But the Major's tribulations had only just begun. He was well looked after at the farm by two ladies who had refused to flee from the advancing Germans. During the night of 24/25th August, Bridges was woken by the sound of horses' hooves and on looking out of the window saw four Uhlans questioning the *patronne,* who was refusing to reveal the whereabouts of the Major, who was now the only occupant of the farm. Bridges went back to bed. The next morning he set off on foot, aided by a stout stick, in the hope of finding his own cavalry.

This was a particularly low point for Bridges. True, he had survived as if by a miracle the debacle at Andregnies, where his Regiment had lost eighty-one officers and men. True, he had got away from the farm, narrowly escaping capture for the second time in twenty-four hours. Now he was on foot, an unhorsed cavalryman, anxiously looking about for enemy cavalry, walking alone down the road to Solesmes, armed with his stick and the Webley. It was very hot, although it was still early in the morning, the 25th August. He had no idea where 5th Infantry Division might be, although he assumed they were in front of him and he had no idea where his own cavalry might be.

Bridges thought of his wife, working as a nurse in the Allied Hospital in Brussels. Was she already in German hands or had she managed to get to Ostend and a boat to England? He marvelled at the local peasant women, bringing in the harvest even as the armies marched across their land. He marvelled at the way the peasants didn't even bother to look up at an RFC scout plane. They put him in mind of William Cobbett's descriptions of Surrey farmworkers in the 1830's. He wondered whether his guardian angel had deserted him.

Bridges had spent his entire life in the Army, first as a gunner and then in the Dragoons. He had been at Mafeking with Baden Powell. His father had been in the Army of the East India Company, 'John Company', before dying in Bermuda, while serving with the garrison artillery. He had left his mother a small pension on which to bring up four boys; a small private school in Oxford, a genteel establishment with no pretence at academic excellence, was all that the funds would allow. His brothers went into the church or died young. All his life had been spent in the company of men until he had met the nurse who was to become his wife. He was as yet childless. He was well-read, taking inspiration from his uncle, the poet-laureate, Robert Bridges.

To be alone is impossible in the Army; in barracks, on manoeuvres, in the Mess, at war, one is never without the society of brother-officers, some rough-hewn, but all drawn from the same stratum of society and all sharing the same belief in the age-old military virtues. Bridges was affable and popular, even if he couldn't afford to be generous with the port in the Mess. But now he was very much alone, walking down a sun-drenched road in northern France, and it was an unnerving experience. He knew that in the next hour or so his life was going to change dramatically one way or the other. Either the next group of horsemen to come down the road was going to be grey-green, with spiked helmets, or it was going to be the familiar khaki, with the Sam Browne belt and the peaked cap.

When the sound of horses' hooves and a cloud of dust told him that a troop of cavalry was approaching from the north, he had no choice but to stand and wait; there was nothing but open fields on both sides of the road and no possibility of concealment. But his guardian angel had not deserted him: it was the 3rd Dragoons, with Brigadier Hugh Gough at their head, his bulbous nose, as red as a beetroot, recognisable at fifty yards.

'I recognised you by your height, old boy. Spotted you as Bridges of the 4th from a hundred yards. I've got a spare charger for you: Greatheart. He's yours until you find a remount. You can ride with us until you find the 4th, or what's left of them after that damn stupid charge.'

Bridges cast aside his stick and was hoisted into the saddle. A mile north of Solesmes they came across a platoon of Lancashire Fusiliers under the command of a subaltern. Bridges had a brief word with the young officer, who told him that they were newly arrived 4th Division troops in 12 Brigade and they were under orders to hold the position at least until night-fall and then to await further orders. Bridges thought their trenches left a lot to be desired but refrained from comment. The young Fusiliers were leaning on their entrenching tools and smoking their pipes and cigarettes; and yet they were the most northerly of the BEF troops in this sector and would soon be in contact with the enemy.

As they approached Solesmes they got mingled up with the refugees and took a route across the fields. They entered the town through the narrow streets to find the Grand Place like Piccadilly Circus on a Friday evening, with touches of an Indian bazaar. Newly arrived 4th Division infantry mingled with the refugee carts, some soldiers, out of pity for the refugees, helping them with their loads. He heard a cockney Rifle Brigade soldier say to an old woman on a wagon, 'Mind how you go missus and I'll send in my bill later', as he passed up a bedding-roll that had fallen off her wagon. Bridges at once recognised that a town centre like Solesmes represented a legitimate and valuable target for German field guns and desperately hoped that Brigadier de Lisle had ordered sufficient cavalry screens to cover the high ground to the north. The Lancashire Fusiliers he had come across earlier hadn't given him much confidence in their ability to keep off more than an enemy reconnaissance patrol. He shuddered at the carnage that would result from even a few well-directed shrapnel rounds, let alone a full HE bombardment. Like all cavalry officers Bridges was trained for war in the open and regarded urban centres certainly as no place for a dragoon and no place for warfare generally. They came across a baggage-train of cavalry stores and Bridges asked a corporal where the officer in charge might be found. He was told that Brigadier Hambro, no less, was at that moment engaged in conversation with General Robertson and would no doubt emerge from the Town Hall in a matter of moments.

Hambro, whom Bridges knew only by sight, duly appeared and introduced himself. Hambro was distraught with the task of trying to reunite the stores with the squadrons, now scattered far and wide between Solesmes and the Cambrai-Le Cateau road. He said,

'Tell you what, old boy; why don't you ride with me in my car? You can give your horse back to Goughie and we'll have a good chance of coming across your 4th Dragoons, or what's left of them, further down the road. I'm going down to Quievy now ahead of the wagons.'

Bridges was getting rather annoyed with everyone telling him how the 4th had been so cut up, but let it rest.

'Capital idea, General, capital.'

Bridges added up his mounts in the last twenty-four hours; three horses and two cars. He noticed that Brigadier Hambro's car was particularly well-appointed, having two Fortnum and Mason picnic hampers strapped to the luggage racks. He looked forward to a slice of duck paté at the very least. He managed to find Gough, thanked him for the loan of Greatheart and told him of his new transport.

The two officers sat in the back of the open car as the driver struggled to get clear of the Solesmes traffic, both civilian and military, past the vanguard of the 3rd Division troops now heading for the Cambrai road. The troops, who had born the brunt of the Mons fighting, looked distinctly ragged. Redcaps waved the car through. Hambro was glad of a sympathetic ear.

'I tell you, Bridges, this is the task of Sisyphus. I've got essential kit for three squadrons and I haven't a clue where they are. Allenby must be having kittens. If the Corps and 4th Division are going to have a battle tomorrow, God knows how the Cavalry are going to get out to the flanks. I've even got all the spare horse-shoes on the wagons and I don't need to tell you about shoes.' Hambro cursed the refugees who he seemed to hold responsible for the plight of the whole BEF. The pitiful sight of the refugees reminded Bridges of some lines from Macaulay's *Lays of Ancient Rome.* He recited the lines to Hambro:

'For aged folks on crutches,
And women great with child,
And mothers sobbing over babes
That clung to them and smiled;
And endless trains of waggons
That creaked beneath the weight
Of corn sacks and of household goods,
Choked every roaring gate.'

'Very appropriate, old boy, but why and how a gate can be 'roaring' escapes me', said Hambro. 'Never was much of a one for poetry; 'cannon to the right of them, cannon to the left of them', I can get the hang of that but anything more complicated is beyond me, I'm afraid'.

As the car approached Quievy, Bridges became more optimistic about finding some at least of his own Dragoons when he spotted a fair number of horses at the water trough in the centre of town. He bid farewell to Hambro and soon got together about a hundred and fifty horse, composed chiefly of the 5th Lancers and some of his own 4th Dragoon Guards. Bridges at once assumed command of this composite force, being the senior officer present and availed himself of a fine gelding. He was further encouraged by the fact that both regiments had their recruiting base in Ireland. They struck out for the Cambrai road and prepared to take up their customary position on the flank of the army and to act as rearguard as the army continued the Retreat. Bridges never did get a chance to sample any of the contents of the Fortnum and Mason hampers.

As far as Major Bridges and his new Commando were concerned the battle of Le Cateau which raged for ten hours on the 26th August was a series of rearguard actions conducted in the orthodox manner. His Commando ranged out to Esnes, made contact with some French cavalry, and bivouacked near Walincourt. He never received any orders informing him of General Smith-Dorrien's Stand and Fight order; in fact he never received any orders at all on the day of battle. He was able to provide an escort for some RFA guns who seemed somewhat lost, although their officer would not admit to it. The battle became just another day in the Retreat and it was not until he reached the northern outskirts of St Quentin on the morning of the 27th that he and his squadrons were presented with an order in the starkest terms: to fight it out and if necessary die like gentlemen.

Chapter 6

26th August, Early Morning, Bertry Lieutenant-General Smith-Dorrien

Horace Smith-Dorrien, feeling all his fifty-six years, managed to sleep for two hours on a folding campaign bed in an ante-room of the Mairie in Bertry between 11.30 p.m. and 1.30 a.m. His ADC, Captain Bowley, woke him with a cup of tea and the news that General Allenby had arrived. General Hamilton was expected shortly and General Fergusson was still out with his rearguard but would be in later. Brigadier Forrestier-Walker was up and about and a staff officer was on standby to take a despatch to St. Quentin. Smith-Dorrien put his knee-length boots on, Bowley giving him a helping hand. An ADC's duty included a fair bit of what came close to a valet's job as far as the General was concerned, although there was a batman to look after things like the creases on his britches. Bowley handed him his swagger-stick.

Horace knew that if orders were to be issued to the divisions it had to be done by 5.30 a.m. at the latest. Even that time would probably be too late to get orders out to the 4th Division. It would take, say, two hours to get a written despatch to GHQ, allow, say, fifteen minutes to receive a reply by wire, assuming that communications had been set up. He couldn't wait for Fergusson. He was still haunted by the near-failure to get the retreat orders out in time to the brigades in the early hours of the 24th. To save time it would be possible to telephone or wire GHQ with the planned battle intentions for the day but the risk of enemy intervention was too great. It's a damn shame that nobody in the Engineers listened to me when I put forward my scheme for using Gaelic speakers in division signals traffic; it would have confounded the enemy. Well, the Engineers listened but as so often in the Army nothing came of it. The only sure way of getting a secure message down to GHQ was by staff officer in a car, and he had better travel with an armed escort. And be damn sure he had a good mechanic with him. He ought to take the Rolls, it was Lord Derby's personal automobile and a good runner.

They were assembled at 2.00 a.m.: Forrestier-Walker, Allenby, Hamilton, Bowley, and of course Smith-Dorrien. All were seated, with their caps and gloves placed beside them on the floor. A map of the front from Le Cateau westwards was spread out on the table; the line of recently dug trenches was marked out in red crayon. Smith-Dorrien started off by saying time was short but they had a 'choice of evils'. He knew from reports already in that there was contact with the enemy all along the twenty mile BEF front, from around Caudry to Le Cateau and at Landrecies in Haig's area. Indeed he had had the most annoying request from GHQ actually asking him to provide troops to go to Haig's help, who claimed to be under attack from at least a brigade of elite German infantry armed with field guns. Ridiculous; and the man has got the whole of the 4th Guards Brigade with him, what more does he want, for God's sake? GHQ is forever eager to hold Haig's hand as if he was a blushing debutante.

'As I say, gentlemen, it is a choice of evils. The choice we have before us is this: we can march away at 7.00 a.m. under the noses of the enemy and turn our backs on him in broad daylight. Or we can make a stand, and trust to our good shooting and the eagerness of the men to fight. As far as the first choice is concerned I don't need to tell you, gentlemen, that there would be a real possibility of a rout if German cavalry got in amongst our retreating columns. And running away when defensive positions, trenches, have already been dug, seems perverse. As for the latter choice, may I tell you our latest intelligence, which is that von Kluck has four army corps at his disposal as well as three cavalry divisions, although they are not all Active Corps.' He pointed with his stick at the map rather vaguely in the area Quievy-Neuvilly, being without his spectacles. 'We would be ordering the men and officers to fight at least three times their number, depending on how Kluck deploys his divisions. And that at a time when many of our men are tired after the rigours of the last three days. Add to that the necessity of breaking off the battle before dark.' The General paused for a moment while an angry fly buzzed around his head. He decided to ignore it. 'We did it often enough in the Transvaal, but not against such numbers. For what it's worth GHQ is all for retreat at all costs as you know, but compared to Mons the ground here is more favourable to us. With friends on both our flanks we have a much shorter line than at Mons, although I hardly need to tell you my views of French cavalry, even if Sordet seems a dependable sort of chap. But when did a commander have everything he wanted in a battle?'

Smith-Dorrien paused and looked at the assembled company, inviting comments from the division generals.

Allenby was the first to speak up, his prominent chin jutting forward, a red line above his eyebrows showing where his cap had rubbed the skin. 'Horace, we don't have a choice. I simply can't vouch for the safety of the flanks of a moving army if we have to move at 7.00 a.m. My horses are tired and some of them blown. My brigades are mostly unreachable. I never did trust this wireless telegraph. I am strongly of the view that we stand'.

Forrestier-Walker spoke up, unbidden, the junior of the officers present.

'I think we have a real chance of dealing the enemy a smashing blow if they come on like they did at Mons. We have better lines of sight for the guns. Von Kluck is a hard pounder as Wellington said of Napoleon, to my mind one of the most over-rated generals of all time. When he came up against British infantry, Napoleon was no match for us. I see Kluck as a general without sophistication who will throw himself at our infantry. Our men are solid in defence. The boche conscript has only two years to prepare for war. And this is not Sedan, as General Wilson at GHQ seems to think.'

'That's enough history', said Smith-Dorrien, 'Hubert, what do you think?' turning to Major-General Hamilton, the commander of 3rd Divison.

'Without question, now is the time to fight. We have a line prepared, at least as good as the one we fought from at Mons and we have more troops and a shorter line. For myself in the centre I couldn't be happier, with friends on both my flanks. Most of my battalions are already in position, with the exception of 7 Brigade, which is causing me worry. I say lets bash the Hun.'

Smith-Dorrien came to his decision.

'Gentlemen, we will stand and fight and I will ask General Snow to fight under me. What I suggest is that you stay here and rest for a couple of hours, then go back to your divisions when the reply from St. Quentin comes back. In that way you can take the new orders with you. To save time we will have them drawn up now. I don't need to remind you that Field Service Regulations gives me considerable latitude in acting without clearing this with GHQ, although knowing French's *idée fixe* about the retirement we can hardly not at least go through the motions. The troops are getting in to position in any case and it will simply be a matter of getting them to fill up their trenches with water and ammunition for a battle. 4th Division on the left of the line, 3rd Division in the centre based on Caudry, and 5th Division here in the west. Cavalry on the flanks. But gentlemen: you must think of this as a stopping blow, no more. Allenby, do please consider the use of at least a couple of RHA guns at Ligny where the ground offers good fields of fire. The Engineers I know are working all night on running out cables. We will use both cable and your own goodselves to pass the orders down the chain of command. I am now going back to bed for a couple of hours. Captain Bowley, will you please see that a message setting out the decision to fight in language that even French can understand is sent immediately to GHQ. Phrase it in such a way that they will have no alternative but to concur. Use the Rolls, with the regular driver. Give him an armed escort. Liaise with Major Hope Johnstone of the AMS. We will meet again when GHQ's reply is here'.

The reply, received by telegraph, duly came at 5.00 a.m., sent with commendable speed, only fifteen minutes after Clegg had arrived with the written dispatch from Second Corps. It read, in clear,

'If you can hold your ground the situation appears likely to improve. 4th Division must co-operate. French troops are taking the offensive on right of First Corps. Although you are given a free hand as to method, this telegram is not intended to convey the impression that I am not anxious for you to carry out the retirement and you must make every effort to do so.'

The generals met again, not exactly refreshed after a brief nap and now joined by General Fergusson of 5th Division. Smith-Dorrien brought Sir Charles Fergusson up to date with developments, but added his anxiety about the right of the line, in Fergusson's Division area. The generals were informed of the telegram from GHQ, with Smith-Dorrien expressing his relief that GHQ was seeing things his way. He expressed his dismay at the lack of information regarding Haig's movements, still shrouded in mystery, although allowance should be made for the fact that he had been engaged in a battle for much of the night. Smith-Dorrien then issued further instructions for Captain Bowley.

'Please be so good as to wire back to French saying that his message is understood and would he communicate with General Sordet of the French Cavalry to the west and tell him that Second Corps will not be retiring. Send in clear, there's no time for encoding. That will be all, gentlemen, now to your business.'

It was now a little after 5.15 a.m. and dawn was breaking.

All over the French countryside between Le Cateau and Wambaux, a distance of about twelve miles, the best part of fifty thousand British officers and men were at that moment on the move, aided by nearly twenty thousand horses of every description: cavalry chargers, draught horses for the transport of guns, limbers, wagons and ambulances, and of course the riding horses of officers like Lieutenant Penfold. To the west, the battalions of the 4th Division were attempting to find their positions, identified from map locations and guided by French liaison officers who were often as much in the dark, in every sense, as themselves. In the centre, around Caudry, most of the battalions were already in their trenches, which they were diligently improving. 7 Brigade were in disarray, however, as General Hamilton had suspected and were trying to establish, without much success, a defensive position to the north and west of Caudry. Firing, both small arms and gunnery, had already broken out all along the line. To the east, the battalions were streaming out of Le Cateau, accompanied by the sound of gunfire, following those that had left before dawn. Gunners everywhere along the line were trying to dig themselves in or at least camouflage their positions. In this they were helped by the stooks of corn piled everywhere in the fields south of the Cambrai road, a road that had borne the tramp of Julius Caesar's legions, and in more recent times, the jackbooted feet of Prussian invaders. 3rd Division battalions between Caudry and Troisvilles were well established, having arrived from Solesmes during the afternoon of the 25th and having had time to improve the trenches dug by the French, dug without military knowledge and resembling nothing more than shallow drainage ditches, but offering protection for the body and a parapet on which to rest a rifle.

To the north of the Le Cateau-Cambrai road came on the best part of a quarter of a million German officers and men; two cavalry corps west of Solesmes with their Jaeger infantry coming on behind with II Corps leading, both Reserve and Active infantry divisions, a total of eight infantry divisions in two army corps on both sides of the Forest of Mormal, the whole panoply of a nation at war, including engineers with bridge-building equipment, the equivalent of a soldier for every yard of front. Indeed there were specialists of every description in the First Army: dentists, sausage-makers, cobblers, electricians. They had come to stay in this land and they had long prepared for this moment. There were shock troops carrying a weapon unknown to the BEF: fusiliers with rifles adapted to fire grenades. Like the British they were a horse-drawn army and they had with them more than 80,000 horses of one sort or another, one horse for every three men. But unlike the British they understood that a machine gun was a weapon of attack and they were massing them accordingly. They had all been on the move since dawn and were soon in contact with British units across a loosely held front of twenty miles. For General von Kluck the 26th August was going to be his best and indeed only chance of encircling, defeating and capturing the larger part of the BEF. His path to Paris would then be clear.

Kluck was an old man in a hurry. Not for him the encirclement manoeuvre beloved of the staff colleges, fixing the British in their positions and then using his superior numbers to roll them up; he wanted to attack the British at first light, now that he realised that he had a chance of bringing them to battle. Even though his scout planes were bringing back conflicting reports of the British positions and movements throughout the 25th, he could tell from the fact that trenches had been dug along a line of ten miles or so west of Le Cateau that the BEF intended to make a stand. The intermittent line of trenches, with their freshly dug earth, had been unmistakable from 10,000 feet, like Morse code without the dots, a photograph having been brought to him before dinner by a dispatch rider on a motorcycle. Now he would achieve what he had failed to achieve on the canal. The trenches told him all he needed to know. All he feared was that the British would once again melt away before his infantry could get to grips with them.

A captain in the Worcesters was pricking his way across the plain, his thoughts on a girl called Phoebe then abed in the Cotswold hills. He was thinking of her unusually dark nipples. A private in the Welch Fusiliers was marching out with his mind still dwelling on the reddish-brown pubic hair around the inviting pussy of a French teacher, still in Le Cateau. A subaltern in the Warwicks was seeing a picture in his mind of his men in flight and he himself left alone to face the enemy; with the fear, the ever-present terror, that he would appear a coward in the face of the enemy. No, not the enemy; in the face of his men. He knew that he was about to face the supreme test of his life.

Chapter 7

26th August, Morning
Near Le Cateau, The Day of Battle
Private Edwards

Most of the men and officers of Second Corps had experienced enemy shell-fire on the 23rd and 24th. Most thought at first that it was beyond endurance, even those who had experience of shell-fire in South Africa, that after a short time all those receiving artillery fire would be dead or wounded. The first whizz-crash of the shrapnel was like a punch in the gut, an assault on the brain, leaving even those in trenches with only one desire, to get to the bottom of the trench and stay there. They were quite quickly to discover that in fact death does not always result and the capacity of the ground to absorb the shock and metal of gunfire is quite remarkable, and that the air-burst of shrapnel lacks killing power beyond fifty yards. Officers were quickly acquiring a studied nonchalance under fire, partly out of bravado but also in the belief that nonchalance would somehow be good for the morale of their men. All the men and officers of Second Corps will learn lessons on this day, the 26th, when the number of enemy guns brought into action was greater, and the duration of fire was longer, than anything they had previously experienced. In fact 600 German guns of all calibres of the 1st Army were ranged against the three divisions of the BEF's Second Corps on this day. Second Corps had 246 guns of all types, including the field guns of 4th Division. Although they were not aware of it that was exactly the number of guns Napoleon massed against the allied line at Waterloo.

At 6.00 a.m. Captain Bowley received a wire from GHQ requesting Lieutenant-General Smith-Dorrien to be at the telephone at the station at

Bertry, to receive a call from General Wilson, the sub-Chief of Staff, but now acting as Chief, General Murray being temporarily in a state of emotional exhaustion. The Mairie still had no telephone. Private Clegg was off getting a supply of requisitioned petrol, or was putting the Rolls in a safe place, no one was sure; the gentlemen-drivers of the RAC Corps were all out in the field on various missions, to the divisional HQs at Haucourt or Reumount, so Bowley put his chief in a small Sunbeam, the property of a staff officer, for the drive to the station.

Smith-Dorrien's only comment on the short drive was that he would rather be speaking to Colonel Macdonough the intelligence chief than Wilson, who was little more than the mouth-piece of the French General Staff, in whose pocket he was. Or perhaps he should say 'poche'. But Bowley told his chief that he had not been able to get hold of anyone at GHQ who could tell him anymore than they already knew: that von Kluck had four Army Corps including his two Cavalry Corps spread out over a huge arc to the north but the RFC would be grounded until the morning mist lifted.

When Smith-Dorrien got to the station, a little more than half a mile away, he was ushered into the station-master's office, now unmanned. It was a cramped space and there was an annoying banging from the goods-handling yard. A portrait of President Poincaré hung over the desk and a government notice listed instructions for the protection of minors from public drunkenness. He waited, pacing up and down, feeling useless, his stick tucked into his armpit. He ground his teeth, a habit of his when agitated. The phone rang and a female French voice spoke into the ear-piece,

'Ne quitez-pas, s'il-vous plait'

Then,

'Is that you, Horace, can you hear me? Henry Wilson here.'

'Yes, just, Henry'

'As you know Horace we, GHQ as a whole, think it most unwise to do as you are doing. Remember the late and not lamented Napoleon troisieme (it was typical of Henry to use the French word) at Sedan. He was enveloped, tout court (again the irritating French, like a tic) and with Kluck's numbers the possibility exists of a repeat performance. You must get away and resume the retirement at the earliest opportunity. With Lanrezac falling back you run the danger of finding your right flank in the air.'

Just then the noise of shell-fire could be clearly heard in the office, the walls even shaking slightly from the reverberations.

'Did you hear me, Horace? What was that sound?'

'Yes, Henry. There are noises off'.

'Well, I must say you sound remarkably cheerful. And yours is the first cheerful voice I have heard in days. Good luck to you.'

'Thank you, Henry. And what can you tell me of the French on my left?'

But the line was dead. Wilson had rung off. Horace put down the apparatus, which he had been holding in both hands, having put down his stick on the desk. Bowley was standing just outside the door, keeping watch. Horace opened the door and said,

'The battle has started. Let's go back to the Mairie. There's very little we can do now.' He picked up his stick and they went out to the car.

Something that Wilson had said about his right being in the air was worrying Sir Horace. Did he mean to say that Haig would not be on his right?

At that precise moment, in a bedroom of a small hotel in Le Grand Fayt, eight miles to the north-east, Lieutenant-General Sir Douglas Haig was sitting up in bed, having been brought a cup of tea by his ADC Major Dawnay. A young staff officer from GHQ, Captain Deedes, was waiting outside in the foyer, having ridden from St. Quentin, a journey that had taken him the best part of three hours. He had left GHQ well before the Rolls arrived from Bertry with news of Smith-Dorrien's intention to offer battle; he was of course under the impression the Second Corps would be retiring soon after first light, as ordered by GHQ the previous day. Haig was feeling delicate, tired and wan, only marginally recovered from a bout of stomach sickness, or to be precise violent diarrhoea. The MO had given him some remedy that had caused his bowels to counter-attack in an equally violent manner. A truce in his intestinal war had now been declared. He had arrived at this small town in the early hours, having fled Landrecies which had been under attack from unknown numbers of German infantry, who had used both machine-guns and a field gun in their assault. It had taken Captain Deedes quite a time to track down the First Corps commander to his new HQ.

'Show him in'.

'Good morning, Sir', Deedes said. 'I have orders from the Commander-in-Chief'.

'Please acquaint me with them. I do not have my spectacles to hand'

'The gist, Sir, is that, in accordance with standing procedures you are free to choose your line of retirement, south-east toward French 5th Army, due south to Etreux, or south-west toward Honnechy/Busigny and Second Corps.'

'As you know, Captain, we were violently attacked in our billets last night at Landrecies. The Germans attacked, using a ruse, dressed as French soldiers. The 4th Guards' Brigade is coming out on the road south, leaving I have no doubt many dead and wounded behind and piles of stores burning even now to prevent them falling into German hands. The Brigade is in no fit state to march west to fight another battle, if such is to take place near Le Cateau. In any case it is clear that the enemy is in strength between the two Corps. My orders to retire stand good as you have just said. Second Corps now has 4th Division as a reinforcement. I shall continue the retirement on the lines I have already laid down. I have already informed Lanrezac of the attack on the Guards' Brigade last night and he is moving troops in my direction. I shall march south to Etreux with both divisions, although 4th Cavalry Brigade will move west in a reconnaissance. The road to Etreux is a good one and I shall be able to double-bank the columns.'

And with that, Douglas Haig sealed the fate of the right flank of Smith-Dorrien's line, the 14th Infantry Brigade, in particular the 2nd Battalion of the Suffolk Regiment.

At 5.30 a.m. Private Frank Edwards, 2nd Royal Welch Fusiliers, was marching alongside Buffy with the Battalion, almost one thousand strong, strung out on the Roman road in four columns, the Company Commanders and the subalterns marching and riding alongside. Those riding would soon give up their mounts to the grooms who would be going to a rear area with the battalion transport, together with the other non-combatants. They all knew now that the whole Corps was to offer battle and in the British Army that meant only one thing: that they would fight until ordered otherwise. The exit from the town had been a hot one, but the 1st Middlesex had done most of the fighting, firing from the doorways of the houses at the dim grey figures of German soldiers coming on in short rushes and small groups through the town. There was fighting in the street where Suzanne's house was, the girl having moved down to the cellar with a supply of water, apples, a boiled hock of ham and her copy of *Madame Bovary*. Edwards remembered he had said he would be back for her. It was a thing devoutly to be wished for. But there is nothing to concentrate the mind as much as marching out, knowing that the Battalion is to take its place in the lines and must meet the enemy in battle, by the dawn's early light.

As they were leaving town they heard the sound of a train leaving the station, the engineers straining to get up a head of steam. Buffy said,

'Just like on the Titanic, the first class passengers always leave without getting their feet wet'.

He seemed to have a bit of an obsession with the Titanic, but Edwards knew that the top brass had long gone. But maybe Buffy is not far wrong with his Titanic thing and it's going to be every man for himself before long. But at least we sha'n't have to worry about the women and children.

Four Eyes had told them just before dawn that the Battalion was to march out to a position south-west of Reumont, near Maurois, where they were to be in reserve and that the whole Corps was to fight it out. This was not unwelcome news, both bits of it, but Edwards was enough of an old campaigner to know that that did not mean they would not be brought up to plug holes in the line. What was worrying Edwards was the presence of two civilians in the ranks with him, the journalist wallah, and a jumpy little man with a French accent, who said he was a salesman for an agricultural seed company. As Edwards said to Buffy, 'He keeps going on about how he had been seeing his long-standing customers in Mons and had managed to get away just before the fighting started, 'and all 'ell broke loose'. I could have told him that bit that for nothing'.

Well, he's got a habit of bringing the Germans with him. The one thing you don't want is a couple of civilians getting in the way, even if one of them is a gentleman, *The Times* man I mean. And if that stray black dog joins us it's going to look like a music hall, what with the seed man's bowler making him look like Charlie Chaplin. The seed man said he was an Englishman and we'll have to give him the benefit of the doubt for the time being. *The Times* wallah may be a gentleman but he has a nasty habit of turning up like the proverbial bad penny. But I'll say this for him, he has pluck that man.

By this time we had left the town by the cutting and were passing the front trenches of the line and the first rays of the morning sun were on our backs, but filtered through the mist and I couldn't help wondering how many of us were going to see it go down this evening. I didn't like the look of the position from the point of view of the poor buggers who were going to have to fight here. First, they were too close to the concealed exit from the town and the enemy were close on our heels, the Middlesex holding them off for the moment. It looked like a full Company up forward and they said they were the 2/12th, which I knew to be Suffolks. They were still digging with their grubbers, officers strutting about. Just country boys in uniform I thought and they are going to find the whole of von Fuck's grey infantry on top of them before long and fighting with their fists to save their lives. They looked to be what was called in the Peninsula the 'forlorn hope', if I remember rightly, the ones who are sacrificed for the buggers behind them. But at least they had managed to scratch enough of a trench to keep their heads down below ground level, which is where I would stay if I were them. The only consolation they've got is that the banks of that sunken lane behind them could provide some protection from artillery blast.

Well, we went on turning left down the Roman road, the cobbles glistening from the rain in the night, the road to St. Quentin I mean, with the weak sun now on our left and damn me if I didn't notice another rum thing. Now I have been in this army long enough to know that gunners don't put themselves up with the infantry in a battle unless they have a good reason. And I could see at least three batteries up on the hill, probably four, with infantry up close and a command post and a machine-gun position nearby. And this wasn't horse artillery, which was going to gallop off when things got too hot. No, these were 18-pounders and howitzers, not 13-pounders. This could only mean one thing and that was that this position was going to fight it out to the bitter end, the guns not dug in like they should be, what with all this being a bit of a last-minute operation. And it doesn't take a military genius to work out that if the gunners on the hill are up there to get a better sight of their targets the opposite also holds true: the enemy can see our gunner boys better. Those poor Suffolks are going to cop the anti-battery fire as sure as squirrels eat nuts; double-trouble again for the country boys. It was still misty which was probably the reason fritz was taking his time, although it was still only just after 6.00 a.m.

And then I remembered the river valley between the town and the hill and the high ground to the east. This spelt triple- trouble for the Suffolks, unless they had some more support over that way which I didn't know about. They said the Guard's Brigade was over there, or was meant to be, which put me in mind of the old saying, 'Steady the Buffs, and let the Guards take up the rear', and there's many a true word spoken in jest. But then I thought that the officers would know the picture and it wasn't my business, unless it was to turn out that we were going to have to come back up and plug the gaps. I was thinking all this and noticing more guns on the west side of the road and more infantry there too, and thinking that this is going to be a hot spot. And the poor buggers in just shallow trenches, dug by the frogs or so I believe. A sergeant called out to me and said they were the Yorkshire Light Infantry, which I knew as the Koylies. I wished him good luck and even called him 'boyo' which was not proper address for a sergeant, but I was feeling all Welsh for a moment, it must have been the emotion of it all I suppose. 'We'll have a bang at the bastards before long.' I called out. He just looked at me in the way a sergeant will look at a private, which is to say not with a great deal of the human spirit, if you get my meaning. We then passed the Yorkshire machine-guns, with the men digging in, their Lieutenant standing over them. I felt sorry for the machine-gunners; always the last to leave a position and never quite knowing whether the gun is going to jam. But they're the boys you want with you when the bulleys begin to fly. They looked well supplied with ammunition, I was glad to see, the teams unloading boxes from a wagon. A man was driving stakes into the ground next to the dug-out, on the left and right, setting out the limits of the field of fire.

The two civvies were still sticking to me like poxy resin, the seed man getting happier the further back we went but bringing his bad luck with him, and *The Times* man, who is called Mr. Moore, getting a good look around. And then I heard a plane overhead and I looked up and saw the black crosses and knew that that meant trouble. There is one thing that you can be sure about and that is that the Taubes have a way of sending messages to their guns, I don't know how but it must be some Morse code transmitter device. Sure enough the pilot did a few circles, out of rifle range of course, and with the mist lifting you can be certain that he had a good view of our position, there was no hiding it stuck out on the hill on the stubble. He didn't drop any flares like I have seen them do before but flew off cool as he could be, set on his mission, which was surely to bring down shell-fire on the poor gunners and soldiers on that hill. We went past the 5th Division HQ at Reumont where General Fergusson was set up in what looked like the school and I had a strange vision of him sitting down at the teacher's desk, while the staff took instructions in the class-room. There were signallers running about with their coils of wire and a dozen cars as well as horses hitched up with grooms holding the halters.

It started, the bombardment I mean, more or less the moment we got to our reserve position south-west of Reumont, off the Roman road and in a farm track with banks on both sides. I could see Four Eyes looking at his wrist-watch for some reason, sort of staring at it, but officers are keen on their watches, it makes them important. It was 6.30 a.m. precisely and the Germans are known for their precision. And this was not just a few Krupp guns like the poor buggers had to cope with at Spion Kop in Natal, this was the whole German artillery of a division. I could see the gun flashes even from here and they were on the far side of Le Catoo, over to the north-east, it must have been four miles from where we were and two miles at least from the Suffolk boys, but I knew those guns, the 77s, had a range of up to five miles, give or take. So that put us at their extreme range. We were not likely to be among their targets for now, although there was an RFA howitzer battery a few hundred yards to our north and the big long-barrelled 60-pounders behind us, the divisional Royal Garrison guns. The big artillery horses were now being led into a temporary corral by a farmyard to our left. So I knew there was a fair chance that we would get our share of the shelling and if Fritz started sending over big stuff like the 5.9's we would be in trouble, but the shrapnel I wasn't too worried about, we'd seen that up at the canal. So I told the seed man he had got nothing to worry about and to take it all like the Englishman he claimed to be. He didn't like that bit and pulled his bowler hat down as if it would offer some protection. He kept down in the lane, although I was watching the proceedings from the bank. The cool Mr. Moore just wrote things down in his notebook, still with his Panama on his head.

The shells were falling on the hill with no pauses, not like a salvo followed by another, but the salvoes of so many batteries together making a continuous roaring explosion, throwing up the earth in spouts or geysers. Woolly Bears they were called, the smoke from the big HE shells, mixed up with the earth and stones and other things I didn't want to think about. Surely it was not meant to be like this, this was not what the brass had in mind when they ordered us to stand firm and fight back. This wasn't fighting back, this was useless slaughter of our boys, putting them on a hill so the fritzes could shoot at them. Well, I could see that our guns were firing back at the gun-flashes on the far side of Le Catoo, I don't think they were getting the range but they were cool customers all right, just carrying on like at Woolwich or wherever they do their training. I could see now there were four of our batteries in action on the hill and another three on our side of the road, all barking with anger, the muzzle flashes visible in the misty air. I knew then that it was a matter of hanging on and surviving until the fritz infantry appeared, as they surely would. And then we would have a bang at them, if there any of us left.

But then I realized why it was that the enemy had the range and the location of our position on the hill so precisely. It wasn't just the Taube; if I knew anything about artillery from my time in South Africa, it was that gunners like to have their officers forward, spotting the fall of shot and calling the correcting shots. And this is what they must be doing now. The question was, where could these fritz forward officers be? And then it came to me: the clock tower of the church, the highest point in Le Catoo. I knew right away when I saw it that it was like a beacon for miles around. The crafty Hun had surely got an officer up there with a telephone cable laid out to his battery; the Hun must have shimmied up there almost as soon as we quit the town. Either that or the local priest is a German spy and is doing their work for them. Look for the priests with the Zeiss, that's what I'd tell the Red Caps.

As soon as I realized this I wanted to tell Four Eyes and get permission to run or ride back to the hill and tell that Suffolk colonel to put some shots into the tower. Those poor farming boys crouching down in their scrapings could not see what I could see from back here, even though I was out of the line of sight of the tower. I could see it in my mind's eye as surely as if I was there, which was giving me grief and pain. But there was nothing I could do, except curse the Hun who used churches against us. Except we would do the same against him, if the tables were the other way around.

Enemy gunners were now getting guns into new positions, well out in the open now, so confident was he getting with his great numbers. I could see our gunners shifting their fire and manhandling their guns to take on the new targets. How could our guns keep up their fire, under such a barrage, and how would the resupply wagons get up there? I knew for a fact that each gun would initially have only a hundred shells and that to send up more wagons from the lines would necessitate running the gauntlet of the open ground.

I thought I could see fire coming from the Cambrai Road in front of the Suffolk boys, but I could not be sure. If so, and if the enemy had machine guns up forward, the farming lads were surely doomed to death or surrender, together with the Yorkshiremen on the low ground on my side of the road. But my guess now was that General Smith-Dorrien under whose orders we were, would soon call us up to go up there; either us or our sister-battalions, the 1st Middlesex, the Scottish Rifles or the kilted Argyll and Sutherland Highlanders. That's what generals do in my experience: when things are going badly for the poor buggers in the front, they throw more poor buggers from the back into the fire. As if that's going to put the fire out. And the poor sods who have to go up there have to go up in the open, which is the one thing an infantryman doesn't want to do.

Just then the two big 60-pounders behind me opened fire with a crash which pained my ears. I was sure I could see one of the shells, the size of a small dog, clear against the sky, and I followed its progress until it fell with a yellow Lyddite explosion on the ridge to the west of the town five thousand yards away. This image of a dog stayed in my mind and I said to Buffy, 'there goes one of the dogs of war.'

Buffy didn't have a clue what I was talking about, or else he was deafened by the firing of the 60-pounders. Mr. Moore barely looked up from his note-book.

I then remembered that the 60-pounders, with their long barrels, God Bless 'em, were really naval guns, so I said to Buffy 'Thank God we've got a navy.' and again he looked at me as if I was mad.

It was going to be a very long day.

Chapter 8

Early Morning Another Part of the Battlefield, Near Caudry: Captain Johnson

At 5.30 a.m. Captain Henry Johnson of the 3rd Worcesters was approaching the village of Troisvilles. He was keeping to the unmade road to the south of the Cambrai road, there just being enough light to make his way. Caudry lay two miles away to the east, across open country, now hidden in the misty half-light. He had left Le Cateau on the piebald mare in the middle of a street battle between what must have been dismounted German cavalry and elements of 14th Brigade. German cavalry had their fearsome reputation but Uhlan lancers in a town should hold no fear for a British soldier with a Lee-Enfield and even Johnson's Webley service revolver should offer some feeling of security. But there was something sinister about the spiked helmet, the lance so reminiscent of medieval times, the unbroken link to the Hunnish hordes of antiquity that lived on in the collective memory, a memory that occupied a corner of Johnson's mind. But take the horse away from the Uhlan and he doesn't make a good foot-soldier. Better still, shoot the horse and you remove a valuable trained animal. Cavalry boots are not made for walking.

Just short of Troisvilles he came across some Norfolks and Cheshires trying to cut down a tree, armed with a ludicrously small cutting tool. It pained him to see a task carried out with the wrong implement but he passed on without comment. The sergeant in charge told him that the tree was an obvious marker for enemy artillery and that they had been trying to cut it down for the past hour; that he had asked some froggies for a decent saw but he might as well have asked for the moon. Johnson knew that they had suffered heavy losses on the 24th at Elouges. He could see and hear shells falling in Caudry itself and it was his duty and his heart-felt wish to re-join his battalion and report to Brigadier McCracken; anything else would have been unthinkable. Into the maelstrom of exploding high explosive he must go.

He came across a group of twenty or so artillery draught horses in the lane, under the care of their grooms. There had clearly been a recent shrapnel burst very close and the grooms were tending to the wounded horses; one man was extracting a shrapnel ball from the flank of a chestnut gelding, the huge horse's eyes swivelling and his cropped tail thrashing the air, the groom's mate holding the horse's head. Other horses were leaning against the banks of the lane as if determined to carry on despite their lacerations. Another burst and they will bolt, thought Johnson, there didn't seem anything to stop them, but there did seem to be some sort of understanding between man and beast. The Brigade vetinerary officers are going to have to get busy. The mare cleared the bank of the lane and they were on their way, now out in the stubble.

The six-gun battery just south of the lane was a fine sight, one that never failed to impress Johnson. The guns had been newly painted by the look of it in a metallic grey to reduce glare, each gun served by six men and NCOs. They all looked as if they were eager to do their business, the business of firing shells, carefully fused, at an enemy who might be anything up to eight thousand yards away. The men were still digging-in the guns, making a pit camouflaged with corn stooks from the field. Engineers were laying out cable to a command post just behind the battery. Ammunition wagons were being unloaded by bombadiers, who were stacking the boxed shells in readiness for the layers. Johnson saluted their Lieutenant and rode on through Troisvilles, an unprepossessing place now deserted, apart from some farm dogs. Johnson was now back on the farm track, grateful for its occasional low banks and the shelter they provided.

A little further on a small group of obviously frightened Frenchmen, local farm workers probably, huddled together under the bank. There was nothing that Johnson could do about them. They were a hindrance to traffic but Johnson felt sorry for them; after all it was their land that was being invaded and it was them the army was fighting for and they had a sort of right to be there. He would have liked to order them to help the artillerymen with the draught horses but they didn't look as if they would obey an English captain. He then had the thought that they were going to be the Germans' problem in a matter of hours. They were sullen, cowed, but one of them addressed him as 'mon capitaine' and touched his cap. They had their blue trousers tied with twine at the knees as well as the waist, making them look as if they had been parcelled up before setting out. He forced the mare through them, the mare now with her ears back.

Shells were falling near him now, shrapnel, but they were bursting high, searching fire he thought, searching for the battery he had just passed. The 18-pounders opened counter-fire, firing six-gun salvos, making the mare jump and buck, almost throwing Johnson off. There was a brigade headquarters just beyond the battery, in the lane, and he thought that it was a bad place for an HQ, that it would receive fire intended for the battery. But they could shift, it was only a few wagons, an ambulance, some runners and signallers like himself, a half-dozen staff officers, 13 Brigade of 5th Division probably, which he knew to be Guthbert's brigade. There was no enemy infantry in sight and he could see a fair way to the north, the mist beginning to lift and sunshine coming through on his back. There were piles of obviously human shit beside the lane, just over the bank; it had clearly been the site of an overnight bivouac by a 5th Division battalion. There were other signs of recent human habitation, a few mess-tins which their owners would miss later. The cookers of the battalion were standing nearby, the horses having a feed themselves from nosebags; he thought it was high time they made off for the rear. The men were dousing the fire of the cooker and steam was rising.

There were larks ascending and descending in the morning sky but their song was not audible to the human ear, drowned out by the crash of the 18-pounders and the roar of falling masonry in the town, now less than a half a mile away. But even if he had been able to hear them, Henry would not have remarked to himself on the paradoxical juxtaposition of the anger of the guns and the sweetness of the song. It was a paradox he would not have recognised; the diary he was keeping and was to keep throughout the War makes no such observations. His diary was to be a record of his own actions, that of his brigade and battalion, and his dismay at the shortcomings of other less well-run battalions like the East Lancashires. He was annoyed, in his practical way, that the stupid Arch-Duke had got himself shot so early in the summer, starting off the War before the harvest could all be brought in. We will all have to pay for that later, he thought.

His mare was skittish but not alarmingly so. He decided to go in to Caudry by the south. The shells were screaming in, high explosive mostly, which he knew was much more effective in a built-up area than shrapnel. He had to give the enemy some professional respect, to have been able to bring so much artillery and high explosive into action so early in the day, although the town was not exactly a difficult target. The enemy seemed to be shelling indiscriminately, perhaps in the belief that the British would abandon the town, but obviously caring nothing for the fate of the civilians. There were a lot of buildings on fire. He could see flames licking around the edge of what looked like a gas-holder. The church tower was still standing.

He found a grain-store at the edge of town and put the mare in; there were other horses there and a couple of soldier-servants, boys looking barely eighteen years old, probably less. There were three things he wanted to do now; find 7 Brigade HQ, where McCracken should be; find Sergeant Rouse of his own Section and find Simon Brett and his old

Company of the 3rd Worcesters, Simon being now second-in-command and a Captain. And with luck find his groom and tell him where the piebald mare was.

He quickly made his way to the main square of this biggish town, about the size of Le Cateau or Solesmes. The confusion was however much worse than in those towns, made a hundred times worse by being under artillery attack. There were infantry of different regiments all muddled up, which he knew to be a bad sign. There was naked fear on the faces of men, sheltering in doorways, who stared at him as if he was a hostile stranger rather than a superior officer in their own brigade. The Royal Irishmen confirmed his low opinion of them by turning away from him, clearly reluctant to accept orders from an officer in a different battalion. So far as he could tell, German infantry had not yet appeared in the town itself; at least that gave him some time to organise a defence, which clearly hadn't been attempted so far. There was no firing line, the assorted men, who appeared leaderless, were huddled around the edge of the square, obviously having been driven in from their positions to the north of the town. Some of them, as he was taking all this in, broke cover and ran, clearly without orders, down the road he had come in; that is toward the south and away from the enemy, even though there were no enemy infantry to be seen. They rushed past him, knocking over tables and chairs which were still on the pavements outside the cafés. Johnson made no attempt to restrain them but he did draw his Webley in case he needed to buttress his authority with its threat. He was dismayed to see that some of these men were NCOs, and further dismayed to see one or two were from his own battalion. He guessed that the terror and panic of the local inhabitants had communicated itself to his men. A man lay dead in front of a café, clearly a waiter by the apron round his middle, the back of his head matted with blood; he must have been hit with the first HE salvoes. A breakfast roll still lay on its plate on the table and Johnson helped himself to it. He put it in a pocket of his tunic.

But worst of all, there were three RFA guns with their horse teams in the square, which had no business being there at all. Presumably they had been driven in from the north of the town, from their initial position, now overrun. Their drivers seemed paralysed, the junior officers in charge seemingly helpless and the horses on the verge of bolting. At any moment they could fall victim to an artillery strike. Johnson looked at his Rolex watch: it was just after 6.00 a.m. He had been in the town less than hour.

In the square there were four roads which converged on it and on the south side was the Mairie, which was partly on fire, from what looked like a direct hit from an incendiary shell. Did the Hun have incendiary shells? He didn't know. Part of it had collapsed by a hit from what Johnson guessed was a large HE howitzer shell, one of the 5.9's. Red-tabbed officers were rushing about, some covered with blood, dazed, others trying to assert some authority. Johnson went up the steps and a signals corporal he recognised, with blood seeping from a bandaged head wound, told him that this was 7 Brigade and 3rd Worcester HQ, that Brigadier McCracken was hurt and hors de combat but would survive by the look of him. It was clear that the Mairie would have to be abandoned. The Colonel was not in the building, but out somewhere in the town. There were some RAMC orderlies binding up the more urgent cases, but it was quite obvious that command had now effectively ceased, as far as the Brigade was concerned. A 4th Middlesex corporal then arrived, pleading for RAMC orderlies to come to the church, pressed into service as a dressing station, where a fire had started. Some quartermaster men ran back across the square with the corporal without waiting for orders, towards the church.

All this Johnson took in in the space of a few minutes. He knew that order must be restored; a firing line must be improvised because the enemy would surely be coming on in a matter of minutes, and that the only way to do this was by gathering together what men and NCO's he could bring together in a scratch force under his command. The men he had witnessed running back would have to be sorted out later. The shelling had now abated somewhat, or rather the enemy gunners had shifted their attention to the southern part of the town. He went round the square, collecting up a variety of men, some of them quartermaster NCO's, some 1st Wiltshires and a few Royal Irish Rifles and Royal Scots, together with some of his own Worcester men, making an ad hoc force of perhaps a hundred and fifty all told. One or two were clerks from Brigade, now shelled out of the Mairie. His orders to all these assorted men were that they would defend the square, under his command. He used the manual signal they were all familiar with, indicating 'Fall In On Me'. A Royal Irish subaltern emerged from a wrecked building, dusted himself down, saluted and promptly passed out. A soldier rushed to his aid.

The enemy seemed to be coming on strong now down the main street from the north, and in all likelihood from other places as well, and it was imperative to form a barrier in the square from which to form a fighting position. To his great relief the gunners had managed to get themselves out of the square and were now clattering down the road to the south. It did briefly cross his mind that they could have been used to fire down the approach roads to the north, but dismissed it as not a practical proposition. But the men were responding to his orders and were getting themselves into firing positions using what cover was afforded by the bomb-blasted buildings.

He ordered a Wiltshire sergeant and a dozen men to use the fallen masonry and other debris that was lying around as shelter from which men could fire from a prone position. Bullets from approaching German infantry were now swishing overhead and striking and ricocheting off the nearby buildings, one of which was a branch of the *Credit Agricole*. He thought that he might hold this position at the north part of the square for perhaps half an hour and then fall back, but where to exactly he had no idea. It was at this moment, to his great relief and joy, that Simon Brett appeared, with about fifty men and two subalterns of the 3rd Worcesters. They rushed up, with Simon at their head, from the road which entered the square at the north-west. Johnson called out, above the cacophony,

'Good to see you, old man. Things are getting a bit sticky here. Come and join the party'.

'Delighted to be invited, Henry. We got a bit held up. Major Crawford has been wounded.'

'I'm sorry to hear that but if de Salis could join us the triumvirate will be reunited. The Brigadier is out of action, I'm afraid'.

At this moment Major-General Hamilton arrived in the square on a grey horse, accompanied by half a dozen officers and men. With astounding insouciance, he rode up to the two officers and said, or rather shouted above the sounds of falling masonry and rifle-fire, his horse prancing like a circus animal,

'Hold this position for an hour if you can. We are bringing out the wounded from the Mairie and the church. We will then evacuate the town and take up positions to the west and south. You will go out to the field west of here and form a fighting line. Good work. Carry on.'

He rode off with his entourage to the south, keeping a tight rein on his handsome horse.

To Johnson's surprise, the German infantry seemed reluctant to press on with much enthusiasm. They were using the doorways of houses and smashed buildings as cover and only came forward when urged on by an officer, or so it seemed to Johnson. Bizarrely, there were still some tables and chairs on the pavement outside a café and the enemy were seen to be working their way around them in a mocking gesture of respect for private property.

'Fire at the officers, watch for the ones with no rifles!' Johnson shouted. The men didn't need to be told this of course but it was useful general advice. Johnson found himself waving his Webley around in a ridiculous manner, so he discharged it in the direction of the enemy, even though they were still a hundred and fifty yards away and extremely unlikely to get hit by its bullet. It did make him feel better and it was the first shot he had fired in anger at the King's enemy in his life. It showed the appropriate aggressive spirit. It would, he thought, need a bit more than one revolver .455 projectile to avenge the burning of the Louvain library, a Hunnish crime that particularly incensed him. Curious how one has time to think of libraries at a time like this.

'Use the upper floor of that Bank! There is a good field of fire from that window!' Brett ordered six men from his company into the building. The men sprinted across the open space, one man getting hit in the leg and going down, but then helped up again by his mate. 'Must remember to put that man's name forward for a medal', thought Brett, the man having added considerably to his own chances of being hit. He saw the men break into the Bank by firing at the door-lock, wondering for a moment whether the directors of the Bank could claim compensation.

Johnson then decided to shift his position to another part of the square, to check on proceedings at the eastern side. He was very conscious of the lack of senior officers. Where was Colonel Stuart? He had lost touch with proceedings everywhere except the bit of the square he was in, and men were being hit now by small arms fire with distressing frequency. Thank God the shelling had stopped, now that the enemy infantry were closing in. He had another moment of giving credit to the enemy for their infantry/gunnery co-ordination. What time is it now, I wonder? He looked at his watch: 6.47 a.m. Later, he was to remember this exact time because it was then that he received a punch in the lower part of his leg and the two events were soldered together in his mind. It was actually at the moment he was looking at the Rolex, with its luminous dial, that he was hit.

It turned out to be, by an incredible stroke of luck, the merest flesh wound, although quite a large chunk had been gouged out of his leg. He bound it up himself with his linen handkerchief, a present from Phoebe. His first thought was annoyance with himself, surprisingly, not with the enemy. How stupid of me to get shot. He thought at first of how this was going to spoil his running between the wickets and then annoyance turned to relief when he realised that it wouldn't.

He was now getting more conscious of the isolation of his position in the square. The rest of the Brigade seemed to have fallen back on both sides and the general had ordered him to abandon the position, but at an unspecified time. Surely that time was fast approaching.

He called out to Brett, shouting above the continuous rattle of fire,

'We must fall back to the south-west of the square by sections. And then out to the field. Each platoon to give covering fire to each other. Get the men out of the Bank. Five rounds rapid. Go now'

They had to leave a dozen dead and severely wounded men at the makeshift barricade, but they made it in small groups and in short rushes to the edge of the square, past the burning Mairie and then out towards the big field of beet adjoining the town, Johnson dragging his wounded leg behind him, and accepting help from a Worcester soldier who took his arm and shoulder in a comforting grip ('Just lean on me, Sir.') They formed a line in the root-crop and made use of its cover, with Brett moving out to the left of the line, the men spacing themselves at two yard intervals. As far as he could tell the Brigade had abandoned the town now. There were no friendly troops on his left that he could see. He could not know that 11 Brigade of 4th Division were fighting a similar action half a mile to the west against Jaeger infantry, and that they would be locked into a fire-fight for the next seven hours. He could not know that the enemy for unknown reasons were not to exploit the gap between his small force and the village of Fontaine to his left. He was to learn much later that further to the west the Essex, the Lancashire Fusiliers and the Inniskilling Fusiliers were already locked in close-quarter combat with Jaeger infantry, and that they would be driven from the field, the enemy having brought up twenty machine-guns into their attack, something that was not even in the BEF Field Service Manual. He was to find out, also much later, that little more than a mile to the south-west the King's Own had been ambushed by a German cavalry force and had suffered three hundred casualties from a field gun and a machine-gun, in the space of two minutes. How could he know that the 1st Warwickshires had already been ordered up in support of the King's Own and were even at this time going in to an attack? An infantry officer in a beet-field, surrounded by the sounds of battle and facing the enemy in that field can know only what he sees in front of him.

What he did know, because he could see it with his own eyes, was that enemy infantry was moving about in the beets a good five hundred yards off and they seemed to be growing in numbers. Bullets were swishing and zapping through the heavy air and hitting the beet-leaves with a disconcerting tearing sound, and hitting his men with a dull thwacking sound. If the German infantry tactics were anything like British tactical doctrine, their officers would be sure to drive their men forward, aided by whatever supporting fire their commanders could lay on. All over the battlefields of France on this day similar engagements were taking place; the belief in the power of the offensive having a strangle-hold on the doctrinal thinking of strategists in military academies from St. Petersburg to Sandhurst. This theorising had filtered down to battalion officers like Johnson and Brett; indeed they would often ask each other, 'Are you going to be offensive today?' and reply 'Only mildly so, old boy.'

His own supporting artillery was not in evidence; he was going to have to hold this position with the men's rifles alone. The 18-pounders that were in the square an hour ago would be well away to the south by now and quite unreachable. But it was a comfort to know that quartermasters, even batmen and cooks, had all been trained to the highest standards with the bolt-action Short Magazine .303 Lee-Enfield, with its ten-round magazine fed with clips holding five rounds each.

Fifteen aimed rounds a minute was easily achieved by most soldiers, and most could exceed that. It was a sturdy, reliable weapon, easier to handle than its French and German counterparts. A fusilier or a rifleman could, and did, achieve impressive results at ranges up to 1200 yards. The ranges involved here were much less than that. Johnson, although a Signals Officer, was trained in, and familiar with, infantry tactics. His leg wound was becoming a bit of a bore, but he felt better being out in the field than in the confines of the town. He put his head up just enough to have a look around, and, joy of joys, here was de Salis coming out of the town with another twenty or so men of his platoon to add to his line. The old triumvirate was complete!

Chapter 9

Morning, The Left of the Line
Lieutenant Penfold

The 1st Warwickshires left Solesmes in a thunderstorm shortly before midnight on the 25th August, unmolested by the enemy. They were the last British troops to quit the town, and the battalion was at full strength. Their Lieutenant-Colonel, Elkington by name, rode at the head of the four columns of marching infantry, alongside the adjutant. Elkington was an unconventional man. Before leaving for France he had shaved off all the hair on his head in the interest of hygiene, and it was rumoured that he had shaved off all his body hair as well. This in fact showed a fair degree of knowledge of the living arrangements of the common louse, although the louse was also more than happy to live in the seams of the shirts of trench-dwellers until such time as the wearer of the shirt took the offensive against his parasitic tenants. But the days of the lousy trench-dweller were yet to come.

To help navigate the route to Haucourt the Division staff had found a French guide and interpreter, Major Trichet, who rode with Lieutenant-Colonel Elkington. It was a pitch-black night, at least at the time when the Battalion set off, and the only artificial aids to navigation were the electric torches of the half-dozen officers chosen to carry them, torches thoughtfully provided by the adjutant from Brigade stores. A fitful half-moon did appear after an hour or so, which illuminated the roadway sufficiently to permit quite easy identification of it. But on the whole, as long as one man followed in the footsteps of another, a trouble-free passage was not out of the question. It was not exactly the first time in the history of the British at war that troops have had to march at night, under threat of enemy action. But enemy action had been in evidence around Solesmes right up to the moment of the Battalion's departure, which was making the men, already tired, nervous and jumpy. It was still only their third day in France.

Lieutenant Bernard Montgomery was of the opinion that the move south to Haucourt, although necessary to conform to the movements of the other 11 battalions in 4th Division, was fundamentally flawed from the outset: to abandon a favourable position on high ground, to move troops at night over unfamiliar ground, to meet the enemy at day-break on that unfamiliar ground, and to co-ordinate this move with that of the whole Brigade, was courting disaster. The Battalion had been busy in Solesmes all day and night, shepherding the refugees through the town, and now had to do a night-march, a difficult manoeuvre at the best of times, quitting the town even as the enemy were closing in from the north, the Battalion being the last to leave the town. To make matters worse the cavalry of the Division, its reconnoitre troops, were stuck below St. Quentin. Its RAMC ambulances were similarly stuck, or impounded by order of GHQ, as were its big 60 pound guns. The Signals troops with their equipment were similarly down the line, all presumably for the reason that GHQ did not want to move equipment up again, only to have to move it straight down again. After all, this was a Retirement. The Battalion was going in to action with the equipment and tactics that would have been familiar to the Iron Duke himself.

Monty was riding alongside Lieutenant Penfold at the side of the columns. In the dark, and because the road was not of even width, the columns lost their cohesion, so that the Battalion resembled more a large party of walkers on a picnic outing, or more exactly a party of blind-folded walkers. Some of the men marched on the roadway, and others on the soggy edge of the fields, and they marched, and stumbled, at different speeds. Some men slipped and fell and bumped into one another. Indeed it could hardly have been otherwise. Some of them kept in contact with each other by using their diggers as batons, like runners in a relay-race. They kept up a constant line of chat: ('If my mum could see me now, she'd have kittens.' 'If the Kaiser could see you now, he'd be shitting himself'). But the columns moved like a series of inch-worms, now bunching and now stretching and then losing contact. The noise of the men's boots on the cobbles was more of a scrape than a tramp.

Before the head of the column had reached Quievy, Monty was seriously worried whether the Battalion was ever going to arrive at Haucourt in a formation of any military value, if it was to get there at all. He said as much to Penfold, riding Charlie alongside him, who had to agree, as he usually did, with Monty, who was now convinced that the Battalion had been going around in circles for the past hour and that Major Trichet was a fool and his name gave more than a clue as to his nature. Penfold had to agree that it did appear that the same burning farmhouse had been passed twice. Monty quite seriously put forward the view that the Grand Old Duke of York was a military genius by comparison with the leadership of this Brigade. He then added some comment about the shaved backside of the Colonel and whether he could tell the difference between that part of his anatomy and his elbow. Monty told this hoary old joke, laughing in a sort of high-pitched giggle, as if unaware that it formed a part of a good many music hall routines; he didn't tell jokes of his own. Monty had been consulting the luminous arrow on the small magnetic compass he carried in his tunic pocket; it told him all he needed to know about the line of march they were taking. It was part of his personal kit, purchased only a week ago from the Army and Navy stores, where the assistant had said 'A very wise choice, Sir, and can I interest you in a pair of binocular glasses?' The field glasses, the compass and five pairs of thick woolly socks had cost him the best part of a week's pay, nearly £2, paid without fail into his account at Cox & Co, 16 Charing Cross.

The two officers, riding to the left of B Company on the edge of a field of stubble, assumed that the men could not hear what they were saying, which was not entirely the case. But Penfold was still thinking about the tricky subject of maps and whether or not he was meant to have one. He thought it best to avoid the subject of maps altogether. But to the great relief of officers and men a half-moon appeared through the clouds, showing up the paved road-way, its wet cobbles giving off a feeble reflection. There was gun-fire somewhere in the darkness, although for all the men knew it may well have been thunder. The line of direction of the march now showed up as south-west on Monty's compass, which he knew to be the correct one.

Just beyond Quievy, shells burst on the road less than a hundred yards ahead of the column, causing the leading company to run off into the adjoining field. Some of them had been struck by shrapnel balls. Others were hit by flying metal from High Explosive shells bursting on the cobbles, a mix cannily put together by the German field artillery commander who was able to fire both shrapnel and HE from the same battery, unlike his British counterparts. There was a good deal of shouting for the bandsmen and orderlies. Monty was impressed with the boche night shooting and wondered how they had acquired their target; random searching fire he thought, probably from at least four thousand yards away; cavalry guns, but without doubt pre-registered on the road, their presence a shocking surprise. The result was further disintegration of the columns leading Lieutenant-Colonel Elkington and Major Trichet to the decision to halt the march until dawn; the officers were told to get the men to rest and resume the march at 4.30 a.m. There was considered to be no risk of actual contact with the enemy, either infantry or cavalry. French cavalry was said to be somewhere out to the north and west and acting as a screen. A night action was in any case an extremely unlikely event, or thought to be. The battalion bivouacked in a field a hundred yards off the road. The ground was wet and soggy from the recent rain but the men had their great-coats which they spread on the ground, now grateful that they had been made to carry them. They did not remove their boots. Each man lay down with his rifle alongside him. Some of them munched on turnips, a pile of which lay beside the road. There was no more shelling. The wagons went into a laager, with the horses munching on their nose-bags. Lumley brought both Penfold and Monty their Burberry's from the officers' wagon.

Small fires then appeared in the surrounding darkness, lit by unseen hands. Penfold was bemused. He thought of the night before Agincourt, fought almost exactly five hundred years ago. He then remembered from his days at Churchers College that this day was the day on which the battle of Crecy had been fought, in 1346. Was this a good omen? He thought it probably was. But then he remembered what the Worcester captain had said about the enemy coming on strong, even in the teeth of our fire.

'Sarnt Fox'

'Sir'

'What can those fires mean? Won't they attract enemy artillery?'

'Possibly, Mr. Penfold. But I doubt that their night-shooting is any better than ours, which is not attempted unless the targets are pre-registered. That will be French territorial troops, Sir, who are uncommonly haddicted to the lighting of fires for their cooking purposes. They will be lighting the corn stooks, not having the hadvantage of our mobile cookers. A distressing lack of discipline it shows, I'm afraid. And I dare say that they are like lost sheep, what with this land being both dulating and undulating'. His aspirated 'addicted' made Penfold think of the French soldiers eating fish for breakfast.

At the same moment that Lieutenant Penfold was watching the cooking fires of the French Territorials from a field near Quievy, Generaloberst Alexander von Kluck, sixty-two years old, commander of the 1st German

Army, numbering 320,000 men, was settling down into his bed in the Hotel Cambresis in the Rue Napoleon in Solesmes. He had had a most satisfying dinner, good solid German pork and potatoes prepared by his personal chef, an elderly sergeant from Strasbourg, with none of the over-rated French cuisine, over-rated like most things French. The sergeant-chef had remembered to bring the General's favourite Strasbourg mustard. He had dined with his senior staff officers, who had been full of foreboding for the morrow, worried about the ability of the divisions to mount an attack after the rigours of the past three days. Mons had been a shock to them, and they knew that the staff-work had been found wanting, although they blamed the airmen for their inability to locate the Tommies. The officers had dined off the tables so recently furnished for General Robertson of GHQ and General Snow of 4th Division. Von Kluck addressed his staff officers, talking to them as if he was in the lecture hall of the Academy in Potsdam:

'You have no faith, gentlemen. The Kaiser has called the English force a contemptible little army and I shall prove His Highness right. They will put all their forces in a line, the English are always predictable. I have seen their trench-lines, I will attack with artillery and then Marwitz's Hussars on the west flank, together with his Jaegers, and the centre will collapse of its own accord. II Cavalry Corps will advance on the axis Avesnes-Bohain. The infantry will do the rest, with the Maxims up close. I know they are eager for battle. Von Armin will take the east flank of the English. We will be in Paris within a fortnight, unless that old fool von Bulow manages somehow to get ahead of me to the Champs Elysées. But old nanny that he is I hardly think that that will be a possibility. And now pass me the brandy. It's one thing the French understand.'

Why should he listen to these staff officers, he, General Alexander von Kluck, veteran of the war against Napoleon III in 1870, named as he was after the legendary Greek military genius? They had had a soft time for the last thirty years, these staff officers, with staff rides and war games their only experience of war. Boxer Rebellion? Hardly a war to be counted alongside the war of 1870/71. Massacring Negroid peoples in south-west Africa? Hardly warfare worthy of the name. Besides, he, von Kluck, was a student of warfare who had studied the battles of the great Napoleon as well as Frederick the Great and he would apply the shock tactics of Napoleon, but buttressed with the power of his 77's, Maxims and howitzers. The zeal of the men, their love of Kaiser and Fatherland, would carry them through the English lines like a knife through kartoffel. This time he would not let the Englanders get away. 'Do you not agree, von Keppel', he said, addressing his ADC. It was not a question.

Von Kluck was not a cavalryman and didn't think like one. Not for him the romance of the sweeping, outflanking movement across open country, with horses leaping over fences like a great steeple-case. He himself was not an aristocrat, the 'von' being awarded rather than given at birth. The constraint of time, the need to march in step with the five invading armies, and in particular von Bulow's 2nd Army, could only mean that his cavalry, despite their lack of firepower, must fight as infantry; didn't they have their Jaegers for just this purpose? They must forgo their ancient aristocratic disdain and learn the harsh lessons of war. And this corner of France will be their proving ground. The musketry of the Tommies that his officers were telling him about, well, that would be dealt with by the proper application of fire-power, by the 5.9 howitzers to which the Englanders had no answer, and by concentrating the Maxim-guns. And he was confident that tomorrow, unlike at Mons, the guns would get into action at first light. And if the carbines of the cavalry were not effective long-range weapons, well, they would just have to get in close with the Tommies. The Anglo-French alliance would fall apart when his Army drove a wedge between the English and the French 5th Army and then the English would flee for their channel ports. All armies, especially when under two different commands, are vulnerable at the hinge and meeting point, everyone knows that. At bottom, von Kluck doubted that the English had the heart and stomach for a battle to save France; they were a naval power rather than a Continental power. In von Kluck's often expressed view, expressed in private anyway, the attempt to build a German High Seas fleet to rival the Royal Navy was an expensive waste of resources.

That did not mean that Marwitz wouldn't be pushing out cavalry to the west. Kluck and Marwitz had agreed this strategy as long ago as Brussels; that the 2nd Cavalry Division would take up position on the right of the line and be prepared to move west in a reconnaissance in force, as far as Amiens if need be. Indeed, elements of the cavalry were already as far west as Cambrai. From there they should be able to detect any westward move by the BEF if they should fall back on their channel ports, and engage their rear echelons. The 22nd Reserve Infantry Division would also be on the right of the line, out toward Cambrai, and would be able to act as an additional buffer, although Kluck had a low opinion of its fighting ability. But if von Kluck was already having doubts about the military need for the great western sweep envisaged by Schlieffen, he was keeping them to himself. He was enough of an old soldier to know that no military campaign is ever conducted according to plans laid down by staff officers in gilded academies. Paris was the prize and going the long way round never did make any sense to him; indeed it contradicted one of the basic principles of warfare, the concentration of force at the *schwerpunkt*. And hadn't he had to deal with Belgian franc-tireurs, who had conducted outrages contrary to the rules of civilised warfare? If he hadn't given the necessary harsh orders to counter the threat it would have thrown out the whole Schlieffen timetable. These Belgians - he didn't care whether they were Flemish or French ones - they were all ill-bred, a mongrel race beneath contempt. Franc-tireurs; shooting was too good for them. They should be hanged. It was one of the lessons he carried with him from 1870.

Kluck was a rarity among German officers of the line in that he had actually studied the American Civil War, albeit superficially, and he had come away with the knowledge that cavalry could disrupt the enemy's lines of communication but must not be used in an attacking role against unbroken infantry unless supported by other arms; or unless they learned to fight as infantry themselves. It was hardly original thinking but getting the cavalry to fight dismounted was flying in the face of centuries of tradition. Kluck gave his staff the benefit of his views on the role of cavalry, in between mouthfuls of rosti. The staff had the good manners to listen in silence, having heard his tactical doctrines many times before. They even kept silent when he delivered his familiar rant against the distressing frequency with which the cavalry seemed to wear out their horses. They kept silent when he told them that a man in an airplane could see a great deal further than a man on a horse. They rose as one and drank a toast to victory in the battle to come. The noise of their heels clicking in the Teutonic manner could be heard by the kitchen staff.

'I tell you, gentlemen, that if I were in Sir John French's boots I would saddle up and make for Rouen as fast as I could.'

The staff made the appropriate noises, indicating that the General had made a particularly witty remark. Von Keppel made sure that the corps commanders were in receipt of the General's order that they should attack at first light, laying particular stress on the importance of the guns keeping up with the infantry. The General didn't concern himself with any level of command below that of corps commander.

At 4.30 a.m. when the 1st Warwickshires' march was resumed, the Cambrai road lay only forty minutes away to the south, and Haucourt perhaps the same distance again or less, so that the expectation of arriving at 4th Division HQ at Haucourt by 5.15 a.m. was not unrealistic. They should do this without a rest-stop, now that the men were rested. Lieutenant-Colonel Elkington knew from his orders from Brigadier

Haldane (10 Brigade) that his immediate rear was secure from enemy cavalry. His position was to be in the vicinity of Haucourt, to be used as a reserve by General Snow, who would respond to events as they occurred on the battlefield, with 11 Brigade roughly on his right and 12 Brigade on his left, as they faced the enemy to the north. Navigating in the dark must have been equally difficult for the enemy; even the wily Hun couldn't see in the dark. The Battalion was admittedly a bit behind schedule, but not seriously. He had had to leave a dozen wounded men in a farmhouse, tended by an orderly and the good lady of the house, which had slowed him down a bit.

They had buried one man, a private soldier in Penfold's platoon, in a shallow grave dug by the light of a storm lantern, the padre intoning the words from Deuteronomy, 'The eternal God is your refuge, and underneath are the everlasting arms.' The service lasted three minutes. Penfold, who had been standing bare-headed next to the Padre, was asked by one of the men, Private Prescott, 'Sir, what are these everlasting arms? Would that be the artillery or the infantry?' which Penfold thought amounted to insubordination, but let it pass. It was the first death of the war for the Battalion. The wounded would have to surrender to the enemy when he arrived, being too badly injured to move in the wagons. There was no ambulance. The doctor, Captain Nolan, did what he could for them, and the kindly farmers arranged space in their barn, with plenty of fresh straw-bedding. But all-in-all at this juncture, Lieutenant-Colonel Elkington was not a particularly worried man.

They reached Cattenieres shortly before 5.00 a.m., at dawn, having crossed the Cambrai road. The village, little more than mean brick cottages strung out along a single street, was deserted. The people had left in a hurry - that much was obvious from the cooking fires still alight, smoke rising from the chimneys. There was muttering among the men of French spies suspected even now of watching their movements from behind the closed shutters. Penfold and Montgomery, if they were pressed on the matter, would have admitted that Cattenieres was a place of ill omen. Crows were perched on the telephone wires that ran along the railway line, adding to the sense of foreboding. Nobody thought to cut the wires, perhaps out of some feeling that being French property it would not be a proper procedure, without specific orders. An Englishman in a friendly country has a natural respect for private property. There were a few Limousin cattle, beef cattle, left hobbled in the yards and chickens and mongrel dogs had been left to wander the open spaces, one of which attached itself to a man in Penfold's platoon. Penfold assumed that any milking cows would have been driven south by the inhabitants.

The Battalion, in four columns, marched through the village street and on south through fields of stubble, turned to a sticky mud by the recent rain. They marched in silence, rifles at the slope, the only sounds being the soft squelch of ammunition boots on the wet earth, the jangle of harness, the occasional rasp of metal on metal and the sucking sound of the horse-shoes on the earth, together with the click of shoe-metal on stone. Each man, with his heavy pack, great-coat rolled on top, the ground slippery under his feet, found himself leaning forward to compensate, one or two falling over and being helped up by their mates.The morning mist was still thick here but a weak sun was attempting to shine through. There were puddles where the rain from the night still lay on the surface, the August hard-baked ground not easily absorbing water.Visibility was about one hundred yards, Trichet the guide looking anxious as he led the columns across the fields in what he was sure was a more direct route to Haucourt than the road.

They continued due south, regaining the road, now marching easier, spread out over nearly half a mile; the Colonel, Major Haddow and Major Trichet, all mounted at the head of the columns. At 5.10 a.m. they crossed the Warnelle ravine, a natural feature in which lay the railway line to Cambrai. They met no other BEF troops on the march and the French Territorials, so much in evidence in the night, had vanished, presumably off to the west toward Cambrai. There was a variety of meadow pippets, skylarks, wagtails, finches and hedge-sparrows in the fields, all birds being known as sparrows to the men. Penfold was again reminded of the hunting country around Petworth. The mongrel dog trotted alongside the column, avoiding Charlie's feet. The enemy were thought to be at least two miles away, at the very nearest, although this distance was of course within the range of field guns and howitzers. But even Germans couldn't see in fog. In any case, Lieutenant-Colonel Elkington was much more concerned with getting to his rendezvous at Division HQ than with any enemy who might be lurking in the fog behind him to the north.

At Haucourt which they reached at 5.20 a.m. it was the familiar story of confusion. Troops of two brigades (10 and 12) swamped the village, more or less abandoned by its inhabitants, although the village priest emerged in his black cassock and offered to interpret. He was asked to enable the battalion MO's to set up an aid post in the church. General Snow had set up his HQ in the school but was out somewhere to the west inspecting 12 Brigade deployment. He had sent out staff officers with orders to resume the retreat 'as possible', but at 5.35 a.m. the new order was received from Corps at Bertry, sent by wire, that the Division was to stand firm and cover the flank. There was not time to contact all the battalions with this new order before events overtook them, so different battalions were in receipt of different orders. It was somewhat of an academic matter; a battalion didn't need to be ordered to fight when the enemy appeared, but it was to lead to confusion in the minds of battalion officers about what exactly was the Division's overall intent. To resume the Retreat 'as possible' lacks military precision and with the lack of signalling gear, further orders were going to be difficult to get down through the chain of command. But Field Regulations gave individual commanders on the spot autonomy in making decisions.

The 1st King's Own, Lancastrian men, were already in the town, having done a night-march from Caudry, and preparing to go up towards Cattenieres as the forward screen, to the left of the 1st Hampshires. They set off more or less at the same time as the 1st Warwickshires arrived. Their orders were to dig in and hold the ground, although they left before the 'No Retirement' order was received. They should have left a good half hour earlier, but for what seemed to Penfold a simple lack of urgency. Two companies of the 2nd Essex, 12 Brigade, were standing easy and ready to go to the west, to take up a position near the village of Longsart. The men were standing by their packs, some smoking, some eating bully and bread, although Penfold couldn't see any cookers. It put him in mind of one of his father's sermons on the feeding of the five thousand. The other three 10 Brigade battalions, the reserve formations, were arriving or were said to be arriving from the Caudry direction; the 2nd Royal Dublin Fusiliers were coming in in dribs and drabs rather than a cohesive force. 11 Brigade, which included the 1st Hampshires, had made a good night march from Solesmes and were in position around Fontaine, across the ravine to the north-east in what was to become an isolated position. Gun batteries were already in place to the north of the village but even a 2nd Lieutenant like Penfold could see that this assembly of troops in the village was not a force ready and in position to fight the enemy if he should appear. An Essex machine-gun team was still hanging about, not knowing whether to set up in the forward line, or take up a position in the rear to cover the retirement. The subaltern commanding the guns told Penfold that he was awaiting orders, from whom it was not clear; he seemed to think that his deployment was a Division matter, and the General was away from his HQ. There were some fine-looking French cavalry but no-one knew what they were doing there. They were said to be on their way to the west, but awaiting orders. Penfold heard a man say to his mate 'And where are the Dublin Fusiliers, I'd like to know', and getting the answer, 'Probably stopped off for a drink'.

Montgomery was fuming with frustration; in his view this was not the way to start a battle. Sergeant Fox, who was rapidly becoming the Company humourist said, to no-one in particular,

'If I had known this was market day I would have brought my shopping basket.'

Penfold thought later, when he had time to piece the events together in his mind, that it was at this moment that the firing began, that is, about 6.00 a.m. It came from the north, the area of the Warnelle Ravine, which they had just crossed and even to his novice ears it consisted of machine-gun, field gun and small-arms fire. 75mm shells, exploding on impact, began falling around the school in the square, where about two thousand men of various battalions were congregated. In fact, although he did not know it, these shells were 'overs', fired at the King's Own, ambushed as they stood around leaning on their entrenching tools, as troops or indeed workmen in general will if not driven with a sense of urgency. The shells had been fired from north of the Warnelle Ravine, and had landed purely by chance and without any warning in the small town of Haucourt, still packed with troops, a distance of more than a mile. The church was immediately pressed into service as a dressing station; even the battalion and brigade veterinary surgeons helping the doctors and orderlies as dozens of wounded were brought in. The wounded were treated on their stretchers, with the altar being used as an operating table, the village priest assisting as best he could, lighting candles in their ornamental brass holders to pierce the gloom. A silver chalice was dipped in the font-water and used for medicinal purposes. The shelling stopped as suddenly as it had started and when the dust had settled the survivors saw that the school had suffered a direct hit and among the wounded was General Snow's ADC, although at first the belief was that the general himself was killed. The German gunners, a horse artillery troop, had got lucky, but they did not know it. Almost without exception, every man and officer had thrown themselves to the ground when the first salvo had struck. Six horses had been wounded, and one killed.

To the King's Own, a mile to the north, the target of the German guns, it was devastating; over three hundred of them lay dead or dying, having been caught in the open, their arms piled, and the men tightly packed, some of them lined up to get breakfast from the Company cooker. Their colonel, Lieutenant-Colonel Dykes, was killed almost at once. His last words to a company commander pointing at the shapes of horses and men in the mist were 'Enemy cavalry? Not possible!' Like Lieutenant-Colonel Elkington he had been convinced that no enemy forces could be that far south that early in the day, having been told that he could rely on French cavalry as a screen. It was their baptism of fire, the battalion having been in France for four days, spending their entire time marching hither and thither, from Le Cateau to Caudry to Haucourt. The enemy had in fact occupied Cattenieres almost as it was vacated by the Warwickshires on their march south, that is to say at about 5.15 a.m. or soon after, the two groups of infantry being unaware of each others' presence. The Warwickshires were convinced for ever afterwards that spies had emerged from the cottages as soon as they had passed through to report their progress to the enemy. The King's Own had been sent unsuspecting into the misty high ground above the ravine. The men who died never even saw their enemy before they were cut down by machine-gun bullets skimming the cut corn. The mist had been on the side of the German cavalry. Von der Marwitz's cavalry machine-gunners couldn't believe their luck when the mist cleared enough to reveal an English battalion in the open, about to have their breakfast. The German cavalry detachment also scored a direct hit on the King's Own field cookers with a 75mm field gun which they had unlimbered with practised alacrity, the cookers brought up to the line with commendable zeal by their NCO's providing excellent targets. The wagons at once caught fire, their four horses collapsing in their shafts in a bloody tangle of twisted limbs and mangled flesh. It was this gun that fired the shells that landed quite by chance in the main square in Haucourt. By soon after 6.00 a.m. nearly four hundred

BEF soldiers had been killed or wounded by one detachment of German cavalry, without the loss of a single German.

The response from Brigadier Haldane of 10 Brigade was swift. The Warwickshires were ordered to go back up the road to Cattanieres, across the ravine and attack the enemy who were expected to be on the north side; to go back along the same road that they and the King's Own had just travelled. Their orders were to stay up there until ordered otherwise, to close with the enemy, and to make contact with the King's Own. The Battalion transport, together with the noncombatants, was ordered to get out to the south, away from the town, and to find a place to shelter and await further orders. Sergeant Fox ordered a young bugler back with the transport, considering him too young to fight, and telling him to mind Major Haddow's horse, although there was a groom already tasked with this job. ('And if the Major's horse doesn't need minding, just make yourself useful and mind yourself.')

It was the very worst preparation for a battalion attack. Lieutenant Montgomery immediately began questioning the operational details but since there weren't any, there wasn't much point. Anyway who was he, a subaltern, going to question? Lieutenant-Colonel Elkington? Brigadier Haldane? It simply wasn't in the realm of permitted military procedure. There was no possibility of providing artillery support, that much was obvious. There was no way of communicating with the guns to the south, XXIX RFA, in time to lay on a fire plan. The guns to the north of the town would need observers forward and signal-wire laid and it was obvious that that was not being done and indeed could not be done. The battalion was going in without RFA fire support and without its own Vickers guns, which lacked the mobility to be used in an infantry attack involving an advance across steeply undulating ground. In any case, machine-guns were best used to cover a retirement, everyone knew that. But there was no doubt in Monty's mind that the enemy were a good deal better at deploying for battle than 4th Division. It was obvious that the

Battalion should have deployed up on the ridge instead of going down to Haucourt and then back up again. They were now going to have to go back to where they had just come from, but this time they were going to have to fight for ground that had been theirs. Once again Monty was put in mind of the Grand Old Duke of York. Even that Hannoverian general would have realised that abandoning high ground without leaving even a skirmishing line and a galloper was contrary to normal practice.

Penfold and Puffing Billy on the other hand were almost ecstatic with the prospect of leading their men into action for the first time. They were keyed up to such an extent that Sergeant Fox, certainly an older and wiser man, said to himself, 'I'll be keeping an eye on those two young gentlemen.' He fingered the rosary given to him by the old crone. As for Lieutenant-Colonel Elkington himself, he never made it his business to try and find out what strength the enemy was expected to be in or where he was expected to find him. He couldn't of course expect anyone to know anything more than he did, there not being any signals connection between the surviving King's Own, the 1st Hampshires on their right, the 2nd Lancashire Fusiliers on their left and Haucourt. He was ordered to take his battalion back up to the ridge and over the other side, and that was the end of the matter. But in the colonel's judgement, that order did not include his own presence in the battalion's forward deployment.

In fact, the distance between the battalions involved was such that they could not give each other covering fire. And unknown to the British commanders at Haucourt the Germans, commanded on this front by General von der Marwitz, an aristocratic cavalry officer, had managed to get to Cattanieres with most of their 2nd Cavalry Division, supported by three Jaeger infantry battalions. The Jaegers ('hunters' in German) were the most skilled of the German infantry, the nearest they had to specialist shock troops, now burning with a desire to close with the British, who they erroneously suspected of using a device on the stock of their rifles to cut off the tips of bullets to create dum-dum rounds. Von der Marwitz was himself up at Cattanieres; indeed his staff were nervous for his safety, mounted as he was and with his uniform of a general marking him out for any lurking British sniper. He had also brought up twenty-two machine-guns to the village, which were mounted on carts and towed by horses. He even had some lorries for the purpose. The British guns, being lighter, were all manhandled by their teams of six. The British mustered three old Maxim machine guns on their immediate front, those of the Lancashire Fusiliers and the Hampshire, one of which jammed almost at once. Penfold knew the words of the Infantry Training Manual, Chapter 3, Tactical Notes (8), which were: 'The only way to avoid the surprise effect of the enemy's machine-guns is by careful reconnaissance'. But in the excitement of the moment these words of caution were forgotten. No advance patrol, no scouts, were to be sent out to assess the strength of the enemy. There were ten thousand enemy south of the Cambrai road, and no-one in Haucourt thought that there could be more than a few hundred at most.

'Take off your packs! Bayonets at the ready! Fill your pouches with ammunition!' Penfold was shouting himself hoarse with orders which Sergeant Fox could perfectly well have delivered with a good deal less hysteria. Penfold found himself for some reason talking to himself, which he found steadied his nerves.

The men haven't had a meal since last night, but that can't be helped now. They will have their water flasks at least, and some hard rations. The thing is to lead the platoon and to show aggression. The boche must be punished for his treatment of those poor Belgians. The men will follow me, they are sure to. Where is Lumley? Ah there he is, get the mare taken into a safe place, load the Webley, oh of course it's already loaded, have to take my sword, the mark of a gentleman officer, oh dear God be with me, my Redeemer. Now we are getting into artillery formation, have the men still got their diggers, we will have to dig in to consolidate, it's only a short way up to the ravine and then up and over and be prepared to use the bayonet. When do we issue orders to fix bayonets, Sergeant Fox will know, now or later? I am an officer in the finest regiment in the army, an officer of the 6th. I will get the men to shout and cry havoc when we close with the boche. It's a miracle that no one in my platoon was hit in the shell-fire.

We are going forward now, a bit of a way to go before the ravine, my God the Battalion looks a fine sight spread out, the mist lifting, visibility perhaps four hundred yards, but uneven, the Colonel and one company back in reserve, up to the bottom of the slope, no firing yet, good scrub cover here, don't bunch up lads, here comes some shrapnel. High thank God, the noise of it hitting the ground just a plop, but here we are coming to a hedge, the men coming on in short rushes they know what to do. Oh that man, his jaw is a mass of blood the shrapnel is getting us now. Don't bunch, but the men have to get through that gap in the hedge, I had better lead. I must lead. I am a leader of men.

Sergeant Fox called out,

'Not through the gap! Through the hedge!'

But the young soldiers knew nothing of the siting of the boche machine-gun which had been trained on the gap and killed the first seven men who used it as a portal to death. Other men ran up and down the hedge looking for a way through, until the older ones steadied them. Men were calling out to each other, advertising their presence, which Penfold knew at once was an unwise thing to do. So far no enemy had been seen and the Warwickshires knew nothing of where the survivors of the King's Own were sheltering, which was in fact in a sunken lane to the right. What fire they could bring to bear was not going to be much help to the Warwicks. But the survivors from the attack had been able to return fire and drive off the field gun.

The Warwicks then broke through into an open field, a field of stubble, Penfold himself following Sergeant Fox through the hedge, but still seeing nothing of the enemy or the men they had been sent to help.

How could they, with the patchy mist still present but sparkling prettily in the early sun? The men went forward towards where they supposed the enemy to be, led by their officers, among them Major Haddow, Lieutenant Penfold, Lieutenant Watkins, Lieutenant Puffing Billy Stephenson and Lieutenant Montgomery. Major Haddow was close to Penfold, and walking with his head turned to the left in a curious way. The men of B Company were keeping loose formation around their officers, but moving forwards to keep close to their friends. They took their pace from their officers, who seemed in no particular hurry. The noise of bees in the air was suddenly very loud and alarming, a strange hissing noise. Was there a swarm? No, it was machine-gun and rifle fire tearing and renting the air. Mostly machine-gun fire. And tearing the flesh of men and officers alike as the invisible enemy found their targets, especially the officers who had become the targets of snipers, marked out handily for the Jaegers by the swords they were carrying. There were involuntary exhalations, marked by gasps of sudden pain, as bullets the size of hornets struck into bodies and skulls, the impact knocking men over, making a dull thwack of sound. Penfold passed a man lying down with his feet toward the enemy and wondered why he was facing the wrong way and how he could have got ahead of him. Penfold kept his head down, his eyes fixed at a point a few feet from him, with the thought that this would save him from a bullet in the face. Not in my face oh God, not in my face. He was not running but walking, walking with a ceremonial sword in his hand, but made sharp by the armourers, walking toward an invisible enemy, knowing even as he did so that if he did meet his enemy he need do nothing because then his work would be done. He would have led his men to the enemy. It was not that he consciously thought about this; his training as an officer and an English gentleman told him, hundreds of years of social history told him, that he must lead his men to the enemy whether they lived or died. Living or dying made no difference; an officer must lead. This is what they have always done.

This is what they do. Men kill and officers lead. We must close with the enemy. Those are our orders. The men will follow. There is no hurry. We will do our duty. I must show aggression.

All the officers had drawn their swords and had attached the hilt to the hand in the appropriate way. The men had fixed bayonets, but Penfold didn't remember the order being given. Some fired from the hip where they had a clear field of fire forward. One man had slung his rifle and had brought out his entrenching tool and was holding it aloft in front of him, as if it were a shield. Some started to bunch up. An officer, perhaps Puffing Billy, shouted 'Don't bunch!' Sergeant Fox shouted, 'Steady, lads!' But the men continued to seek shelter, one behind the other, as they moved forward, now moving slightly to the right as if drawn by an invisible cord. The officers were armed like their forebears at Waterloo, the Major even having a bugler near him as he would have had at Waterloo or even Malplaquet. They pointed their swords forward toward where they supposed the enemy to be. And then they waved those swords as if they there the baton of a conductor. They did this perhaps in unconscious imitation of pictures of Victorian officers dressed in red tunics going in to battle, pictures by artists such as Lady Butler which adorned many an officers' Mess. The men were still tending to the right, a dexterous tendency some say that goes back to ancient times, in order to keep the shield arm facing the enemy. Penfold became conscious of his binoculars in their leather case around his neck; it was flapping about and banging against his Sam Browne in the most annoying way; should he stop and adjust the strap? Should he stop and put it in his tunic pocket? Where it could join his toothbrush which Lumley had so thoughtfully brought this morning. But with his sword in his hand he was one-handed. He had a ridiculous thought: I am going in to battle armed with a sword, a revolver and a toothbrush. He carried on, bent forward, up the slight incline.

Penfold observed the men and officers falling as a phenomenon unconnected to himself. He asked himself, why are they falling down? Why can't they get up and carry on? Then he realised that the angry bees, the air-borne bullets, were killing his friends and would soon kill him. He was going to be killed and there was nothing he could do about it. He put his sword-arm out to his right, extended, in the hope that a bullet would catch it. An honourable wound. To be greatly wished for. He then wondered whether to put the sword back in its scabbard and draw his Webley, but the effort involved did not seem worth it. He thought with clarity; if I get to the enemy I can draw the Webley from the leather and the lanyard will keep it from falling to the ground. I will then be doubly armed. Should I remove my glove from my left hand? No, an officer should wear gloves. He watched the white puffs of exploding shrapnel and thought how beautiful they looked. He saw Major Haddow spin round, clutch his shoulder, and saw a patch of blood form on his tunic, dark and red; the major looked startled and faced toward Penfold as if about to say something, but not sure how to form the words. His mouth formed a silent 'O'.

But then it came to Penfold that if he fell down he might avoid the bullets and the shrapnel and that he might live and he now had a great urge to do that. It made no sense to walk across a field and be killed by something he could hear and not see when he could lie down like the others and rest from the noise. There was still no enemy he could see to attack. He wanted very much to kill a Hun, but there were none to see. What was the visibility now? Four hundred yards? Hard to tell. But the men had followed him. He had done his duty. So he fell down like the others. He saw Monty do the same. He saw Puffing Billy do the same.

At this point a staff officer appeared, mounted on a beautiful black charger. Penfold thought it must be a dream. How could such a large target escape the swarm of bullets? The mounted staff officer was shouting something, but it was impossible to hear above the noise of the exploding shrapnel and the constant, insistant chatter of the Maxims. He must be shouting the orders to abandon the attack. My God he is a brave and good man that officer on the horse, he must be from Brigade. Or another place unknown to us. A bugle was heard but whose meaning was not clear. And then some of the men who were lying down got up and began to run back in the direction from which they had started. Many lay still on the ground but it looked like half the Battalion was now going back, the men bent over as they ran. So Penfold did the same and followed the running men back to the hedge, pursued by the angry bullets, which were now flying high. And other men began to crawl back toward the hedge, knowing that that was where safety lay.

The survivors somehow got back through the hedge and into the scrubby field on the other side. They looked back to the south at the ravine they had just crossed for the second time that morning. They had left perhaps two hundred and fifty of their comrades on the field beyond the hedge, some wounded but many dead. Puffing Billy was among the dead, shot through the heart, although Penfold was not to learn with certainty of his death for months. Haddow came back with the survivors holding a shattered arm, being helped by his young bugler. Haddow stared around him as if expectimg someone to explain things to him. He seemed to be the only Company Commander to have survived, to have come back through the hedge. Monty also was among the living. He and Penfold started to get the men digging with their grubbers in a line four hundred yards back from the hedge. A boche counter-attack was expected. Or a counter-attack was not expected. Nobody seemed to know where the Colonel was. Then they remembered that he was not in the attack. Men dug and dug with a new sense of urgency and asked after their friends. They marvelled at the tears and rents in their clothing and haversacks. They marvelled at the appearance of the mounted staff officer, who had vanished as quickly as he had appeared. Had he appeared to stop the attack because it was never intended? Is that why the Colonel was not with them? Had they just blundered into the mist without specific orders? Some had wounds that they didn't remember getting. Some men had wounds being dressed by their comrades, using the emergency dressings they all carried. Water bottles were passed around, the men finding themselves suddenly very thirsty. It looked like they might be here some time. None of them had seen any Germans at all. But they were ready for a German counter-attack, if it should materialise.

A plane with black crosses on the undersides of its wings flew over. It didn't drop any flares but the men knew that it was a bird of ill omen. They fired at it, but it was too high. It circled over them lazily, almost with disdain, and then flew off to the north.

Penfold found Montgomery. He wanted to know how it was that they were alive and others weren't. He didn't know how to say it. He had led his men but he had thrown himself to the ground. He had saved himself. He then realised that his left hand was covered in blood and knew at once that he had cut himself with his own sword, through the glove. He wiped his hand on his britches. Just a scratch. A memory came back to him from his hunting days. He had been bloodied.

Monty said,

'That damn sword strap, I've never managed to get the proper hang of it. Got in a terrible muddle and the bally thing tripped me up. Sent me flying.'

'Same thing happened to me, old man. Next time, no sword for me.'

It was still only 7.30 in the morning but the sun had banished the mist. The Warwickshires burned with a desire to get their own back on the enemy, to avenge the death of Puffing Billy and all the others. Their time would come. For those who died it was their first and last encounter with the enemy and their third day in France. Two orderlies, Red Cross armbands clearly visible, went back out beyond the hedge with stretchers, to try and get wounded men back into the line; they were shot down and after that no further attempt was made for the time being. For Penfold, everything was so damnably unfair; the boche seemed to see us, silhouetted in the mist, but we could not see him. For Monty it was quite simply a lesson in how not to go about an attack.

Von der Marwitz's cavalry had placed two Maxims, with their teams of six, under a leutnant, seven hundred yards back from the hedge. Once again the Germans had got lucky. They had only been placed there ten minutes before the Warwickshires came through the hedge. And the mist cleared at just the right moment for the gunners to identify the hedge and the men advancing through it. The shouts of the British NCO's had told the gunners exactly what was happening. They fired into the mist, knowing that their bullets would find British flesh and bone. The guns, fixed on their tripods, were set to fire just above ground level and were easily traversed from side to side, firing a thousand rounds per minute.

Chapter 10

The Right of the Line
Private Edwards

Frank Edwards of the 2nd Royal Welch Fusiliers at 10 o'clock in the morning was still watching the bombardment of the hill on which the 2nd Suffolks, the 2nd Manchesters and the gunners of XV RFA batteries were now enduring the fourth hour of ear-splitting hell. No. 11 Battery was almost completely knocked out, only one of its six guns still firing; it was perhaps the most exposed of the four batteries on the hill, being on the right of the line, although in truth all the batteries were equally exposed. It made no difference to the German gun-layers north-east of Le Cateau whether the path of a shell on its flight through the air caused it to fall one hundred yards east or west. No. 11 Battery was nearest the clock-tower of the church, which may have been the reason for it being singled out for the most prolonged and accurate fire, singled out by the forward controller in the tower. The battery and the other batteries were also coming under enfilade fire from enemy guns to the east, firing across the Selle Valley. From where Edwards was watching - the bank of the lane - it seemed unlikely that many gunners or infantry were going to survive. Edwards knew enough about gunnery to tell that the volcanoes of smoke and earth were caused by the 5.9's firing from the other side of the town, and the air-bursts were caused by the more mobile guns firing from new positions east and north, as well as from the hidden position to the north-east. And it worried him that the hill was now surrounded on two sides by the enemy.

Edwards knew it was 10 o'clock because the seed man told him the time. The clock on the church-tower no longer told the time, although it was of course out of sight from the sunken lane where Edwards and his battalion was still in reserve. The clock had been hit by machine-gun fire from the Suffolk guns, when the gunners had at last realised that an enemy observer was up there in the tower and that a machine-gun had also been positioned there.

The enemy, under the overall command of General Sixt von Armin of IV Corps, were now beginning to mass infantry on the hill a mile and a half or so to the north of the Cambrai road, between Rambourlieux Farm and the western edge of the town. There was only one reason that the enemy commander was now contemplating a massed assault, and that was that he had now come to the conclusion that the British garrison was no longer capable of any serious resistance. Since soon after dawn he had been infiltrating troops along the Selle Valley, the dead ground that lay to the east of the hill. He had massed machine-guns, their crews going forward with persistence and bravery, immediately in front of the Suffolks on the Cambrai road by using the banks of the road as shelter from the fire of the Suffolks. The first German machine-gun crews had been shot down by the forward company of the Suffolks as they left the shelter of the edge of town, but others had pressed on in their wake, crawling over the dead bodies of their comrades. The Suffolks' forward company was the one that had made Private Edwards think of the Forlorn Hope; it was an accurate comparison in that this company would be sacrificed early in the battle, although most of them would spend the next three hours keeping their heads below their parapet.

By 10.30 a.m. the RFA 4.5 inch howitzer battery on the hill was nearly out of ammunition. Lieutenant-Colonel Brett of the Suffolks, an officer distantly related to Simon Brett of the Worcester Regiment, had been killed almost with the first salvos that landed at 6.30 a.m. The fifteen hundred troops of the East Surrey's and the Duke of Cornwall's Light Infantry had been driven off the hill to the east of the valley, the hill where the Suffolks still vainly looked for salvation from Haig's brigades.

The ammunition for the Suffolk's Vickers guns, aligned north-east, wasn't going to last much longer at the rate they were firing, and nearly half the 18-pounders were out of action. Haig's First Corps battalions were nowhere to be seen and were in fact marching south. In short, the situation of the garrison on the hill was becoming desperate. All Edwards really knew was that the poor farming boys, as he called them, were not going to have a chance of getting away unless something of a miracle was going to happen. And he was enough of an old soldier to have lost any faith in miracles a long time ago. He could tell, however, that the Yorkshire machine-guns he had passed on the road this morning were keeping up a good fire on the enemy to the north. But he knew that they were only two guns against many regiments of German infantry, who were even now massing for an assault.

It was now that Lieutenant-General Smith-Dorrien ordered two battalions of his reserve up to Suffolk Hill as it was already being called; the 1st Middlesex and the 2nd Argyll and Sutherland Highlanders. Edwards was able to watch them both go off to the north. He knew that this was not the miracle that the Suffolks needed; this was just stoking the fire with more fuel. 'The Die-Hards' as the Middlesex were known throughout the Army looked set to live up to their motto. He knew of the exploits of their sister battalion, the 4th, up at Mons. And the Highlanders who had been the original 'thin red line' at Balaclava, in William Russell's words, were going up the hill into a storm of shell and small-arms fire without any immediate chance of hitting back at the enemy. Another military debacle was in the making, to rank alongside Moore at Corunna and Raglan at Balaclava. All this was seen as clear as day by Edwards.

Arthur Moore of *The Times* now was consumed with a burning desire to get closer to the main action. All his short professional life he had been an admirer of his predecessor William Howard Russell. And Russell had not reported the charge of the Light Brigade from the safety of Scutari; he had been an eye witness. Moore could have requested permission to go up to the hill from an officer superior to Four Eyes, but that would have been unlikely to be granted. In any case the great Russell didn't always observe the niceties of procedure. *The Times* readers numbered in their many thousands and they had to be told of the events now taking place near Le Cateau which would rank alongside the campaigns of Wellington and Marlborough in the annals of military history; not to mention the fame and fortune that would await Mr. Moore when his graphic account was published, an exclusive report, there being no other reporters present to the best of his knowledge. So he requested Four Eyes' permission, in his politest tones, for the use of Private Edwards as a guide to accompany him to view the action from a closer vantage point. Moore said that the Royal Welch would soon be famous the length and breadth of England for the deeds they would do this day. He did not mention that the Censor would certainly not permit the naming of any individual units in any published report.

What Mr Moore said was,

'Lieutenant Boasanquet, may I request, in your capacity as the senior officer here present, that Private Edwards accompany me on an excursion up to the lines to see for ourselves the fighting against the Hun invaders?'

To his surprise this request was granted. 'Bring him back; we might need the old bastard later'.

'Thank you Lieutenant Bosanquet'.

'Good luck, Eddie', said Buffy, which was a bit rich coming from him, considering that the only luck he believed in was the bad variety.

Edwards, who didn't have much choice in the matter, and Moore set off up the Roman road towards Suffolk Hill. Shells were falling all around them, looking for the howitzer battery and the big 60-pounder battery, but also searching for the artillery horses in the lines; the German gunners were sending over both High Explosive and shrapnel, the HE coming in with a shriek, a bang and then the sound of metal through the air. The enemy seemed to have limitless ammunition and were shelling the rear areas without discrimination. Edwards asked Moore, after a few hundred yards,

'Are you sure you want to go any further? Have you seen enough yet?'

'My readers will want to know what the men are suffering'

North of Reumont the two men kept off the road and then swung to the right so as to keep under the lee of Suffolk Hill. There were artillery horses in a farm track and Edwards couldn't see how they were going to be restrained by the grooms much longer; some were not going to survive in any case, being already wounded.There were other men there, Manchesters, who probably shouldn't have been there at all; they must have got back from the hill on some pretext or other, probably helping their wounded mates get back to the dressing station at Reumont and now not eager to return to their lines. On the left of the road the West Kents were in support, tucked up nicely in good but shallow trenches, three lines of them, about half a mile back from the storm of steel on the hill. Edwards saw with astonishment that an officer appeared to be reading a newspaper. Beside him lay a pile of musical instruments, drums and pipes, discarded by the bandsmen, now prepared for their role as medical orderlies. That'll be the last they'll see of those items. There was some machine-gun fire landing around the road but they were more or less spent bullets, fired from the cutting on the Cambrai road, over a mile to the north. An ammunition wagon, with a wounded gunner on board, came rollicking down the road, back from the hill, the driver whipping the horses without mercy. Edwards was reminded of posters he had seen in Shrewsbury advertising Buffalo Bill's show. Edwards said to the plucky Mr. Moore,

'This looks a good place to stop and get a good view of the action. We can find a handy billet here.'

But Arthur Moore was made of sterner stuff.

'We will go up there a way and see what is happening with our own eyes.'

This seemed to Edwards a course of action designed to serve no purpose other than to bring about their death or capture. He didn't want to die for the readers of *The Times*, a newspaper he had never read. He could already see that some of the guns on the hill were twisted into abstract shapes, standing starkly against the sky, struck by the High Explosive shells of the 5.9's. Ammunition wagons were upended and the shafts pointing skywards, as if in the act of surrender. Woolly Bears were throwing up geysers of earth. This was a place of death and destruction. It was as if the earth was tearing itself apart.

The intrepid Moore had seen the Middlesex go around the southern part of the hill and take up a position overlooking the valley to the east. He now saw that the kilted Argylls were going to go straight up the hill, led by their officers. He saw their six-man Vickers teams, heads bent as if in a storm, going up towards the gun-line, the man carrying the water-cans struggling under the awkward load. Edwards knew that they would become the target of every fritz gun as soon as they crested the rise. Moore thought that if they could go there, so could he and Edwards. He could do nothing less. And Edwards had no choice but to follow up the hill to what must be a dusty death; death not for King and Country and for the love of his friends but for Mr. Moore, who was certainly not his friend. And a death that would be a lot more than dusty if the amount of hot metal flying through the air was anything to go by.

They passed through the trench-lines of some East Surreys, who being out of the main action seemed to be asleep, although some of them gave them a cheery wave. They must have thought the both of them daft buggers, especially the man in the Panama hat. The intrepid pair, one reluctantly, were now approaching the gun lines; the shelling was continuous, with the surviving XV Brigade gunners firing back with steely determination, the officers manning the guns along with the bombadiers.

The two men squatted down in a shell crater, which gave them some protection from shot and shell. Small-arms fire was zinging and zapping through the air, coming from which direction was not clear, the shields of the 18-pounders affording the gunners some protection from the bullets. The gunners in any case seemed to ignore the bullets; such was their concentration on feeding the breeches of the guns, setting the fuses of the shells, working the firing mechanisms, adjusting the range, the officer in touch with his controller by telephone. Their dead comrades were tenderly placed to one side. An ammunition wagon was being unloaded with calmness and efficiency by men from one of the batteries, seemingly oblivious of the hail of shrapnel. About one third of the guns were still in action, but even this small number could put fifty shrapnel shells into the air every minute. An ammunition wagon was on fire and Edwards watched with amazement as two gunners calmly went about off-loading the shells. Piles of discarded brass shell-cases lay everywhere, glinting in the sun. Dead horses lay round about. The crashing and bellowing of the guns and the blast of the in-coming howitzer shells deafened all those on the hill. And yet he could hear one shout from a bombardier up at the gun-line: 'Ammunition expended, Sir!'

Two hundred yards to their left front an ammunition wagon, pulled by four horses, galloped up to an 18-pounder battery, the battery on the left of the line, the two drivers crouched low in their saddles. It seemed to get stuck in some obstacle on the ground about a hundred yards short of the battery, perhaps telephone wire, and the horses reared up, plunging and whinnying, while the drivers tried to urge them on. A burst of shrapnel caught the team and small arms fire was directed on to them, horses and drivers being hit. The noise of whinnying horses, exploding shrapnel, the discharge of the guns, was all-encompassing. An officer and a gunner ran out from the battery and set about off-loading the boxed shells, each box being about the weight a man could carry. Edwards watched with great admiration as the officer took out his revolver and shot the hysterical lead horse behind its ear, then grabbed a box and set off back to the battery command post, which was partly dug in. The gunner took hold of one end of the box by its rope handle and tried to help the officer but stumbled and fell, clutching his chest.

The two men looked at each other without speaking. Edwards could now see what the RFA gunners were firing at. Across the Cambrai road, about four thousand yards to the north, he could see lines of grey-clad infantry, in parade ground formation, advancing down the slope. Even to a fusilier it was obvious that this was a target that a gunner is going to get only in his dreams. This was what Smith-Dorrien and his Chief of Staff Forrestier-Walker had been hoping for, the chance to bash the Hun; the chance to lay low their gathering, to meet out justice for the rape of Belgium, to give them a stopping blow. The piles of shrapnell shell-cases were growing; the spent cases clanged onto the brass piles as they were discharged and ejected from the chambers. Edwards could see the white bursts of the shrapnel two miles away, the explosions satisfyingly close to the grey figures in the stubble. The gunners worked with rolled-up sleeves, hatless, the officer every now and then calling out a correction to the range, as the grey masses grew closer and larger. There was no need for forward observers now and the hill-top position was working to the advantage of the guns. Edwards marvelled at their work, which he had never in all his years as an infantry-man observed at such close quarters. He could understand how it was that the gunners could become so attached to their guns, could even grow to love them. And when the time came to abandon the guns, as it must, the gunners must destroy that which they had served so loyally. Did they not tend them and serve them as a servant tends his master? Did he not love his own Lee-Enfield in his own fashion? He had another longing for Suzanne and the memory of entering her, he on his knees and she on the settee, came back to him. He vowed again to return.

He wished there was a Hun visible for him to fire at, but the only ones were more than three thousand yards away and now becoming more scattered as they sought shelter from the storm of shrapnel that was falling on them. The fritz machine-gunners on the Cambrai road were hidden from him by the banks of the cutting. The enemy in the valley to his right was a waiting and lurking Hun. There must be fritzes closer judging by the small-arms fire but he was damned if he could see any. He then decided that there must be a nest of snipers on the hill the other side of the Cambrai road, close up to the town, and loosed off a half-dozen rounds at what might be a likely spot, a large collection of straw. But with a target half a mile distant he was not hopeful of hitting a Hun. And then two yellow explosions erupted on the far hill, fired from the big naval guns back at Reumont, each shell capable of killing a whole platoon.

The two men then saw a gunner, while in the act of taking a shell from the limber, clutch his side, stagger and fall to the ground, although he made an effort to get up and return to the limber. Edwards then watched with admiration as a soldier of the 2nd Manchesters leapt out of his shallow trench, ran across to the wounded gunner, lifted him and carried him back to his own trench. And he saw other Manchesters, on his right, run to the guns and put their shoulders to the wheels as the gunner officers sought new targets.

Edwards saw a Suffolk officer, together with an NCO, running across the shell-strewn field to the Manchester machine gun position. He watched them pick up some bandoliers of ammunition, drape them around their shoulders, and run back across the shell-pitted stubble to their own guns. He saw the officer stagger and fall into the gun-pit. But the guns went on firing at the exits from the town. He saw an artillery officer lifted into the air by an explosion of HE and come down to earth in pieces.

Edwards called out to Mr. Moore,

'Write this down, Sir. The people of England will not believe this unless you tell them the truth. Never mind that those Huns on the far hill are daft buggers or drunk or their officers are mad. Write that we are doing our duty and the only tragedy is that we do not have the machine-guns to finish the job. Write that we did it on the canal and we will do it again until the Hun goes back to his country. But we need the guns and the men. Or the scrapings that are the only shelter for the Suffolk boys are going to become their graves.'

'My dear Edwards, you are an invaluable military adviser. I shall have to quote you in my report. The pen and the sword shall go hand in hand and shall be mighty yet.'

This was the longest sentence Moore had yet uttered to Private Edwards. It was not exactly recompense for the mortal danger he was now exposed to, danger directly due to the determination of the journalist to see the action first-hand. But Edwards was no stranger to danger; it was an accepted part of his life as a soldier. So he decided that having come this far he might as well make the best of a bad job, so to speak, and take up the new job of adviser.

Edwards addressed Mr. Moore in the educated manner he had picked up from his mother, who had learnt it from her social superiors while in service up at the Manor. In fact Edwards had learned a great deal about the world of the gentry from the Manor. Although he had played up there as a child with the children of the gardeners and chambermaids, the Squire had encouraged him to read the books in his library, a library hung with suggestive and improving pictures by Pre-Raphaelist artists. He could recall the aquatic world of *The Water-Babies*, the pinkness of Charles Kingsley's babies and the pink of the Empire on the globe in the library merged together in his adult mind. The Squire had let him run free as a fox in the kitchen garden and the stables. The young Edwards was honoured among the farriers and woodsmen. He could pinch the dimpled bottoms of the laundry-maids. He played at tilting in the yellow-stone yard. And even though firmly on the servants' side of the green baize door he had observed with the sharp and uncritical eyes of youth, almost as a child-anthropologist, the Victorian world of tennis and croquet, of shooting parties and cucumber sandwiches and strawberries and cream, of the vicar coming to sherry before lunch on Sundays. His heroes were W.G. Grace and Captain Oates, middle class to the core. Even Sherlock Holmes, to whom he had been introduced by the Squire, was hardly a working class hero, yet hero he was. In spite of this cross-cultural confusion, he knew his place in the Edwardian social structure just as he did in the Army's, but he had observed at close quarters the manners and speech patterns of those placed by birth above him. He would have been an officer but for the accident of his birth to a domestic servant. His own father, a gardener, was long dead.

'Thank you, Sir. And as your military adviser may I point out that the enemy on that far hill are not exactly being wiped out but are in fact being reinforced with fresh troops, they are taking evasive action and they are likely to reach the Cambrai road in a matter of an hour or so. And even if the gunners and the rifles of the Suffolks and the Koylies succeed in killing a good number of them, there will be an awful lot of them still left and intent on doing us harm. Not to mention the enemy even now in that dead ground over there, who will surely spring upon us like grey wolves should the opportunity arise. And not to mention that a company of those brave kilted Jocks have just gone to their deaths in a charge at the enemy on the road that defies belief. And those other Jocks arc lying down either because they are fucking dead or because if they stand up they soon will be. If you can find words for such deeds you are a better man than I am Mr. Journalist. Because if you write merely that their honour is bright you will do no more than echo the words of that impostor Baden Powell and all the other jingo-wallahs.'

It was curious how Mr. Moore's style of speaking was becoming infectious. Perhaps something more than just knowledge of the customs of the upper classes had stayed with him from his days at the Manor. 'If I'm not careful I shall become an officer', thought Edwards. And he also thought, 'if we don't get the fuck out of here toote sweet we're done for, as sure as foxes kill chickens.'

There then occurred one of those events which occur on battlefields which are not often talked about by the survivors with satisfaction, but which rank at the time as important and potential battle-changing moments. On this occasion it was not the miracle that was going to save those still living on Suffok Hill and those up by the Roman road. As Edwards had so correctly observed to himself, a miracle of that sort does not occur in real life. Edwards knew that the Angel of Mons had not really appeared with a flaming sword to hold back the Hunnish hordes, but may well have been the product of the fevered imagination of the exhausted troops, helped on its way by not a few men of Mr. Moore's profession. There was to be no Angel of Le Cateau. And Haig's battalions were as likely to turn up as Russians from Archangel, with snow still on their boots.

What did occur at about 12 o'clock, was that a battery of German gunners on the high ground to the north-east of Le Cateau, freshly arrived at the position, for whom the low ground at the foot of Suffolk Hill was out of sight, fired salvo after salvo on their own troops, who were at that moment reaching that low ground. The observer in the clock-tower had been chased away, or even killed. The markers with which the German assault troops had been issued to show their position were unfamiliar to the gunners of the new division. The result was very pleasing to the beleaguered British garrison, who at first believed it was their own guns which was causing the enemy to turn about, but then realised that it was enemy fire. The shells, well fused, fell on the Forlorn Hope of the Suffolks, but also on the massed Germans in the Cambrai Road cutting. It was a moment of quiet exultation. Gunners looked at each other and with their instinctive knowledge of how such things happen made no comment. But it could only put off the inevitable end which Edwards could see as plain as the Panama hat on the head of Mr. Moore: the complete destruction of the garrison on the hill. The German gunners to the north-east of Le Cateau soon lifted their range, as their artillery spotters frantically flagged instructions back to the batteries.

It was at about this moment that Edwards said for the third time to Mr. Moore that it was time to head south. What he actually said was 'Shall we continue with our Cooks Tour before a fritz bullet finds a billet in you or me, seeing as how we can leave this scene of death whereas those poor sods do not have that luxury?' And for the first time, Arthur Moore agreed. He had seen enough. Mr. Moore could have been forgiven if he had thought he had seen enough death and destruction to last him a lifetime. They edged themselves out of the shallow crater in which they were lying, turned around and started to crawl back. They came back to a gunner with an arm almost completely severed from his shoulder. He had made a shelter for himself, using straw, or someone had tended him, it was hard to say. Edwards helped the man, a corporal, to his feet, but he could hardy walk far in his condition. He seemed pathetically grateful. Edwards fashioned a sling from one of his own puttees. The corporal did not seem as surprised as might be expected to have been rescued by a man in a Panama hat and a private soldier in the Royal Welch Fusiliers. Edwards noticed that blood was seeping from the gunner's ears, which he knew to be caused by the roar of the 18-pounders.

The three of them now more or less upright, the gunner being supported by Moore and Edwards, set off down the reverse slope of the hill. They came across more sights which moved them to pity, wounded men who had evidently crawled back, only to succumb to their wounds or perhaps hit again by artillery fire. They had died without succour. Ammunition boxes lay around, fallen off the wagons in the scramble to bring them up through the shrapnel fire. A horse lay dead, cut loose from its team and abandoned to die.

They could see Reumont about half a mile away, with plumes of smoke from a recent bombardment. Edwards and Moore half carried and half supported the gunner, who remained cheerful in spite of his wound, although he kept giving out small gasps of pain. They knew that there was a dressing station there in which they could leave the gunner. They could then return to what seemed the haven of the sunken lane where Edwards hoped to find his battalion still in reserve, his mission accomplished and his man delivered, thanks to the writing that Mr. Moore would do.

And if the gentlemen of England could learn of the deeds done here, instead of the usual patriotic guff, it would become a day of glory. When the Argylls went up to the hill and without flinching went at the enemy, even though half of them were shot down. When this field of glory will become a field of praise. And even though glory may fade, their deeds will live on, and those that died will not have died in vain because other soldiers will come and take up their fight against the foe.

The dressing station, set up in the church, Geneva Cross flying from the steeple, was a scene of acute suffering. Men were lying on stretchers outside the door, unattended, some wounded again by recent shrapnel shells. The most urgent cases were inside, being treated with surgery or by the ministrations of the RAMC orderlies. Edwards could do no more than leave the NCO outside, to wait his turn, but an orderly came out and told him that a morphine injection would be given him as soon as a doctor was free. The orderly tied a ticket to the gunner's top tunic button, just like in a lost property office at a railway station, the gunner being now double-ticketed, with his name tag in vulcanised rubber worn around his neck, like all soldiers of the BEF. Edwards and Moore set off for the sunken lane, after wishing the gunner good luck. Edwards told him to keep an eye on his wedding-ring and ask for it back if they took off his arm. They had learnt his name; it was Major. Edwards knew that the chances of a safe evacuation of the entire hospital were slim. The best that could be said about the prospects for the wounded was that they stood a better chance of fair treatment from the Hun than if they had been left to the mercy of Pathan tribesmen on the Frontier. So far as Edwards knew, the Hun didn't make a habit of cutting penises off their prisoners and stuffing them in their mouths.

Edwards turned to Mr. Moore. The lowly private soldier felt now a certain comradeship with the gentleman-journalist, both of them having witnessed deeds of heroism that they would never forget. Edwards dimly remembered from his schooldays in Shrewsbury some words from *Henry V*; 'He that outlives this day….will remember with advantages what feats he did that day.' And gentlemen in England should think themselves grateful they had a nice bed to go to.

But Mr. Moore still had his mind on Russell at Balaclava.

'Tennyson, thou shouldst be living at this hour.'

Back at the sunken lane, Buffy was eager to hear about the Hill. Edwards merely said that it was 'a bit hot' and that things were likely to get 'a bit sharp' before too long. It was now 1.15 p.m. The men were dozing in the sun, seemingly oblivious to the battle raging to the north of them. Four Eyes was still looking at his wrist-watch every five minutes. The bowler-hatted seed-merchant was nowhere to be seen. 'I hope he's taken his bad luck with him' was Buffy's only comment.

Chapter 11

Caudry
Captain Johnson

It became clear to Johnson that the enemy were now in complete control of Caudry and that the battalions of 7 Brigade had been driven out to the south and west by the heavy shelling. Much of the town was on fire. He had no idea what was happening on the other side, that is to say the east side of the town. He had no idea what was happening further to the west; the field of beets stretched for half a mile or so up to the village of Fontaine, which was in German hands, although no fire was coming from there. The 'Triumvirate' of de Salis, Brett and himself was now in the beet-field for better or worse and there they looked like staying for quite a while, stuck in a salient. They had a collection of men from various battalions, but mostly 3rd Worcestershires, 2nd Royal Irish Rifles and some oddments from Brigade, quartermasters and the like: about 300 men all told. Johnson was the senior officer present. They were lying down in a line facing north, their only cover being the green leaves of the beet crop. It was the sort of crop that he had often shot over, in the days when he had gone rough-shooting with Brett and De Salis. There were other 7 Brigade men lining the edge of the town, clinging to the shelter of the buildings like sailors clinging to the wreckage of a ship. British wounded were being taken on to make-shift stretchers and carts and being carried out to the south and the enemy did not seem to be firing at them. The shelling of the town had stopped but Johnson was certain that the enemy gunners would soon switch their attention on to him. There was small-arms fire coming from buildings and what looked like orchards about six hundred yards away to the north. And enemy infantry was still active in the beeet-field, their spiked helmets just discernable at a distance he reckoned as about the same as the length of the cricket field at Winchester, from the pavilion to the edge of the water-meads.

He was suddenly overwhelmed by a desperate need for sleep now that he was lying down. He hadn't had a proper sleep since, when was it, four days and nights ago. His thoughts turned to Phoebe and the murmur of distant voices in a pavilion beside the Itchen; Phoebe and the dark aureoles of her breasts, the nipples erect, the thorax taut; the rest of her body, the forbidden fruit, a consummation devoutly to be wished; his penis straining in the constriction of its cricketing box-strap inside his white flannels; Good old Simon offering some more lemonade and talking about the prospects for the forthcoming match against the 2nd Battalion XI. How he envied the men what he assumed to be their enjoyment of uncomplicated sexual congress with barmaids when they were given their week-end passes from the barracks......He made a promise to himself that when he got back home, if he got back home, he would cast off the bonds of bourgeois sexual morality. In a curious way, this nearness to death endowed him with enhanced power and entitlement, would enable him to choose the road yet untravelled, and to sample delights there. It was becoming perfectly clear; he let his mind wander down that road apiece.

Shrapnel exploded above him and he felt a sharp pain in his lower back. Damn, are they shooting at me or are the guns shooting at the buildings and these only stray bursts? He could see where Brett and de Salis were lying further out to the west, about three hundred yards away, the occasional man becoming visible every now and then as he bobbed up to fire. The men were spaced out at about two yard intervals. He shouted for them to stay put; they had no choice but to fight from here if the enemy were to make an attack. If only he had a Vickers on his right, somewhere by those buildings would be useful. He could even mount a counter-attack with a Vickers on his flank. The enemy was showing no aggression, he could drive them off the field with a determined attack with the bayonet if they came on to him. Their musketry seemed pretty poor with most of their shots going high, their soldiers bobbing up and down in the beets and taking snap shots, just like ours. Where was Sergeant Rouse, he hadn't seen him for two days, had he been killed or wounded? The pain in his back was getting worse.

A Worcester soldier to his left called out 'Red Cross flag two o'clock!'

Johnson got his binoculars out. True enough, four men with a distinct Red Cross flag, but wait a moment, they were carrying rifles, that can't be right. Obviously a ruse. And that cart I can see, that's an ammunition cart not a Red Cross stretcher. A Hunnish trick. He shouted,

'Fire at will! Ignore the flag!'

It was now nearing noon. The enemy brought up a Maxim which quickly found the range and position of the small scratch force. Damn gun must have been brought up on the cart. Bullets began hitting the ground in front of Johnson and a ricochet struck him high on the thigh, making him feel sick and faint. He took deep breaths. The Maxim seemed to have galvanised the enemy who were now coming on through the beet. There must be at least a whole battalion coming on. Some were falling to the marksmanship of his men. He realised that his whole force must make a move and that for the second time he was going to have to co-ordinate a manoeuvre. What was happening in the town? Were the men on his right fighting the enemy in the streets? The shelling had ceased but that could mean several things. Nothing was clear. He heard shouts and small-arms fire coming from the town; what did that mean? His leg and his back were now getting extremely painful. He didn't want to end his days in a root field on the edge of a nondescript French town. A terrible thirst came upon him.

For the first time he was terrified. Fear was new to him; he was not equipped for it. But his brain was grappling with the possibilities of the situation. It was clear that his force was outnumbered by at least three to one. He could not see how they were going to get out of the field into a place where the Maxim and the shrapnel couldn't hit them. Or could he? He shouted to Brett and de Salis to get the men on the left to crawl back to where he thought there was a patch of dead ground and to stay there; and looking back, there did indeed seem to be gap in the beet that might be a ditch. He shouted to the men on his right to do the same. He then shouted 'Covering fire, Covering fire!', but was aware that he had not given instructions as to who was to cover whom. The NCO's would have to work things out. He shouted again, 'Move now! Move back!' He felt a surge of hope. He was not going to die in this Godforsaken field. There was a way out and he was going to take it. The terror drained away from him. It was a spur. It had driven him into action.

When he started to crawl back he found at once that the leg that had been hit by the ricochet simply refused to work. His first thought was how damned annoying! The ditch was about forty yards back, just an irrigation ditch probably, but at that moment it represented everything that Johnson held dear in the whole world. The ditch was safety; it was a place that held the promise of life and a future. Most of the men, and now Brett and de Salis, seemed to be getting back there. Bullets were still hitting the earth all around him. Think of it as a matter of will, like going for the second run, or enduring something agonising like the Bishop's sermon at Easter in Worcester Cathedral. No, mustn't think like that. It's just a question of getting from A to B.

Johnson, by using mostly the leg that did work and dragging the useless one, by half crawling and half hopping, made it to the ditch, which extended well out into the field. The ditch led into the town and the town itself offered an uncertain place of refuge. The ditch also served as a foul water drain and Johnson was at once covered in evil-smelling mud. At this moment General Hamilton reappeared, still mounted, at a lane which led through the back gardens onto the open field. He was too far away to make himself heard but he was clearly taking charge of reorganising the defence, of reforming a line at the southern edge of the town. If the General is here on horse-back things can't be that bad. The town, or at least this part of it, must be again in British hands and Johnson saw that his best move should be to go back in there. The General will be sure to give us fresh orders and we will be able to get ourselves out of here. And join a new line.

The General had, in fact for the second time, rallied and organised men of different 7 Brigade battalions into a fighting force and ordered them back into the town from the south, where they went in with the bayonet. What German infantry there were took flight back through the streets, back to the square and on again, with Colonel Stuart of the 3rd Worcesters leading a hastily assembled force of about three hundred men, screaming and shouting to one another as they rushed from house to house, screams audible to the men in the beet-field, screams which Captain Johnson had heard himself. For the second time, the majority of Caudry was in British hands, although there were pockets of German infantry scattered about, some of whom might become snipers. The scratch force commanded by Johnson, Brett and de Salis was now back in the foul ditch, but with about twenty of their men lying dead in the beet-field, or too badly wounded to move. The enemy, emboldened now, were coming on through the beet and using the wooden shacks in the orchards at the edge of town as cover. It was a little after midday. And more German infantry were coming on down to the Cambrai road from the high ground, where Johnson was pleased to see exploding white puff-balls of British shrapnel shells, too far way to hear their explosions. A corporal along the line from Johnson was calling out the range of the advancing Germans in the beet: 'Two-Fifty, Fire at Will'.

Brett managed to work his way over to Johnson, by crawling through the ditch. They were just able to keep their heads below ground level. Brett looked at Johnson's leg, bleeding and with what looked like a chunk of flesh removed, and said,

'I say old man that looks as if it could do with some attention. Hang on a sec while I put an emergency dressing on it'.

'It is bothering me a bit. Makes running between the wickets a bit tricky. I've been hit in the back as well.'

Brett put another dressing on Johnson's back.

'I'll edge over to those buildings and see if I can find out what's going on'.

The two hundred and sixty-odd men and NCO's now had a better fighting position and they continued to fire at any German soldiers who presented a target. Johnson noticed that not all of his men were firing, which of course necessitated exposing most of the upper part of the body and calling for a steadiness beyond what many of the young soldiers possessed. But many of the men were driven by a desire to hit back at their enemy which gave them the determination to overcome the natural fear of exposing the upper body and head. And bravery has its own reward in the eyes of one's fellow men. Johnson wanted Sergeant Rouse with him, damn the man for not being there when he was needed. Most of Johnson's personal kit, his copy of Housman's *A Shropshire Lad*, his valise, not to mention the signals equipment, were all scattered to the winds, if not blown to pieces.

Johnson realised that his leg was now making him worse than useless as an officer and that he would be best to look for an ambulance. His thirst was becoming a craving for liquid; he had only whiskey in his flask. To the great relief of everyone the Maxim had stopped firing, which seemed to dampen the aggression of the German infantry; perhaps it had run out of ammunition. A very young private soldier of his own Battalion lay next to him, his acne spots covered with mud from the field and ditch, his eyes wide with fear. Johnson wanted to give him words of encouragement but couldn't think of anything to say that wouldn't sound a bit hollow. He managed to say something about being on our way in no time at all. The young soldier, no more than eighteen, if that, had never spent any time in physical proximity to an officer; the social niceties were unknown to him. He merely said, 'Sir'. But he got into a kneeling position and fired off a few rounds in the direction of the enemy in the beets, whose spiked helmets could be seen bobbing up and down in a comical way. 'Good work, Private,' said Johnson. The young private soldier pushed his cap back, revealing very pale skin on his forehead. Johnson noticed that the man's cap badge was missing, but now was hardly the time to reprimand him. Both officer and private soldier ducked as a salvo of shrapnel burst high and behind them.

Brett then managed to work his way back into the firing line in the ditch and along to where Johnson was lying. He said,

'The General has gone back to his HQ at Bertry. Colonel Bird of the Irish Rifles has taken over the command of the Brigade from Brigadier McCracken who has been evacuated. By pure luck I managed to find the Brigade Major. The Brigade has gone back again to the south of the town to take up a new position and we are to join that line. The situation is still confused, with pockets of boche here and there, but our men have shoved most of the enemy out with close-quarter street-fighting. There is an advanced dressing station not far from here. From there you should get a nice comfortable ride out to safety.'

Johnson then became convinced that there many worse off than himself who needed attention. Brett cut him off.

'Nonsense, old man. You come with me back to the buildings and we'll find the dressing station. We'll have to run the gauntlet but we haven't much choice. To stay here in your condition would make the enemy a present of a valuable Englishman. There's no point staying on here in this slough of despond'.

Johnson submitted to the logic of the situation. Good old Simon, always a sensible chap. He was in any case now feeling decidedly weak; he had been fighting for six hours now with no food and scarcely any water, never mind his leg wounds. His head ached. His throat cried out for water. Simon found a water bottle and offered it to Johnson; he drank greedily and then he took a swig from his own hip-flask, which was still half-full with Bell's. 'Afore ye go', well, he was going now with Simon. He remembered that he still had a croissant from the café table in the square; he fished it out of his pocket and ate it. He had never tasted better. He took another swig from Brett's canteen. He issued orders that the men in the firing line should keep up their fire while he and Simon and three other wounded men crawled along the ditch; the men in the line to cover each other with rapid fire as they then made their exits in small groups and the whole force to get out to the south to join the new line; they would hug the edge of the town where the garden walls could give some protection; de Salis would remain in charge of the rear-guard. All these orders, written on an order-chit by Johnson, were taken down the line to de Salis by a corporal. Ammunition was running low in any case, and he told the men to share around what spare clips they had. The men had been splendid; there was no doubt about it, at least after the initial panic in the town when the bombardment opened. He could not know that the enemy were already calling his force the 'sugar-beet swine', but he would have been highly gratified with this description. Curiously, his own men, as far as he knew, had no terms of abuse for the enemy.

The two officers, together with three wounded men, set off ('Officer coming through! Make way for the officer!') and reached the cottage-gardens without mishap. The enemy to the north had gone quiet, although the field gun was still sending over the odd round. Perhaps they were waiting for fresh troops to come up. They stopped for a while for Johnson to catch his breath. His three wounds were now throbbing and causing him to hover on the edge of consciousness. He took deep breaths. They rested in the back garden of a terrace house, marrows and leeks growing among the dog roses. An ornamental pond with about a couple of inches of water provided him with another drink; a painted gnome grinned at him. One of the wounded men, a corporal called Grant, who appeared to be less badly wounded than the others, offered to help support Johnson, Captain Brett to take his other side. The corporal still had his rifle, the only weapon the five of them had apart from the Webleys of the officers, not counting their swords, and the rifle doubled as a walking stick. It was a distance of perhaps eight hundred yards through the rubble-strewn and burning streets to reach the new line, formed from about two and a half battalions of 7 Brigade. The streets through the town offered a route away from the enemy in the field, but held unknown danger. Johnson was struck by the absence of civilians who must have fled *en masse* from the earlier bombardment, fleeing without having had time to gather up their precious belongings; unless the poor souls were in their cellars or coal bunkers.

'We'll just go easy and find a way through and keep an eye out for any lurking snipers left behind after our last attack', said Brett with a confidence he didn't really feel.

They went down a path that led alongside the surprisingly undamaged houses into the street and turned right, the same lane where the mounted General had recently appeared. Some of the houses were burning, black smoke rising from the combustible furnishings, giving off an acrid smell. Brett began to worry about how to approach the new line; would they be fired at by their own troops as they emerged from the town? A Red Cross flag might help, although from what he had heard it might not prevent the boche from firing on them.

The sad little group of five hobbled along the deserted street. They passed a dead German soldier lying on his back, his hands gripped around his stomach from where Brett could see the man's pink entrails oozing out. Corporal Grant said, in a quiet voice, 'I'd rather a bullet than the steel, if it comes to it.' A house struck by an HE shell was exposing its front room to the world; Johnson felt a sense of embarrassment at being given an intimate view of its interior, just a few hours ago the pride of its occupants. Chairs and a settee were grouped around the tiled hearth.

They went a hundred yards and then sat down on the bench of a bus stop. They needed to catch their breath, Johnson especially. The gable-end of the house on the opposite side of the street was covered with an advertisement for Dubonnet. The absurdity of the situation was too obvious to make a feeble joke about, but Simon Brett could not restrain himself from attempting. He was about to make a comment about the reliability of French buses when a shot from a Mauser '98 rifle was heard a fraction of a second after its 8mm round struck his upper chest at a slight downward angle and exited from his lower back. Simon fell back under the impact of the bullet, with blood already gurgling and frothing from his lips. Henry Johnson knew at once that his friend was dead. The sniper for some reason known only to himself decided that his work was done, having killed the only Englander who seemed to be unwounded. He put his rifle down. Simon's last sight on this earth had been the Dubonnet advertisement.

Johnson's first thought was that if he was killed as well then Phoebe would be alone, that she would have her parents of course but the two men who loved her as brother and unofficial fiancé would be gone from her life and that she would be bereft. He thought with startling clarity that he would somehow get out of this place of death, that he would survive, that he would tell her that they would be married and keep alive the memory of Simon Brett. All these thoughts came to him in the few seconds after Simon had been killed. And he thought again of the promise he had made to himself in the beet-field, of how he would throw off his old sexual reservations. Johnson knelt down and gently removed the only thing he could find in Simon's breast pocket, a letter from his mother. He took his revolver and sword and told Corporal Grant to carry them with him. He told Grant to tuck the sword down his trousers, in case he was to make a more inviting target of himself by displaying it. He also had the notion that one day he would give it to Phoebe in memory of Simon. He laid Simon's body out and simplified it, with his arms across his chest and his legs together. There was no more firing and no shelling; a lull had fallen over the battle, at least in the town. They set off again for the British line. I will tell Phoebe the truth, that Simon died without pain, and in trying to rescue the wounded.

Henry Johnson was now on the brink of lapsing into a state of delirium, but the image of Phoebe in the straw hat drove him on. Corporal Grant was all but carrying him, and the officer and the NCO helped each other along like a duo in a three-legged race. They came to the edge of the town and could see the 7 Brigade line in a field about four hundred yards to the south. The men were only partially dug in and visible in the stubble, using the corn stooks as extra cover. It was clearly not a line to be held for long. From about a mile back gun flashes showed where the RFA batteries were keeping up battery fire at German troops on the Cambrai road. German artillery fire was falling on the British line but there was no enemy infantry in sight. The white bursts of the shrapnel were too high to cause serious damage, at least to Johnson's eye. 8 Brigade was heavily engaged with enemy infantry up on the Cambrai road to the east, but this line south of Caudry was a temporary bulge in the Second Corps line left after the enemy had been driven back by the counter-attack from the 3rd Worcesters. After the last Worcester counter-attack with the bayonet the enemy seemed to have lost his appetite for close engagement and Lieutenant-Colonel Stuart had abandoned the town for the second time, preferring to position himself out in the open rather than in Caudry where the effect of HE had been so uncongenial to his battalion. He and Lieutenant-Colonel Bird were now positioned a few hundred yards back from the line in a new command post.

A lull in the shelling gave Corporal Grant the chance to yell out,

'Wounded coming in! Don't fire!'

'Who are you?' came the reply.

'3rd Worcesters'

'Advance and be recognised!'

The four men went forward, stumbling and dragging themselves along across the stubble and were helped into the line. A battalion orderly was sent for. Dead horses lay round about which made Johnson think again of his mare and the missing Sergeant Rouse. He asked the orderly if he could send word for him. He was then taken on a make-shift stretcher to the rear, where a track led to the village of Audencourt, in front of which 8 Brigade were fighting. He was told he would be taken to the Advanced Dressing Station behind Audencourt, where there remained an ambulance for evacuation to Reumont. Audencourt was being heavily shelled and was in flames. He lost consciousness again somewhere on the way, being carried by four RAMC orderlies. He had finally retired hurt. Colonel Stuart was informed. It was now 1.30 p.m. De Salis brought his force back out safely, losing only a handful of men, although more than twenty men had to be left on the beet-field, both dead and badly wounded. They came out in a staged withdrawal, the enemy unaware of their departure.

The RFA 4.5 inch howitzers of XXI Brigade started shelling the southern part of Caudry, although it was doubtful if there was more than a handful of Germans in that part of it. But it was by any standards a brilliant piece of infantry/artillery co-ordination. The enemy had gained control of the town but they couldn't for the moment exploit it. They had failed to realise that their best route of attack lay through the beet-field to the west, covered as it was only by long-distance 11 Brigade Vickers fire from Ligny and the field guns of XXIX Brigade, now that Johnson's force had abandoned it. Perhaps they still feared the 'Sugar-Beet Swine', lurking unseen in the knee-high vegetation. And the British still held the eastern and southern ground, effectively bottling the Germans up in the town. Matters had developed more or less as Smith-Dorrien had predicted, although it could hardly be said that there was any overall plan. But the Worcesters had shown that they were the masters of street-fighting, when led by their fighting colonel. By some miracle the gas-holder on the edge of the town was still intact, while black smoke rose from a myriad of fires.

Chapter 12

South of Cattanieres
Lieutenant Penfold

The surviving 1st Warwickshires, 10 Brigade, 4th Division, about three hundred of them, were dug in, having used their grubbers to give them firing positions from which they could just about get most of a man's body below ground and rest the Lee Enfield on the parapet. Without the recent rain even this amount of digging would not have been possible, but the men did not have to be told twice about the need for digging. They used their mess-tins to scoop out the earth and their bayonets to loosen it. It was mid-morning and the disaster of their recent futile attack had been an hour and a half ago. Some wounded men of their Battalion had crawled in, but there were at least two hundred of them lying dead beyond the hedge. The hedge was four hundred yards away, the range at which the Warwicks now set the v-sights of the Lee Enfields. At that range if the enemy appeared through the hedge the men could hardly miss. The enemy were, however, not being so obliging as to present themselves as targets. So far not a single German soldier had been shot by any of the Warwickshire soldiers. Their own RFA gunners were firing at targets a long way away, probably counter-battery fire, which at least had the virtue of drawing the enemy fire on the guns and away from themselves, a very considerable virtue. The officers, one of whom, Major Haddow, was lying down with a shattered arm, had no clear idea where their own neighbouring battalions were. And of course none of the subalterns had a map showing the disposition of friendly troops; they didn't have maps at all. There had been no communication of any sort with Brigade, after the staff officer had appeared on the battlefield and brought them back from certain death, the staff officer now granted superhuman status by all those who had witnessed his intervention. In the absence of any orders they stayed put.

They could hear continuous small-arms fire to the north-east, the position being held by 11 Brigade, like them north of the Warnelle Ravine, but beyond the sound of battle they knew nothing. On their left the Lancashire Fusiliers were likewise holding off large groups of Jaeger infantry, but they were about to fall back toward Haucourt, although the Warwicks could not know that. The Warwickshires were strangely unmolested for the time being. The enemy were showing an uncharacteristic absence of initiative in not exploiting the gaps between the more or less isolated BEF battalions. The surviving King's Own were hanging on somewhere to the right, but there was no contact with them. The Warwicks weren't sure where they were, although they could hear the sound of small-arms fire and the occasional burst of a Maxim.

And of course they could know nothing of the plight of the Suffoks and the other battalions on Suffolk Hill six miles to the east, now enduring their fifth hour of artillery attack and the appearance of infantry on two sides of them, their accompanying guns reduced to a handful of still firing 18-pounders. Nor could they know that Caudry had changed hands twice and that 7 Brigade, 3rd Division was hanging on to the south of the town in a temporary firing line. They did know that their orders of 6.00 a.m., to stand and fight, with No, repeat No, Retirement, held good in the absence of any further orders.

Lieutenant Montgomery and Lieutenant Penfold got together and took stock. They decided Major Haddow was hors de combat and that Lieutenant Montgomery being the senior lieutenant was now in charge of the force, effectively the Battalion. Monty said,

'I think you had better take Sergeant Fox and go over to the right, get in touch with the King's Own, see what their position is and orders are and come back here. I'll send another small party to the left with the same mission. The Adjutant has volunteered to go to Brigade HQ and report back. The main thing is not to get left behind if the two battalions on either side fall back under new orders. We can't be sure whether Brigade knows where we are. The boche could launch an attack at any minute and you should set off now while this lull continues….oh, and Stephen, good luck'. His use of the Christian name made Penfold uneasy.

'Righto, Monty.' Penfold was happy to let Monty's leadership establish itself and happy to take the role of courier rather than remain with the main force; with Sergeant Fox with him he felt sure of finding the King's Own and getting back.

'You'd better allow me an hour and a half to get there, find the senior officer and get back here. After that time if we're not back you'd better regard us as a lost cause.'

The two men set off, Lieutenant Penfold leading. He had left his sword with Monty, at what Monty was now calling his Command Post. Monty had rather ceremoniously stuck it in the ground like Excalibur, in a romantic gesture uncharacteristic of him. Penfold now carried a rifle, acquired from a man too badly wounded in the shoulder to be able to use it effectively. Sergeant Fox was also of course carrying his Lee Enfield.

They skirted the first field, a beet-field, keeping close to the hawthorn hedge on the southern side, and came on to a large field of stubble, the stooks piled, drying and ready for collection, threshing and transport to the mill. A covey of partridges flew off with a whirr of wings, their red legs, the colour of the pantalons of French soldiers, tucked up neatly.

'I fancy, Sir, that we had better keep to the edge of this field as well, but we should stay the other side of the tree line. We should stick out like a couple of walking scare-crows if we traipsed across.'

'Yes, Sarn't, of course'.

The sound of firing from the east and north-east intensified. They had the hedge, or rather a row of recently planted poplars, between them and the field to the north. They crossed a railway line, which lay in a cutting.

The ravine lay to their right. They could see Caudry to the east.

'That firing must be the King's Own, we'll make contact soon.'

'Let's just take it slowly, Sir,'

The bullet that passed between them came simultaneously with the crack of the Mauser that fired it. Both men instinctively dropped to the ground as the next bullet struck a poplar a couple of inches from where Penfold's head had been half a second before. The two shots were about two seconds apart. The man was quick, but the second shot with the necessity of working the bolt could not be so good. The first shot must be the one to kill. All this Fox could see in his mind. His thoughts were strangely speeded up. And the sniper's first shot had missed.

Sergeant Fox lay flat on the loamy soil. Penfold did the same. The sergeant seemed remarkably calm as if he often spent his days dodging snipers' bullets. Penfold was the very opposite of calm.

'We can't spend the rest of the day here, Sir. You stay right here and I'll go to the left. I'll move as quick as I can and stalk this sniper and kill him. You remain behind the tree line and don't show yourself. We cannot have this fritz chalking up notches on his rifle-butt.'

Penfold lay on the earth, marvelled at its warm dampness and felt reassured at its touch. He was alive, it was a miracle and his first thought was, 'Ohmygod I have soiled myself - I can't let Sergeant Fox see me like this; but I know that my Redeemer liveth.' He knew that he was not in control of the functions of his body. He did however have an idea, coming to him from some atavistic memory. He said,

'I will draw his fire'.

'Just be careful, Sir,'

The sergeant went left, which drew one more shot from the sniper. It went high and left. Fox knew now that the advantage still lay with the sniper, who could see more or less where they were, and whose own place of concealment remained undiscovered by the two Englishmen. But it had to be one of the corn stooks and it had to be about five hundred yards out, or thereabouts. Fox's instinct told him this. Fox reckoned that there was only one sniper, so that the man was outnumbered two to one. And the fact that he had now missed three times showed that he was not a first-class shot. Fox liked the odds. He wanted very badly to kill this man. He wanted his own Hun and he wanted him dead. And when he shot him he was going to take something from him as his prize.

Fox settled himself behind a poplar. And waited. The sniper was not going anywhere, that much was obvious. It was a matter of waiting for him to make a mistake and reveal which corn-stook was his hiding-place. Then they could pour shots into it until the man was killed.

Penfold in his way knew this too. He then did what boys all know from their scouting days and their days in the CCF, and what all infantrymen know by instinct. He placed his cap on his rifle and raised it six inches above his head, while lying prone on the good warm earth.

The sniper did as Penfold hoped. He fired at the raised cap, with its antelope cap-badge, the 8mm bullet making a neat hole through the stiff material. Fox shouted 'Now!' and let off a round followed by another two seconds later into the base of the corn-stook from where he was certain he had seen a movement and a puff of smoke. He had fired before the sniper could put another round into the chamber with his bolt. He was quicker than the sniper. He shouted 'Stook, two o'clock, five hundred!' Penfold got his rifle into action and got off two shots. No movement from the stook. Could mean anything. Both men fired three more shots, aiming again at the base of the stook. And then three more shots. Then waited. Surely he must be dead.

Penfold was the first to emerge, gingerly at first and then with more confidence. Fox emerged from behind his poplar and walked the five hundred yards into the stubble-field. The two men walked up to the stook and removed the yellow-brown stalks. The body lay neatly, arranged as if for their inspection, blood oozing from a head wound, the bullet having gone clean through the man's Jaeger head-gear, a cap resembling the nineteenth-century shako. The shako had absorbed the man's blood so that the body was clean, as if already laid out for burial.

'That's for Puffing Billy'.

Penfold was breathing in large gulps of air. He had never realised, how could he, that it could be such intense pleasure to have come so close to death and to have survived. He allowed himself this gratification, the sense of having done a man's job, but not knowing how to express it or what gestures were appropriate or even what to do with the body, the first German he had actually seen, the first corpse he had seen at close quarters in his life of twenty-four years. None of this could he discuss with Sergeant Fox. What a silly Hunnish thing the Jaeger-shako was, a corruption of the hunting esprit de corps. The man had red hair, he noticed.

'And we'd better get you cleaned up, Sir'.

The plain truth was that Stephen Penfold, a vicar's son from Petworth in Sussex, had looked into the abyss, had seen the angel of death, and had soiled himself. As his father might have said, he had conjoined the scatological with the eschatological.

There remained the matter of what souvenir Fox was going to select. Penfold found himself brought into this matter, somewhat reluctantly. The shako-hat was too big to carry. They looked in his tunic pocket and found some saucy pictures of ladies in underwear, some with their breasts exposed. They would do for a start. The idea did cross Penfold's mind to have himself bloodied, as if the Hun was a stag, but he dismissed the idea as being too Germanic, of sinking to the level of the sale boche. Fox briefly considered cutting an ear off the sniper but he was not sure if his bayonet was sharp enough to do the job cleanly and the officer might not have the stomach for it. The German had no watch. In the end, Fox chose the man's belt, with its brass fastening clip engraved with the words 'GOTT MIT UNS'. He attached it to his own middle. He could always sell it later to a base-wallah. Penfold took the man's paybook to show to the battalion intelligence officer; it showed he was a reservist from Cologne with the name of Erhard Muller. 'Suum Quique' was printed in the German gothic script on the first page. They examined his rifle and thought that actually they preferred the Lee Enfield as being better balanced and easier to handle. It had no notches on the stock. Both Penfold and Fox were now losing interest in the German, but Fox the Methodist made one last comment on the man's crucifix hung round his neck: 'Didn't save the bastard, did it Sir?' And then added:

'He's got no use for mittens now, silly sod. We're alive and he isn't, and that's our souvenir'.

'I think we should be pushing on, Sarn't.'

'Yes, Mr. Penfold'.

At the next field they could see what must be the King's Own, partially dug in and firing at a small wood to their right, about six hundred yards away from them, and on slightly higher ground. They were also using a farm track, not exactly a sunken lane, but with useful low banks which the men were resting their rifles on. Penfold and Fox made their way gingerly up to them and identified themselves as 1st Warwickshires. Penfold asked the first man he came across, part of a Vickers team, to point out where his commanding officer could be found. The man pointed along the line. They crawled along the line of men – Lancastrians - with considerable difficulty, the line being merely a series of shallow scrapings in the soil. They passed an aid post, with orderlies tending men who looked to Penfold to have been hit by shrapnel. Some rifle fire was coming from the wood but there did not seem to be a Maxim. Penfold guessed that there could be no more than a company of enemy in the wood, perhaps two hundred and fifty or so.

The commanding officer, Major Jeffries, in command since the death of Lieutenant Colonel Dykes early that morning, was politeness itself. Penfold introduced himself. Jeffries spoke to him while looking at the wood through his binoculars.

'Good of you to come and see us, Lieutenant. You've come just at the right time to join in our little show. We had some nasty shelling earlier but the boche gunners have shifted to other targets. There are some boche lining that wood who are a damned nuisance. I don't know how they got there but while they are there they are preventing me from moving. I am going to shove them out. I have my Vickers on the left flank and with fire from that quarter, B Company will attack in short rushes from the right, with platoons and sections covering each other. C Company will advance and then go to ground and provide more covering fire. They will be in the nature of a feint. The final rush will be done with the bayonet. Fire and movement, that's the key. A couple of field guns would be nice, but this is not a time for luxuries. You may have heard of the losses we suffered this morning; we are now going to show the boche that the King's Own are not finished with.'

'I must decline your offer to join in Major. We need to return to the Battalion. May I take it that you have received no order to retire? Our orders are to stand until ordered otherwise.'

'We stay until we receive further orders, Lieutenant. My orders are simply to stay, hold the ground and retire 'as possible' and that time has not come while we are in contact with the enemy. You and your sergeant are welcome to stay and watch the show. The men are just going to have a bite of their hard tack; they have had nothing to eat since last night, the Boche having had the bad manners to knock out our cookers. And then you are in the grandstand seats.'

Penfold was very impressed with this Major, who must have been under considerable strain. He thought he had time enough to watch what sounded like a good scheme, so unlike the unplanned attack his Battalion had carried out that morning. This was a chance to see how it should be done. Monty was right about that fool Elkington, the man shouldn't have been allowed to command a platoon, let alone a battalion.

'My sergeant and I will observe and then leave. I will report back to my Battalion now that I have seen the situation here.'

Orders were being passed along the line and the two companies, actually two companies reformed from that morning's disaster, were checking their equipment. They spoke in low voices to one another. They made nervous jokes about helping themselves to fritz's sausage for lunch. One man said he would not eat sauerkraut if you paid him. They were ordered to fix bayonets and have a round up the spout, with the safety catch on. Penfold overheard a sergeant say to the youngsters of his platoon,

'Shove the steel in and give the bastard a round for good measure; never mind what the drill instructor told you, they're all hot air, do what I say and you'll be all right. If you give fritz a round in the gut it makes it easier to pull the bayonet out; remember that your bayonet is the blood-brother of the bullet. Now, on our way across what I want you to do is this: when I lie down you lie down; when I get up, you get up; when I fire, you fire. Don't stop for anybody on the way over; the wounded will be looked after. For God's sake don't bunch up. Artillery formation. Let's get the bastards for what they did to us this morning. And if they try the white flag surrender trick, remember that's what it is: a trick. I will give an extra tot of rum to any man who kills a fritz carrying a white flag.'

One or two of the men crossed themselves. For all of them this was their first time in attack. They had six hundred yards of open ground to cross but they had Vickers on the left to suppress the enemy fire and the men had trained in fire and movement. The men had been warned that the Vickers would be firing over their heads. They had practiced extended order attacks on manoeuvres in the High Peaks of Staffordshire, when their officers had urged them to 'attack' the 'red' battalions with suitably aggressive shouts. They knew all about attacking in short rushes, platoon by platoon. But that was in England. Now they were to do the attack against an enemy who were going to shoot at them.

The buglers blew the attack notes and the whole two companies set off, less Major Jeffries, who decided that since he was now the senior officer in the Battalion his place was at his temporary headquarters, with the adjutant and forty other men and officers including the MO, the padre, and the young batmen. Jeffries also saw to it that the youngest of the buglers, the eighteen year-olds, were kept back. Penfold saw, from the safety of this HQ, men go down within a minute but then could not tell on the left whether they were deliberately going to ground, or whether they were being shot. B Company was pressing on with commendable drive, only a few men being hit as far as he could tell. They were well spaced out in artillery formation. The Vickers were firing long bursts, with the two guns alternating their fire, firing left and high. B Company were approaching the wood with the leading platoons, as far as he could make out, from five hundred yards away. The Vickers ceased fire, from fear of hitting their own men. Other platoons were giving covering fire from a prone position. The B Company front was about three hundred yards. Penfold literally held his breath; they were nearly there and then surely they would triumph.

It was then that a Maxim opened up at the edge of the wood opposite the B Company front. Penfold watched with a mixture of professional interest and horror at the unfolding tragedy that must surely befall the Company. The Maxim must have been withholding its fire deliberately. It was now firing in long bursts, at the rate of 600 rounds a minute, effectively adding another thirty men or more to the defence. He could see that the men in the front platoon were at least a hundred yards from the Maxim post in the wood. He could even see the faint smoke from the machine-gun's fire, or was it steam from the cooler, but the muzzle-flash told him all he needed to know. He saw the men all going to ground. Surely they would all be pinned down, a fire-fight would ensue, the attack would lose momentum, the men would never go forward, they would be hit again and again out in the open as they were.

He had not got the measure of this battalion, previously unknown to him. It was after all in a different brigade. What the men did now before his eyes was remarkable. Some of them it is true just hugged the ground, too terrified to raise themselves into a firing position. Others were already dead. But others, just enough of them, could work out the direction of fire of the gun, could bring fire to bear, and perhaps for a minute five hundred rounds poured into the gun position. They took their inspiration from their sergeant. The gun went silent. Penfold could make out what looked like white flags appearing on the edge of the wood. The B Company men, maybe two hundred of them, rose up and within thirty seconds were into the wood with the bayonet, their officers leading. The white flags were disregarded. Penfold could hear the cries, the wild cries of men enraged. Most of the enemy fled before the men were on to them, away into the depths of the wood, but there were some who did not get away and they were all killed with the bayonet. And there were some killed with the bayonet and a simultaneous .303 round for good measure. The men had earned their shilling for that day. And the dead had earned their glory. Some words of Milton came back to Penfold from his days at Churchers….. '*the cheerful ways of men…and wisdom at one entrance quite shut out'*. He turned to Sergeant Fox and said,

'I think we had better be getting back to the Battalion now'.

Right you are, Mr. Penfold'.

They picked up their rifles and went off.

Chapter 13

12.30 p.m., Bertry Lieutenant-General Smith-Dorrien's HQ

At the Mairie in Bertry, his battle HQ, almost equidistant from Caudry and Le Cateau, Lieutenant-General Sir Horace Smith-Dorrien, veteran of Isandhlwana, Omdurman, and the Boer War, was sitting at the desk of the Mayor of Bertry. Bertry had been well chosen as an HQ; it lay just outside the range of the enemy field-guns north of the Cambrai road. There was an ante-room, and he and his immediate staff of Brigadier George Forrestier-Walker, Major Hope Johnson AMS, Captain Bowley ADC and Colonel Rycroft AQMG were using both rooms. There was no telephone, but a telegraph link had been established, by dint of all-night work by the Engineers, with Haucourt, where Major-General Snow of 4th Division had his HQ. Major-General Hamilton of 3rd Division had his HQ just across the square. Major-General Fergusson of 5th Division had his in Reumont, a mile away to the east, on the Roman road to St Quentin. Both generals were out on horseback up at the lines for much of the morning, both of them surviving only by the merest good fortune. General Snow had effectively lost touch with his brigadier-generals, who in their turn, with the exception of Brigadier Hunter Weston of 11 Brigade, had also lost touch with their Lieutenant-Colonels.

There was a desk and desk-chair on which Sir Horace sat, a gate-leg table, six more chairs, the obligatory photograph of President Poincaré in full fig on the wall, and that was about all. The town of Bertry had five thousand inhabitants, most of whom had now fled to friends and relatives in the countryside and villages to the south. Maps were spread out on the gate-leg, the Mayor's siver-framed photograph of his fine-looking wife having been removed and placed in a cupboard.

The Mayor, a greengrocer by trade, was hanging about in a vestibule off the foyé, running his fingers through his beard and adding nothing to the proceedings of any value whatsoever. Nobody knew what to do with him, so he was left alone. His beard gave him a remarkable resemblance to the King.

At 10.30 a.m. a two-seat scout plane had landed in the stubble to the south of the town, having flown from St. Quentin, out to Esnes, and via Cambrai, Le Cateau and Honnechy. The pilot brought little information of any use, beyond a note that GHQ was still adamant on retirement as soon as practically possible. He reported that the line seemed to be holding all the way from south-west of Le Cateau to Caudry and Esnes. When pressed, he admitted that he could not be sure whether or not Caudry was in British hands and was doubtful whether 4th Division was holding on to Esnes. Horace did a bit of clearing his throat and harrumphing. When the pilot had left to take off back to St. Quentin he said to Forrestier-Walker,

'The trouble with these RFC chaps is that whenever you need to know some actual bit of information, they can't tell you. Of course they can't. From 5000 feet how can you tell our side from theirs? I must go up in a machine one day and see for myself what it's like from up there. We could have done with a machine in the Transvaal though, I will admit that. Those heliograph balloons were never much use, damn bulky things to carry around'.

Another plane landed half an hour later, but it caught one wheel in a rabbit hole in the stubble and the nose up-ended, breaking the propeller. The pilot was slightly hurt with a broken nose and spent the next hour and a half not knowing what to do, while transport was being sorted out to take him back to his Squadron. He talked to the Mayor-King in his schoolboy French. It is not known what they discussed. Unknown to Sir

Horace, a third plane flew over his Mairie on its way to find Sir Douglas Haig, somewhere to the east. It never did find him, coming down in a field where the pilot spotted some British cavalry. Unfortunately they turned out to be German and the pilot took off again in a hurry. That was the RFC contribution to the battle, beyond a fourth plane whose pilot had the novel idea of bringing up a 4.5 inch howitzer shell and dropping it on a concentration of enemy troops north of the Cambrai road, fused to explode on impact. It was one of 30,000 or so shells fired at the enemy on that day. By contrast German planes were over the battlefield all day, and reporting back to their artillery batteries. It was spooking the men and officers.

There was absolutely nothing that Smith-Dorrien could now do to influence the actual fighting, beyond calling up his only reserves. This he had done at 10.00 a.m. when he ordered the 2nd Argyll and Sutherland Highlanders and the 1st Middlesex up to Suffolk Hill to reinforce the stricken garrison. The losses incurred by the Argylls in getting up the hill were considerable and further losses were incurred when Major Maclean, with two hundred men, charged at the enemy on the Cambrai road in an attack that was more an act of suicide than an act of war. The 2nd Royal Welch and the Scottish Rifles were to remain out of the action until such time as he might call on them later.

Colonel Romer of his staff had been out since first light to deliver the new orders to the brigades up by the Cambrai road and had been lucky to escape with his life when the bombardment started at 6.30 a.m. He had come back to Bertry by a roundabout route and was able to confirm that the battalions were in serviceable trenches and were holding firm. He told his Commander-in-Chief that the field-guns were firing back from their positions up with the infantry on the hill. This worried Smith-Dorrien; why were they not back behind the reverse slope? He realised now that that RFA Brigadier he had met in Le Cateau (Headlam? Something like that) was one of the old school that liked to be able to see their targets. A commendable view to take, he conceded, but putting the guns up front with the infantry is bound to increase casualties. It was much more likely that the man was a damn fool.

Reports came in throughout the morning from 5th Division at Reumont and 3rd Division. 3rd Division in the centre of the line was not seriously threatened. The right was the main worry; if it collapsed there was a real danger of the whole of 5th Division being rolled up. Their right was now known to be unsupported by friendly troops. 4th Division was thought to be holding, although their line had been shortened and ground given up in the west. Of Sordet's cavalry out to the west toward Cambrai nothing was known. The Territorials in and around Cambrai under General d'Amade were known to have some fast-firing 75mm guns, in which the French set great store.

Smith-Dorrien like all commanders was thinking about the integrity of the line. During the morning he gave little conscious thought to the fact that men were being killed because he had ordered them to stand, to fight, which he knew full well that as professional soldiers they would do until ordered otherwise. The British were renowned for being steady in defence, ever since the Peninsula. But he also knew that some individual commanders, Lieutenant-Colonels and Majors, would decide in the crisis of battle when the time had come to save what they could of their battalions, in effect to take the initiative themselves in the absence of further orders. He knew that men would abandon their posts in extremis. He would be a fool to think otherwise. He had been in such a situation himself. It was never his intention to fight to the last. But he desperately wanted to deal a blow to the enemy, to fight more than just a rearguard action, to kill as many of the enemy as possible; and that meant no premature retirement. He didn't need to point any of this out to his staff. His concern at the inevitable loss of life, although genuine, was thus eased by military necessity, and by a breaking of the link between his order and the consequent deaths of individuals; Lieutenant-Generals in any case find it hard to think of soldiers as individuals rather than items that need feeding, clothing and occasionally resting. Smith-Dorrien was no exception. He had not, of course, started his Army career as a private soldier. His pay of £5000 per year was, after all, nearly two hundred and seventy-five times that of a private soldier. When he did think of the ordinary soldier, a rare occurance, that object became an abstraction, part of a larger unit, but a thing without a will of its own, more like a child who needs guiding and leading, without a fully-formed personality. If pressed, the General could argue that the integrity of the line was essential for preventing a rout which would result in more deaths than would otherwise be the case. Generals, the military mind in fact, fear loss of cohesion, the resultant rout, as much as they fear anything. The General knew enough military history to know that most deaths on a battlefield occur after one side breaks through the line of its enemy, after which the number of casualties would depend on the energy with which the victorious troops hunt down and kill those fleeing for their lives. He remembered something from his Harrow days of the Normans breaking the shield wall of the house-carls at Hastings, and not without more than a bit of subterfuge. Subterfuge was as old as warfare.

At 12.30 p.m. General Sir Charles Fergusson of 5th Division came over from Reumont to see him. He was a little breathless.

'Horace, I have been up to the front and I can tell you that the situation is now worrying and finely balanced. The enemy are in strength in the Selle Valley, probably as many as a division, with more troops to the East. They are also coming down on to the Cambrai road. Many of our men are dribbling back; I personally had to restrain some of them, with Colonel Stephenson of the KOSB. I saw some Manchesters coming back on my way up there. They have never been in such shell-fire. The guns up front are shattered. The machine-guns are silent. I suggest that the time has come for the retirement to begin; the line on the hill cannot hold much longer.'

At this moment however, 12.30 p.m., there was a lull in what had been a relentless German artillery bombardment on the east flank. Both generals could hear the guns fall silent. In fact the pause was experienced all along the line. Was this an opportunity to get the men away? Or did it indicate that an infantry assault was under way? In which case, the men could hardly break off now that the crisis was approaching. Now was the time to catch the Allemand in the open while he was forming up his battalions. And if it was going to be anything like at Mons they would be cut down by the British riflemen, who were the best in the world. The fear of a rout was now secondary to the need to keep the guns firing.

'Charles, I think it would be best to hang on for a little while yet. An hour, maybe. There is some fight left in our men. We didn't pull back at Mons until 4.00 p.m. and the men did it then.'

'An hour, Horace, then.'

'That fool French, I can speak frankly to you, all he understands is Retire, Retire, Retire. Doesn't understand the complexities of pulling out in the middle of a battle. Thinks he knows about cavalry but doesn't even understand that. The man's an old woman, even Haig agrees on that. But Haig is going to have some explaining to do about his whereabouts when this day is done. At least at Mons he sent a brigade to plug Hamilton's line, but today, nothing. Not so much as a galloper'.

'I'm off back to my Headquarters, Horace. This is a day to reckon with, for all of us'.

Smith-Dorrien had no doubts in his mind: the men must fight it out a while yet. He knew in any case how difficult it was for orders to get from Division, to Brigade and up to the fighting colonels and company commanders. Even if he issued a retirement order now for all three divisions, it would be at least an hour before the order could have a hope of reaching the most exposed companies. Probably a lot longer; the only way to reach them would have to be by mounted staff officer, the last few hundred yards on the belly in all likelihood. But there were at least seven hours to go before sun-down. There was still a lot of fight left in the battalions.

He thought for a moment of the Royal Welch, the men he had talked to briefly the other side of Le Cateau. They wanted to have a bash at the Hun, no doubt about it. A splendid body of men. The light of battle in their eyes. Their time would come. He called for Colonel Romer.

'Colonel, please be so good as to draw up orders to the Scottish Rifles and the Royal Welch of 19 Brigade, my compliments to their colonels and would they move up to the north of Reumont in preparation for acting as rearguard when 14 Brigade pull back. See that the order is delivered at once. General Fergusson tells me that the enemy is coming on in strength down the Selle Valley and please inform the Colonels of this fact'.

'Yes, Sir, I'll go myself'.

Captain Bowley, Horace's ADC appeared.

'Sir, a sandwich for you. The best local ham, a speciality of the region. Our friend the Mayor does have his uses, arranged a supply with the charcuterie. And I've taken the precaution of having your horse and car removed to a safer place. Can't have Lord Derby getting upset if anything should happen to his Rolls-Royce. It's quite possible the boche might find us with their big guns, their equivalent of our 60-pounders.'

'Very good, Tom, and thank you.'

Smith-Dorrien wanted to talk further to his young ADC. He had not known him long, a few months, but he impressed him with his efficiency and good sense.

'Tom, can I ask you something? Suppose for a moment you are von Kluck. You think you have us on the run. You've got more men than us and more guns. Would you be happy to stop for the night when we disengage or would you risk all and push your tired troops on in pursuit?'

'My guess, Sir, for what it's worth, is that he knows his men are dog-tired already. They've marched through Belgium after all, when all we had to do was to get to Mauberge. You know what it's like after a day's hunting, Sir? You want your whisky and a bath. You don't want to go out to dinner. Well, I know the men, boche or ours, aren't going to get a bath and a drink but it's damn hard to get men to start again when the day's work is done.'

'I think you may have a point there, Tom. Let's hope so, anyway. But if you're wrong and they come on with a will we are in serious trouble'.

At 1.00 p.m. General Snow came through on the telegraph wire to plead for troops to plug a dangerous gap between Caudry and Fontaine. Horace wired back that he had none to spare. But it was gratifying to learn that there was no German breakthrough and the British line was holding, albeit a shorter line than at dawn.

Horace thought that 1.45 p.m. would be about the right time to order the retreat. This is a stopping blow, no more. This was our only field army. He had a duty to keep it in being.

He called for Colonel Rycroft. It was time to get the Quartermasters and the Service Corps busy. They were going to need an awful lot of wagons to get the wounded out on to the roads south.

At 2.00 p.m. the RFC pilot decided that since there was no chance of getting his machine - an Avro scout - airborne before nightfall he had better go out with a can of petrol and set light to it. It burned easily. He then set off on foot on the long road to St. Quentin, hoping to get a ride on a wagon, his cavalry boots being ill-suited to walking.

Chapter 14

Afternoon, Near Audencourt
Captain Johnson

At 1.30 p.m. Captain Henry Johnson of the Worcester Regiment was being carried by four RAMC orderlies to the forward aid post south of Audencourt. In the absence of stretchers he was being carried on a shutter torn off from the window of a house in Caudry. They reached the post at 1.45 p.m. without incident. The aid post was in a sunken lane and consisted of only one ambulance, draught horses munching from nose-bags in the shafts, and four orderlies, although others came and went as they brought in wounded. Blocks had been placed around the solid rubber tyres. The Geneva Cross and the Union Jack hung from cross-bars on the ambulance roof, fluttering slightly in the wind and visible above the banks of the lane. There was continuous fighting only half a mile or so to the north where the 1st Gordon Highlanders and the 2nd Royal Scots held a line between Caudry and Beaumont. The enemy were not able to break through what was a well-constructed defence, held with great skill and determination. Two batteries of 18-pounders were firing from south-west and south-east of the aid post, at both enemy infantry positions and enemy batteries and were clearly under fire themselves. Audencourt, which lay inside the British line, was in flames, but the British had long since abandoned it. It was about eight hundred yards north of the ambulance. Henry was conscious enough to hear the orderlies talking to each other.

'We've got another customer for you, an officer this time so look sharp.'

'What is it?'

'Mostly a leg wound, but could be more, hard to tell. He's conscious some of the time. Probably lost quite a bit of blood. But this one will live'.

'Lay him down there and we'll have a look at him.'

The RAMC orderly, a corporal, deftly cut through the cloth of Johnson's britches, having first removed his boots. A still-bleeding wound was revealed under a lint bandage, crudely applied. The corporal was keeping up a constant line of chat, although Johnson was barely conscious.

'Are you hit anywhere else, Sir? It's funny how they come in sometimes and you can easily miss a real stonker. Oh yes, here on your upper back, that's a nasty one, let's just have a little look shall we? I may have to cut out some foreign body that may have got into it. Half a mo'. ...There, just lie still as you can, Sir, that's better, it's the bits and pieces that get in that does the damage not just the wound itself. And the piece of metal, I can see that now, we'll have that out in no time. You can have some morphine later but I'm not allowed to give you any without the doctor and we haven't got one here, although I do have some discretion. You're not in Piccadilly now. You're somewhere in France although exactly where I couldn't say, but it's near a place called Le Catoo. There's a bleeding war going on here is what I can say, although you probably know that already. Would you like some water? Here you are, Sir. It's only the stomach cases that we can't give water to.'

Johnson listened to all this and felt deeply grateful to this man. But what he wanted above all else was not just water but his mare and if possible his sergeant. He felt sure that if he had the dependable Rouse with him again and if he could be helped up on the horse he could be on his way and back to the Battalion, to de Salis and his signals section. It wasn't too much to ask, surely.

'Just patch me up Corporal and I'll be out of your way. I'll be all right without morphine. I'm sure there are others coming in in more need than me of treatment.'

'Oh it's like that is it, don't like the facilities here, is that it? Now we've just got room for one more in the ambulance and then it's gee-up and off we go to the road to St. Quentin. First class travel. No ticket required. Soldier on, as my old mum used to say when I was a nipper.'

The corporal and his mate, another corporal, then lifted Johnson on his shutter and put him in the one remaining berth in the horse-ambulance. There was no question of Johnson protesting his ability to carry on. There were now just the two orderlies at the ambulance, the others having left to bring in more stretcher cases. They busied themselves for a while attending to the other cases in the ambulance, one of whom was doing a lot of groaning. He had a head wound and a stomach wound and looked to Johnson as if he wasn't going to live. The sounds of battle were all around them, outgoing fire from their own batteries and in-coming fire aimed at the batteries, which were well dug-in. Johnson looked at his watch; it was 2.30 p.m. He could smell burning, the smoke from the burning buildings of Audencourt drifting over the ambulance. The ambulance horses gave off whinnying noises the way horses do when they are agitated. He thought vaguely that a stray round could strike them at any moment. One of the corporals, the one who had dressed his wounds, went outside, probably for a smoke, thought Johnson.

'Fuck! Would you fucking believe it! The horses have gone, all four of them! Some thieving bastards have come along and taken them. Here, corp, come and have a look for yourself.'

Johnson heard all this and instantly understood. He remembered the French farm labourers in the lane from his ride this morning, the ones with the string tied around their knees. They must have come along the lane while the two corporals were in the ambulance, unhitched the horses and made off with them. He realised that he was now immobilised, wounded, stuck in an ambulance that was going nowhere and that he would be captured by the enemy when the British battalions withdrew, as they would before nightfall. This must not be allowed to happen. The RAMC corporals couldn't very well abandon their cases and go in search of help, on the uncertain hope of finding four fresh horses, in the middle of a battle. Well, he thought, maybe one could go and the other stay, but the chances of one corporal finding four serviceable horses were not good. But he knew that as RAMC orderlies they would be duty-bound to stay with their wounded. He himself was determined at all costs not to fall into the hands of the enemy. He owed it to Simon.

It was not that he feared the frightfulness of the Hun. He had never really believed all the propaganda of the German atrocities in Belgium, the nun-raping and the sticking of babies on bayonets. Indeed among his fellow-officers, de Salis and Brett, the reality of whose death still eluded him, 'frightfulness' had already become a figure of speech rather than a thing of truth. They would say to each other, 'The Colonel is exhibiting signs of frightfulness today' and think themselves jocular fellows. No, since he was convinced that the War was going to last a long time, at least until next spring, the prospect of being transported to some camp in eastern Germany where it would be cold and cheerless and there would be no Phoebe filled him with horror. Simple pleasures like a bath and a drink and an hour with Thomas Hardy would be impossible.

It was not the frightfulness in general that he was worried about; it was the thought that the first boche to come along might be Uhlans. They might not be bound by the rules of civilised warfare; they would not be the carefree hunting types of our own cavalry regiments he had met many times at hunt balls or point-to-point meetings. They were men with duelling scars whose antecedents were of a different sort than the hunting squire so familiar to him. They were not the sort of men in short by whom one would wish to be captured. Prussians more than likely, they lived as far as he was concerned on the edge of the steppes from where all the European invaders had come. They were tempered in a different school of warfare; not likely to appreciate his old College motto,

'Manners Makyth Man'. The great GA Henty didn't think much of them as far as he could remember but of course Henty had a dim view of foreigners in general.

He lay on the bunk listening to the groans of the other five wounded men. It seemed to him certain that none of them could walk unaided. He thought that in an hour or so he might have recovered enough strength to make it out of the ambulance and have a try at getting away. Quite how, he wasn't sure, but he would find a way. He would drag himself out somehow, crawl or even limp southwards when surely some passing soldier or officer would take him up to a place of safety. He would go towards the nearest of the two batteries still firing about half a mile away. They had transport in the form of limbers that he could hitch a ride on. That seemed a good plan.

He took out the letter he had taken from Simon's pocket. It was from his mother. He read.... 'Your father and I are both so terribly proud of you and at the same time so frightened, but we know of course that you will do your duty. The newspapers tell us so little of what is happening ....do please write as soon as you get the time.....the chickens are laying more eggs than we can eat and we have given half a dozen to the vicar......Phoebe sends her love and says she is missing dear Henry dreadfully .....' Johnson would write to her soon, he promised himself. It was another reminder of what he was fighting for, to keep faith with the dead. Our dead. And he would write to Simon's parents. The words, from *Macbeth*, said by Ross to a man who had lost his son in battle, came to him;

Your son, my lord, has paid a soldier's debt; ...
Your cause of sorrow
Must not be measured by his worth, for then
It hath no end.

Ever since first reading *Macbeth* and *Henry V* at Winchester, Johnson had known that Shakespeare had been a soldier, once. And Henry's little army, grossly outnumbered as it was, also retreating back to its base, had turned on its enemy and struck back with such devastating effect, when all had seemed lost. Next year would see its anniversary, as well as that of Waterloo. I must prepare a few morale-boosting words for the men, to remind them of their inheritance. And a few stirring words from *Henry V* wouldn't go amiss.

He was impressed with his clarity of thought. Morphine would have clouded his mind. It was better with the pain than the opiate. He drank some water, which revived him. He would have to be insistent with the orderlies, but after all he was an officer and he could insist that it was his duty to return to his Battalion. He looked at his watch. 3.15 p.m. Time to go. He strapped on his Webley and sword, which the orderly had left by his side. He put on his boots, which reached just below his leg wound. He knew now that rejoining the Battalion in his state was not the best plan; far better to make for the battery.

He lifted the good leg onto the floor. So far so good. Then the injured one. Not so good. Never mind, crack on, ignore the pain from the back. Out of the ambulance on his bottom. The RFA batteries were still in action, being re-supplied with wagons of ammunition, which he could see racing up at the gallop.

At this point the chatty corporal was very much in evidence.

'I'm all right, Corporal, just going out for a bit. I may be some time. Gives you a spare berth, which you will no doubt need. But since this ambulance is stuck here I don't intend to stay with it.'

'Yes, Sir. Mind how you go, Sir. This may help a bit', handing Johnson a stout piece of oak, fashioned into a sort of crutch. He gave him a canteen of water. Johnson still had some whisky in his flask.

Well that bit was remarkably easy. Now comes the hard part. Now this is a handy walking stick. Off to that battery to the south-east, it doesn't look more than a thousand yards way, should be able to make it in a jiffy.

Hang on, there's a horse coming along the lane now, what luck, perhaps the rider will take me up and get me to the battery. Oh and now isn't that something, I do believe that's Sergeant Rouse and what's more he's riding my mare, I'd recognise that piebald anywhere.

'Well met, Sarn't. I could do with a ride.'

'They told me you would be here, Sir, and I found the mare so I thought I would come along. Seems I came just at the right time. I would have found you earlier, Sir, but I got caught in the midst of some fritzes and had to hide in a house, but managed to escape under cover of a bombardment.'

'Good work, Sarn't. I'll take the mare and go off in the direction of Bertry. I may still be of some use to somebody, even if I'm not much use as a signalling officer, with or without the signals cart. You rejoin the battalion. If you could help me up I should be able to manage the rest.'

The good old mare stood steady as Sergeant Rouse helped his Captain up into the saddle. She'd been pulling a cart in the Malvern Hills for a solicitor and his wife before the army requisitioned her and was a reliable animal. Johnson felt no sentimental attachments to animals, except possibly his spaniel which he used for rough shooting. She was kept at his parents' house near Broadway so that in any case he didn't have care of her. He didn't even have a name for the mare.

They set off south-east, the unnamed piebald mare and the Captain, along a farm track getting gradually further from the RFA battery and the British front line. He knew he would be getting in to the 5th Division area of operations, from where he had started out that morning. How long ago that already seemed. He saw the lone tree to the north, the one he had passed in the early morning; the soldiers hadn't managed to cut it down. He realised he had no further need for the oak walking stick, so he threw it away. He passed a howitzer battery, four guns well dug in, with an ammunition wagon nearby, shattered from an HE explosion, the horses still in their traces and mangled into unnatural shapes. The bombadiers were looking intently at the nose-cones of exploded shells, which he knew was an attempt to estimate the range of the enemy battery. This was clearly a pause in their action. The gunners gave him no acknowledgement. Their dead comrades lay alongside the battery, covered with a tarpaulin.

The pain from his two wounds was now an annoyance rather than an acute pain. He was going to live, but he said to himself that the one piece of luck which had come his way in the shape of Rouse and the mare couldn't possibly be repeated. Nobody gets that lucky twice in one day.

Chapter 15

Near Reumont
Private Edwards

Orders brought by Colonel Romer from HQ at Bertry to Brigadier-General Drummond of 19th Brigade near Reumont, coming down through the chain of command from HQ Second Corps to Brigade to Battalion to the Company commanders, finally reached Lieutenant Bosanquet of the 2nd Royal Welch Fusiliers at 2.15 p.m. On this occasion the orders were passed down more rapidly than might be expected because 19th Brigade was an independent Brigade, outside the structure of 5th Division, so that a whole level of command was bypassed. The order-chit contained the appropriate map references, but Bosanquet knew that they would sort themselves out as the situation dictated.

He addressed the platoon.

'We are to move to a position north of Reumont and form a rearguard to the east of the Roman road in the event of an enemy breakthrough. Prepare to move off in columns of four. Full magazines but nothing up the spout. We will adopt artillery formation as soon as we get to the main road. We will have the Scottish Rifles on our left. We will now walk-march south-east and then north-east when we come to the Roman road.'

This was not unexpected to any of the members of the platoon. They could hardly have expected to be able to move out and find a comfortable billet near St. Quentin for the night. The men picked up their rifles and packs, adjusted their webbing and formed up, rifles in the marching position, and moved off at the order 'By the right, quick march'. The Battalion transport, with the non-combatant personnel, had been long ago been sent down the St. Quentin road.

Then Edwards remembered Mr. Moore. Not that he'd forgotten him; it was just that a decision had to be made about what to do with him. The seed-man seemed to have disappeared, much to his relief. It was possible someone had found a use for him.

Edwards needn't have concerned himself with the ubiquitous Moore, who had now been granted the unofficial rank of Captain. He noticed the Panama hat bobbing up on the outside of the column. He caught up with Edwards.

'I couldn't go on without my invaluable guide, so I'm coming with you, Edwards.'

'Just as long as you know that there might be a bit of shooting, Sir.'

'I think I know well enough what to expect, but I want to see it for myself, for my readers.'

'They don't give medals to civilians as far as I know.'

'There will be more than enough medals given out today I'll be bound.'

'Every man up there on the hill is a hero.'

They reached the Roman road. Ahead of them was Reumont, where the RAMC had set up the forward hospital in the church, where Edwards and Mr. Moore had left Gunner Major. Ammunition wagons were moving up the road, the drivers showing no mercy to the horses. There was broken down motor transport, pushed to the side, one Albion lorry left blocking the road. Shells were falling in an indiscriminate pattern. Walking wounded were coming down from the hill, helped along by their mates. One man had so much blood on his trousers that they looked like the pantalons of a poilu. An 18-pounder, with its limber, pulled by four horses came down the road, one of the drivers with an arm that appeared to be only just connected to his body. The big 60-pounder long-barrelled guns were firing from the left side of the St. Quentin road at targets not visible to the Royal Welch. The howitzers, a battery of six well in front of the 60-pounders, were firing battery salvos of High Explosive, the stubby barrels pointing skywards at 45 degrees, the gunners bent to their sweaty task, not looking up at the passing traffic. There was no problem with re-supply of High Explosive here, unlike the howitzers on the hill which had long fallen silent for want of shells. Enemy HE shells were straddling the road, throwing up debris. A wounded horse lay against a pile of straw; for some reason no-one had taken a gun to its head. Edwards sensed that the men were almost glad to be on the move after all the hours hanging about in the lane.

They went on, staying off to the right to let the wheeled traffic pass. Buffy and Edwards were marching together, five yards apart. They passed through the straggly village of Maurois, where civilians were still about, strangely unmoved by the commotion. General Hamilton, accompanied by a staff officer, passed through on his horse, going south, and a woman with a stall called out to him: 'Chocolat, mon General?' He rode on with a wave of his baton. Refugees were coming down the Roman road on foot, old men in their Sunday best and their wives with shawls wrapped around them, although the air still had the heat of the day in it. Some of the mothers were pushing prams, babies sharing the space with provisions such as apples and carrots. The Battalion passed Reumont and came again to the place where the West Kents were in reserve, on the left of the road. The East Surreys were up ahead of them. The hill rose to their right. A man from the West Kents was heard to shout 'Give 'em hell, boyos!'

Orders came down to Four Eyes. He started to wipe his spectacles, which Edwards recognised as a sign of nerves.

'This is far enough for the moment. Spread out and keep down. We are staying here a while until further orders.'

Edwards sought out Mr. Moore.

'Well here we are again, Sir, about to get stuck in, and I'm wondering whether an educated man like yourself can tell a private soldier why, because some archduke, or whatever he was, gets himself shot in a town in a place I can't pronounce, we have to fight the boche on this Godforsaken hill in France. Did the mayor of this town have an argument with the mayor of a town outside a hill in Germany? You know about the newspapers, Sir, so perhaps you can tell me if it is all true about the Germans cutting open the Belgian women and tearing the unborn babies from their wombs?'

'You are now a philosopher as well as a military guide, my dear Edwards. You should write my dispatch for me. I have not seen the German atrocities with my own eyes but the Hun is a rapacious animal and he must be driven back whence he came. The Hun is probably no more prone to rape than the rest of humanity but he will indulge in it if given the chance and if we do not stop him he will have us all at his mercy. War is what men do; it is not an aberration. We must defend our sisters and our daughters as much as our hills and valleys. This is a civil war, as all wars are, and there will be barbarity and killing without mercy. The English are slow to anger but they fight when they have a mind to it. We did it with Napoleon and we'll do it with Kaiser Bill. I've heard that he has called your army a 'contemptible little army.'

'Cheeky old bugger. We'll have to show him about that.'

Up on the hill the tempo of the battle had changed. The shell fire seemed to have slackened and there was now continuous rifle fire. There must be close-quarter fighting now, the enemy from the valley to the right emerging on to the high ground and the enemy on the front closing in. Were the gunners firing shrapnel direct at the troops coming up from the valley? Edwards knew the Suffolks and the Highland Scots couldn't hold out much longer. Unknown to the Royal Welch, Smith-Dorrien at 1.55 p.m. had ordered all the divisions to disengage from the enemy and start movements for the retreat to be resumed; the retreat to be commenced from the right, here at Suffolk Hill, and then progressively eastwards to the 4th Division around Haucourt. But as Smith-Dorrien and every staff officer knew, translating these orders into operational orders and then getting them through to the fighting battalions was quite another matter. An order issued from a town hall in Bertry doesn't make much difference to a man who can see a hundred grey-clad enemy with spikes on their helmets working their way toward him with seventeen-inch bayonets sticking out in front of their Mausers; enemy fusiliers who may be not in the mood for accepting that man's surrender after he has seen his comrades lacerated by British shrapnel; fusiliers who could launch a bomb with their rifles and land it in a shallow trench a hundred and fifty yards away.

Edwards called over to Buffy,

'Let's give the gentleman a song, the one that goes to the tune of the old hymn'.

And they got several Welshmen to join in the song they had sung on the march down from Valenciennes:

'We are Fred Karno's army
The ragtime infantry:
We cannot fight, we cannot shoot,
What earthly use are we!
And when we get to Berlin,
The Kaiser he will say,
'Hoch, Hoch, mein Gott,
What a bloody fine lot,
Are the ragtime infantry!'

The words, just audible over the rifle and shell fire on the hill, delivered in a Welsh baritone, moved the journalist to tears. The thought of these men swinging into horrors undreamt of was almost too much for him to bear. It saddened him that he had not got the words to express it. It saddened him that the censor would never allow him to publish an account of the battle in which individual units and individuals could be named. From over the hill he heard the mournful sound of a dozen bugles blowing.

Then a team of horses appeared, followed by another, coming up from the lea of the hill. Two teams of six, with two officers riding alongside the teams, both teams being driven by three drivers. They were pulling limbers, the vehicles for hooking up guns, and they were going north, into the battle and they could only be going for one reason. They were going up to rescue what guns they could. The West Kents stood up, the better to view their passing; they quickly sensed, as did the Welch Fusiliers, that something extraordinary was about to happen. All of the fascinated onlookers could hear the shouts of the officers: 'Come on Boys! Come on my Beauties!' The onlookers gave rousing cheers; these were men and horses going up to what must be certain death. And they were going with a will and with an eagerness which took the breath away, galloping through the exploding white puff-balls of shrapnel, the horses' ears seemingly pinned back, nostrils flaring and eyes bulging.

A Manchester private came running down the hill toward them; Edwards noticed that he still had his rifle. If he had abandoned it would have been a court martial offence. But the man was otherwise beyond reason. He had had enough; eight hours of shelling and now the enemy on him with rifle and bayonet. The Welch Fusiliers took him into their ranks and enveloped him as one would a child. He was trembling uncontrollably. He said he was the sole survivor of his Battalion. He was babbling about the enemy coming on shoulder to shoulder and firing from the hip. It will be every man for himself up there soon, thought Edwards. And then we'll have to face the bastards.

A gunner came running towards them, an officer by his side. The officer seemed wounded in the left leg and was faltering but getting on. He was carrying the breach mechanism of an 18-pounder in both hands. Edwards thought it strange that the officer and not the bombardier was carrying the heavy load. The gunner stopped long enough to say: 'If the fuckers could shoot straight we'd all be fucked.' The officer didn't seem to mind this language.

'Christ, that can only mean one thing,' said Edwards to the ever-present Mr. Moore, 'We are disabling the guns'.

Edwards noticed Four Eyes wiping his glasses.

'Steady lads, steady the 23rd!'

'Seen enough yet, Mr. Moore? Enough to freeze your blood?' Edwards felt again that satisfaction in having a civilian see what they had to do for a shilling a day. Enough to buy a good bottle of vin blanc, with not much left over. Which made him think of Suzanne again, with her Pre-Raphaelite hair, who was only a matter of a mile away at the most, but a mile that might as well be a million miles. The thought of her at the hands of the Uhlans made him shudder.

Another cheer broke out from the entrenched East Surreys to the north, audible above the constant rattle and crack of musketry, the West Kents joining in; the horse teams were back from the hill! No, only one was back, one must have been shot down. They were towing two howitzers, a miracle, but now Edwards could see only two drivers, one must have been shot and fallen from the saddle. But a miracle none the less. Heroes all. The officer was still riding alongside, acting like another driver, holding on to the reins of the lead horse. This time there were no shouts of 'Come on boys!' But they all three used the whip with ferocity; Edwards was reminded of Egyptians - Gyppos - he had seen beating their donkeys in Alexandria. Not like the Hindoos with their cows. And Buffy says the Indian regiments will be arriving here before long; well, if that happens we'll know that things are getting to a pretty pass.

The retreat order had been issued but the order had gone out in any case too late to save the Suffolks. They were facing the ultimate test that any man can face: to lay down his rifle and put himself at the mercy of his enemy who up to that point wishes him dead; or to fight on and invite more certain death. Up on the hill the German buglers were blowing the British cease-fire notes. Edwards could hear the familiar sounds but suspected them of being a German ruse. A British infantryman will take his orders from his own officers and not from the enemy, that much he knew. The rifle-fire flared up and then stopped. The Suffolks and the Highlanders saw that behind them, as well as to their front and right, the stubble was filled with grey-clad soldiers emerging from the valley. There was no dishonour in laying down their arms.

Chapter 16

Lieutenant Penfold

Lieutenant Stephen Penfold and Sergeant Fox, whose first name Penfold didn't know, skirted once more the stubble-field in which the dead Jaeger sniper still lay. After the next field they found their way back to the Battalion, or rather the remnants still active on the field of battle. There were about one hundred and fifty men and officers back with the transport, over a hundred had made off for St. Quentin with the shaven-arsed Colonel, and two hundred or so lay dead beyond the hedge, in what was now nomansland. Major Haddow was still too badly hurt to exercise command and all the other company commanders were dead, picked off by snipers in the early morning disaster. Lieutenant Bernard Montgomery was now in command, with Lieutenant Penfold as his second-in-command and Lieutenant Watkins acting as a Company Commander. They numbered now 300-odd men, about sixty of them wounded, more or less severely. Some of the wounded had been carried back to a temporary aid post, using the bandsmen as orderlies. Captain Nolan, the MO, was with them and without him many of the wounded would be dead by now. Monty had organised the Battalion into three companies, A, B and C to be commanded by Watkins, himself and Penfold, in that order.

It was now 1.00 p.m. Montgomery was very glad to see Penfold back with Sergeant Fox.

'I'd almost given up hope for you; we got shelled a bit, and very unpleasant it was, especially when a Taube came over and dropped some flares to show our position to the enemy guns. But our batteries silenced them. Some Jaegers tried to get round us on the left but Watkins went out with half of A company and drove them off. It's a damn shame we don't have the Vickers. I've pushed some men out as a picquet by the hedge. Still no orders from Brigade. We've managed to get some wounded men in from the other side of the hedge. The adjutant is out looking for Brigade now at Haucourt, but he's been gone two hours and I fear he must have been captured on the way, together with the two men he took with him. The men I sent out to the left looking for the Lancashires have not returned either. I sent some men over to that farmhouse on the right and they found some fencing wire which you see now fifty yards in front of us. We think it might slow the Jaegers down if they try a frontal attack; it's got some spiky barbs in it at regular intervals. I rather think they might attack and if so you are just in time to join the fray.' He pronounced it 'fway'.

'We took a while to deal with a sniper. The King's Own are holding on and have just carried out a successful counter-attack. They are staying put until they get further orders. They are about a thousand yards on our right. I can't understand why the Jaegers or cavalry don't come through between us'

'They must think we're stronger than we are. Or they are under orders to attack us where they find us, to destroy us rather than bypass us, which I think is more likely. But I'm extending our line to the right now up to the farmhouse. I have a sergeant and a dozen men in the yard. If the enemy attack in strength, say in Brigade strength, I intend to go into the farmhouse and its buildings and use it as a redoubt. We will be safer in there from all but High Explosive. And if the King's Own are standing fast, then we must do the same'.

As Monty was uttering these words, a salvo of shrapnel came in and exploded at twenty feet or so just in front of the line, followed by another. A piece of sizzling metal landed at his feet. The men got as low as they could in their scrapings. Penfold thought it might be the prelude for an attack, especially in view of the attention from the Taube. And he thought the boche would come round their flanks as well. There was a call for stretcher-bearers. He got into a space in a shallow trench on the right of the line, about a hundred yards from the farmhouse. Sergeant Fox was about twenty yards away. The farmhouse, undamaged, with its solid walls and half-brick, half-stone construction looked inviting. Penfold then remembered that he had had no food since first thing this morning and thought of the egg and ham that must surely abound in the larder of the house. What a good idea of Monty's to go into the farmhouse; it would be their castle and keep. Penfold's mind went back to the Vicarage at Petworth, when as a child he would play with his lead soldiers and his wooden castle and defend it against the 'enemy' soldiers, who wore the blue and red uniforms of the dastardly French. His men in the castle, many of them in tartan and green, always triumphed against the red and blue, who lined themselves up in column and were easily shot down. The 'enemy' would have more numbers but would fall victim to the steady British fire and Penfold the General would show no mercy. His father, the vicar, did not discourage his martial juvenilia, believing in the Church Militant, and that 'Onward Christian Soldiers' applied exclusively to those white men born within the dominions of the King-Emperor.

Penfold was brought back to the present by a new salvo of shrapnel exploding fifty feet away. Again, he was surprised at how little bodily injury was caused to the men, with such little protection that the scrapings afforded them. But it surely must herald an assault. Their presence was hardly unknown to the Jaegers.

And now an assault was definitely on its way; the sound of bugles was in the air, another salvo of shrapnel and then another and now the piquet was running back to the line, through a gap in the wire so cunningly placed at Monty's order. Then the first of the curious green shakos could be seen at the hedge four hundred yards away and men with rifles were now visible, scrambling and hugging the ground, and taking up prone firing positions even as the order 'Fire At Will: Four Hundred Yards Front!' was shouted by Montgomery and passed down the line.

Penfold to his surprise found himself observing them with interest even though bullets were tearing the air above and all around him; he found himself counting the shakos and speculating on whether their owners were being killed in numbers sufficient to render them a nugatory threat. It was curious how that word sprung unbidden into his ken. He wished he had a rifle; he didn't even have his ridiculous sword, but he drew his Webley, checking to make sure it was loaded. It made him feel stronger; it was his badge of office, his mark of a Gentleman, its weight a comfort in his hand. His own men were keeping as low as they could in the scrapings. They would pop up and loose off a round every now and again, resembling to Penfold's mind the ducks at the annual Fair at the pistol range at the big house at Petworth; so must his men appear to the enemy. This sort of shooting was what all British infantry had been trained for and the shako-soldiers were being killed one after the other.

All the advantage of the fire-fight that ensued lay with the 1st Warwickshires. The Jaegers seemed perplexed by the wire, which was in truth only a few strands held down with metal spikes and supplemented with spare coils found in the farmyard. It must have been intended for the fencing of cattle but barbed wire fences did not form part of the farming landscape and the Jaegers were at a loss as to how to get through it. Penfold was confused at first by the pinging sound coming from the front and then realised that it was the sound of bullets hitting the wire. He wondered again why the enemy did not go round their flank and attack them in enfilade. And then he saw, at least seven hundred yards off to his right, opposite the farmhouse, a machine-gun cart emerging from a culvert. There were men in green-grey crouched around it. He shouted to Sergeant. Fox, 'Machine Gun Half Right Seven Hundred Yards: Fire at Will!' He had a vision of horrible clarity of the Maxim getting in to a position to fire into the Warwick line from the right and killing them all.

He needn't have worried. The dozen men in the farmyard, of whose presence the machine gun crew seemed unaware, caught the crew in a well aimed and well timed fusillade. Two of the crew were killed instantly and the rest went to ground. But the German manoeuvre had shown Penfold that their position was untenable, with the other friendly troops so far distant. They were, as Monty would have said 'in the air'. Penfold decided to edge over to Monty's position and have a word with him about what to do next.

Penfold collected Sergeant Fox and they both made their way gingerly along the line; the men were spaced about ten yards apart, having used their grubbers to good effect. They got to Monty's Command Post; he still had Penfold's sword stuck excalibur-like in the ground and Penfold put it back in its scabbard. Monty said straight away,

'I have had a casualty report; we have about fifty wounded with us and they can't be moved, although some of them can still hold a weapon. The dead number about twenty. We have maybe two hundred and fifty active men. Watkins on the left reports enemy trying to get round on the flank. My view is that it would be wrong to abandon this position altogether, but we should break out with the larger part of our force, and the rest should stay with the wounded and the MO. I would like to seek shelter in the farmhouse; there will be water there at least. The wounded may have to be handed over to the enemy when the main force has made good its escape. A new attack may develop at any moment and my sergeant tells me that we have the equivalent of 150 rounds per man. But it does look as if the Jaegers on the hedge-line have gone back. Stephen, what's your view?' That 'Stephen' made Penfold uneasy.

Penfold was not for the first time happy to allow Monty to decide things, although they both held the same rank. But he felt he ought to make his presence felt. He said,

'I think I ought to stay with the rearguard and the wounded. We should let Watkins take the main body out and try and find their way back to Haucourt. I agree that it is a good idea to seek shelter in the farmhouse, and hope to break out after dark. The wounded as you say,

Monty, will have to be surrendered, with the MO. But at least while we stay we are maintaining the line, such as it is.'

Montgomery turned to Sergeant Fox: 'Sergeant, can you get Captain Nolan to join us here?'

When Fox had gone, Monty said to Penfold,

'I will stay behind myself; as acting commander I can do nothing else. We will stay together, Stephen.' He consulted his watch. 'We have now four hours until it gets dark. The men should have another bit of hard tack before setting off. The time to go is now, before a new attack develops. Watkins should lead the battalion off. Agreed?'

Captain Nolan, the Battalion doctor, appeared at the Command Post.

'Captain, we have no choice; the main body of our force must try and find a way back to Haucourt, under Lieutenant Watkins. Lieutenant Penfold and myself will stay behind with the wounded and a small number of active men, B company men in the main, including Sergeant Fox, as rearguard. We will try and get the stay-behind party into the farmhouse and wait for dark. Those that can, will then make an attempt to rejoin our forces. Those unable to move will have to throw themselves on the mercy of the enemy.'

'Lieutenant Montgomery, I will of course stay with the wounded. I have five orderlies with me.'

Lieutenant Watkins took advantage of the lull in the fighting to take his Company-sized group of men off to the south, towards Haucourt, mostly men of A Company, and as many of the walking wounded who were judged capable of the journey. The stay-behind men wished them a cheery 'Good luck chum' and they were away. They had to cross the Ravine with enemy patrols, both mounted and dismounted cavalry and Jaeger foot-soldiers, known to be active. They had some two thousand yards of terrain to cover. The situation at Haucourt was not known, nor even if it was still held by 4th Division troops, but Watkins was ordered by Monty to find an officer from Brigade to report to. The 1st

Warwickshires had left it soon after dawn on their disastrous attack, when the small town was under shell-fire and they had had no communication of any sort with anyone at Brigade or Division since that time, apart from the heroic mounted staff officer who had aborted the morning attack, an officer who vanished as quickly as he had appeared. The rump of the Battalion had seen small parties of enemy making their way round to their right and left and had heard only sporadic gunfire which told them nothing. There was no established 4th Division line in any sense; the excursion of Lieutenant Penfold and Sergeant Fox out to make contact with the King's Own had established that. Most of the firing throughout the day had been by the artillery. Monty would have liked to send a reliable man back to the nearest gun battery to inform them of his position, but the chance of such a mission being successful was too remote to consider it seriously. But they were still under the No Retirement order, received at 6.00 a.m.

It was now 4.30 p.m. The artillery duel was slackening off, although small-arms fire was almost continuous. Penfold guessed that the RFA gunners were preparing to pull out, which would leave them even more exposed. He had, ever since first thing this morning when they had learned that Corps did not intend to retire, had the private thought that orders to resume the retreat would come through from Brigade well before darkness. But in their exposed position how would such an order get through to them? Had the battalion on their left, the Lancashire Fusiliers, stayed put or gone? The adjutant had not come back from his search for Brigade, which did not bode well. He knew the King's Own were going to stay put, but for how long? The Worcester Battalion, the 3rd, was out there somewhere on their right, but God knows where. He knew so little of the overall situation. He knew that Brigadier Hunter-Weston's 11 Brigade was fighting somewhere to the north-west of them, but nothing more. Both Penfold and Montgomery were of course aware that to abandon their position, in front of the enemy and at a time when not under direct attack, was simply not in the Officer's Manual. They were in the line and even if it was not a continuous line, in the absence of orders to retire, they must maintain a presence. This is what they were now doing with the wounded, both ambulant and hors de combat, and a cadre of twenty-five officers and men. Together with the small garrison in the farm buildings, that made a stay-behind force of say thirty-five effectives. Both Montgomery and Penfold had now armed themselves with rifles taken from wounded men. They now prepared to move the whole stay-behind force, wounded and all, into the farm, to defend themselves if need be from all comers.

At 5.30 p.m. Montgomery went to see Major Haddow. He was lying with the other wounded in a hollow behind the line. His shattered shoulder was bound up, but Captain Nolan was not sure if he would ever regain the use of it and he was nervous of septicaemia if he could not get him to an aid station. The Major had lost enough blood to make him weak but he was aware of the situation they were in. He'd refused morphine. He approved Monty's plan of using the farm as a redoubt. He gave Monty his FS map, which marked the farm and its buildings as Le Coquelet. The one-inch map covered only a small area, but it included the area to the south of Caudry, as far as Selvigny. A cursory glance at the map showed Selvigny to be a good five miles to the south-west, with the villages of Ligny and Caullery in between.

'The 6th shall fight as they always have done.'

For Major Haddow there was no more to be said. The Warwickshire lads would stand their ground, the halt and the lame and the fit; even if they were tired and weary and if there was no-one by their sides.

While Monty was with the wounded a shot rang out and a call of 'Sniper' went up. A man had been shot through the chest and was going to die of a punctured lung and a great deal of other internal damage. The enemy were clearly still active in the hedge. It was time to seek the shelter of the farm buildings. The problem was how to get the wounded across the three hundred yards of stubble that separated the hollow from the farm. Monty crawled back to where Sergeant Fox and Penfold were lying in a shallow pit.

'I'll wager that the boche High Explosive boys are going to pack it in soon. They won't worry themselves about one farmhouse in any case. So when we get there it will be a defendable place. And we shall defend it'.

Penfold thought about his lead soldiers in the castle. And so two young officers, both sons of clerical gentlemen, both schooled in the art of war, decided to defend to the last a farmhouse near the Frenco-Belgian border with a force of thirty-five men. 'I know that my Redeemer liveth'. The words comforted Stephen Penfold, words from the Prayer Book spoken by the Padre last night.

Chapter 17

Second Corps HQ, Bertry

Lieutenant-General Sir Horace Smith-Dorrien called for Brigadier George Forrestier-Walker. The Chief-of-Staff to Second Corps was by his side in a moment, his knee-length boots gleaming, moustache trimmed that very morning by his batman as if they had nothing better to do on a battle-morning. It was now 2.30 p.m. The sound of Fifth Division gunfire was all around them, particularly the 60-pounders firing the naval shells at a steady rate of one per minute, seeking targets on the Montay Spur across the Cambrai road.

'Chief, tell me how goes the dispatch of orders to the Divisions and have they acknowledged?'

'The wire to Haucourt has been cut by shell-fire but the signals Engineers are out repairing it now. It's a ten mile run of wire so it will take a little while but we expect to get through in about half an hour. 5th and 3rd Division HQs have received their retreat orders, with the tactical arrangements and timing to be left to the brigadiers. 3rd Division report that nowhere is their line breached. 14 Infantry Brigade are disengaging but I fear XV Brigade RFA guns will be lost in some quantity because of their forward position. The Suffolks are unlikely to get away, being the furthest on the right. If they hold fast they should prevent a breakthrough. I hear of reports of great bravery from gunners and infantry on that hill, the gunners firing as if they were infantry themselves. They have undoubtedly done good execution on the enemy, which have been caught forming up in the open on the Montay Spur. The two 19 Brigade battalions are on their way to take up their new positions. There are signs that the enemy are not exploiting the gaps in our line which must mean that their leadership is faltering. We have hit them hard all along the line but Snow at Haucourt reported an hour and a half ago, before the wire was cut, that he had lost touch with all the battalions of 12 and 11 Brigade and at least two battalions of 10 Brigade. Our information is necessarily sketchy and the colonels must be fighting their own independent battles. We have no knowledge of the whereabouts of the Warwicks or the King's Own for example. It must be pell-mell out there but it's not Sedan, as Wilson would have it. Still no information on Sordet's cavalry but I know him by repute and he is an old warrior even if his men are all spit and polish. The trouble with these French cavalry chaps is that they don't understand that guns and infantry and cavalry have to work together. They didn't get it right at Waterloo and it's the same story today.'

'We must have faith in our battalions. I know what they can do. The Rifle Brigade is out there with 11 Brigade and I know Colonel Biddulph; if anyone can fight a skirmish line the old 95th can, just remember what they did at Waterloo at La Haye Sainte. Some things don't change'.

'I'm just a humble staff officer, Horace, not a fighting soldier, but I know the Riflemen.'

Smith-Dorrien looked out of the window at the Square and the school-building where 3rd Division was housed. No trouble getting orders there or 5th Division for that matter. He felt a moment's pang of emotion at the desperate plight he knew 14 Infantry Brigade were now in; he remembered Lieutenant-Colonel Brett of the Suffolks from an Aldershot staff-college TEWT designed for Majors and above. The man was an officer of the old school, which in his eyes meant a lot; rock-solid and dependable. My God we are going to need officers like that in spades now. He glanced up at the photograph of President Poincaré. The tricoleur which had been draped around the frame had been taken down, a concession to the fact that this was temporarily a small part of Great Britain. The Union Jack flew from the mast-head of the building.

'George, do you suppose the French have the same problems with their frock-coats as we do? I mean, our lot are in thrall to the Navy; if the Navy want a couple of new Dreadnoughts all they have to do is snap their fingers and they get it, but when it comes to fighting here in northern France what good is a shiny new battlecruiser? We're going to need more big guns, mark my words, and I don't mean more of these old Boer War pieces. Asquith knows nothing of these matters and is too fond of a drink, so I've heard. Churchill is untrustworthy and as for Lloyd George, well, he's a clever Welshman so let's say no more about him. They make good soldiers but poor politicians.'

There was a knock on the door and a Signals sergeant entered, saluted, and gave the Chief of Staff a message from the pad. The message had been decoded. He saluted again and left the room. Forrestier-Walker held up the message, with a look of disdain. He said,

'It's another message from GHQ reminding us of our duty to get the retreat underway as soon as possible. As if we needed reminding. And as if it was worth encoding: it could hardly come as a surprise to von Kluck. It reminds me of the complaint from Collingwood at Nelson's plea that they would do their duty. Of course they would do their duty; they didn't have to be told that. And I'll bet a golden guinea that when it comes to the retreat no-one will do it faster than old Sir John French; he was damn quick to get out of Le Cateau yesterday. Haig and French, Scarlet Pimpernels both of them, too damn quick at the disappearing act. We could have done with the 4th Guards' Brigade on the right. But it looks now as if our line of retreat is towards Noyon. My guess is that Sir John wants to get the Somme between the enemy and Second Corps. Good idea, but the Engineers had better look sharp when it comes to blowing the bridges; a lot of the trouble at Mons was to do with the bridges not being blown in time. But if we go across the Somme, are we going on down to defend the western approaches to Paris? Is it going to be like 1870 and the siege of Paris? If I were in Paris now I would lay in a good store of potatoes. They say all the fish in the Seine were eaten in '71 and they have never recovered. But my guess is that Sir John will want to look to his own lines of communication and leave the defence of Paris to the French, if Kitchener will let him.'

'George, we should be prepared to move out from here before too long. I think we should go out to the Roman road and see for ourselves the state of the troops as they come out from the front. We must see that the rearguards are in place. We might have to rally the men and see what wagons we can muster. Requisition orders may be needed and hesitant officers may need hectoring. You know these quartermasters need badgering before things get done. And see that my horse is kept close to me; I may want to ride out across country. I'm still a brigade commander at heart and I want to be out there with the men. It will be good for their morale to see their Corps Commander up at the front.'

'Horace, reports are coming in from all along the line from brigades all saying the same thing about the German planes. There's no doubt that they have a way of sending wireless signals to their batteries from the air. They are way ahead in this and we are going to have to badger our signals people to see what they can do.'

'I'll bring it up when I'm next at GHQ. Just remind me of the best man to talk to about this. Robertson may well be the man; very sound chap and a quartermaster who understands the ins and outs of the business.'

'Horace, one thing I have learnt from staff rides is that the 'enemy' are always as tired and confused as our own people. We can be sure that this applies to the enemy today.'

'Let's hope so, George.'

Captain Bowley, ADC to Smith-Dorrien, entered the room after a brief knock. He saluted.

'General, there is a Captain Johnson of the Worcesters in the ante-room. He's wounded in the leg and back, but he'll pull through. He's just come in from the Caudry area and I thought you might like to hear his report.'

'I would indeed, Bill. Show him in, if you please.'

Captain Bowley went out and came back with Captain Johnson, helping him to a vacant chair, on which Johnson sat down heavily. The Worcester Captain was pale, there was blood seeping from a bandage on his leg, his uniform was covered in foul mud, but he seemed composed. He had managed a salute. Smith-Dorrien asked him if he would like some refreshment but Johnson said his staff had been most kind and had given him a cup of tea and his horse water. He was invited to give a brief and frank account of the state of affairs up at Caudry.

'General, we have lost Caudry and it is partly in flames. I can't tell you about the situation of 4th Division to the west of the town but I think there has been no breakthrough by the enemy. We are holding them on the southern outskirts of the town. Audencourt is in flames but our line there is holding. The gunners are doing good work. The RAMC is hard-pressed and I had to get away from an ambulance after some Frenchmen made off with the horses. On my way here through the rear of 3rd and 5th Divisions there was no sign of any break in the line. Their artillery is active all along the line and shows no sign of letting up and they are shelling the front lines and the rear as well as the batteries.'

Here Johnson paused partly to recover his breath, but also because the windows of the building were rattling and shaking to such an extent - the gunfire was increasing in intensity from the batteries to the east – that the General was straining to catch his words. He continued….

'One encouraging thing is that the enemy are not exploiting as one would expect. They seem to think that their artillery will do all their work for them. But I must say that their planes are directing their guns in the most effective manner, with flares and other means.'

This speech took a lot out of him. Captain Bowley gave him a glass of water. Smith-Dorrien seemed pleased with the report, which confirmed the situation as he knew it. He asked about casualties.

'Brigadier McCracken was an early casualty this morning when Caudry was heavily shelled. My friend Lieutenant Simon Brett of my regiment was killed alongside me in the town. I will say that even if casualties are generally not heavy it must be the case that if another battle is to come soon the Division will reach the limit of its fighting ability, but that is not for me to say of course, Sir. My Brigade was in a poor state at first light; their night march was poorly disciplined and they were not in battle order at first light. They were in an exposed position in any case. But they rallied and fought well, even if town-fighting is not congenial to them, to put it mildly. They don't like it with the civilians all over the place; it worries them and the general panic is infectious. Our men and officers did not know whether or not a general retreat was in progress which added to the confusion. There seemed to be no scheme worked out for the defence of the town. But when enemy infantry do attack, they attack with machine-gun and shrapnel support; they are learning from their losses at Mons. I had to defend a line without our gunners' support. General Hamilton himself rallied the defence; the boche are inclined to run when they see our men with bayonets at close quarters.'

'Thank you Captain Johnson, that was most helpful. I suggest you make your way back towards St. Quentin as best you can. You have clearly done enough for one day. I will pass on your comments about the German air and gun cooperation to our RFC people; it would seem that they have stolen a march on us in this area and you have confirmed what we have already heard. And if I had a French liaison officer at my HQ I would raise the matter of those thieving Frenchmen, but that's another matter.'

'I have done no more than anyone else, Sir.'

Johnson was helped out and put back on his mare.

'George, it is too early to say the day has gone well. We must go and see for ourselves.'

The Lieutenant-General and his Chief of Staff went out to the front of the Mairie where the Rolls was waiting, Clegg saluting smartly and the General's horse and groom standing by. The two senior officers got into the back seat, with Captain Bowley in the front passenger seat. The car was flying a small penant with a badge that Bowley didn't recognise. He didn't want to admit his ignorance, but when asked Forrestier-Walker told him that it was the badge of the Sherwood Foresters. 'It was the first regiment that the General served in and he's had a soft spot for them ever since'.

It was nearly nine hours since the first shells had fallen on the Corps positions. No-one in the 3rd and 5th Divisions had had more than a few hours sleep since the 22nd. They weren't going to get much more sleep tonight. Bertry and Reumont were about to come under shell-fire, as the enemy guns moved forward and shifted their range. Whatever problems the Germans gunners faced, shortage of ammunition was not one of them.

Chapter 18

Private Edwards

Private Frank Edwards, his mate Buffy, Mr. Moore, and Lieutenant Bosanquet, known as Four Eyes, and the rest of 2nd Royal Welch Fusiliers, minus their transport, numbering about seven hundred men and officers, were about a thousand yards behind the hill-garrison of 14 Brigade, with their sister-battalions of 1st Middlesex and 2nd Argyll and Sutherland Highlanders up on the hill in close support, or what was left of them after their advance in the open. Four Eyes was rubbing his spectacles. It was 3.30 p.m. Edwards had noticed a runner coming up to the company commander with an order-chit and he knew something was about to happen. It was never welcome news in his experience. Edwards looked back the way they had come up the Roman road and could see that the enemy were now shelling Reumont, Maurois and Bertry comprehensively, parts of which were on fire. Fucking marvellous. Now we are in a spring-trap like a fox: shell-fire behind us and fritz infantry in front. And maybe behind us already.

'Platoon! We are now ordered to fall back eight hundred yards and take up a new position as rear-guard to the east of the road. The Scottish Rifles are moving up and will be on our left. Prepare to move in five minutes. Ensure bayonets fixed at all times. Maintain artillery formation'.

'Mr. Moore you are having an education today. We go back, we go up, we go back and forth like the Grand Old Duke of York. And we still haven't had a proper bang at the bastards. But back is better than forwards, at any rate.'

Just then a dozen or so soldiers of the KOYLI came down the road. Edwards could see that they were beaten to the wide, a few were obviously wounded but they were all driven beyond what a man can reasonably endure. Edwards stopped a man, who lingered long enough to blurt out:

'There's none of us left except what you see here. There's Major Yate up there who's as mad as a hatter and will charge the fritzes if someone doesn't stop him. The fritzes are coming on and they will be in Paris at this rate in a week.'Another Yorkshireman, a Private, stopped by Edwards and Mr. Moore long enough to say,

'It's all right for you lot; we were first in at Mons and now last out at Le Catoo.'

But his mate was heard to say, 'In and out, but a fuck of a lot quicker out than in.' There was laughter even though it was becoming a familiar refrain. Another man said, but without bitterness,

'And where were the Guards we'd like to know? Taking up a position in the rear!' More laughter.

The man went on with his mates. A mixed bunch of men came next, also without officers: some Scottish Borderers, a few Dorsets who were a mystery to Edwards coming as they did from a different brigade, a few gunners. All were bug-eyed, foam-flecked like race-horses, but none had thrown away their rifles, although they had abandoned their personal kit, which would normally be an offence. The bombadiers carried nothing, except one who had another of the 18-pounder breach-blocks. So they weren't blowing the barrels with premature charges, thought Edwards. Probably no time for such a measure, things being as they are up there. An officer of the East Surrey's now came down towards them, this time with his platoon in formation, even looking as though on parade. A fine sight, but they had been in support, Edwards knew, and had been spared most of the relentless bombardment. They looked no more in a hurry than as if they were going to catch a 'bus. The officer spoke to Four Eyes;

'We stood our ground to the end and formed a temporary stop, but the boche are biding their time. There are some of our chaps holding on up there, or at least there were a few minutes ago. We had to hold our fire when our chaps and the boche got all muddled up. We are pushing on; good luck to you. If you see any of the gunners tell them they are all heroes. And there's a Highland officer up there who keeps calling for his gamekeeper to pass him his shotguns; mad as a March hare.'

A couple of Taubes were overhead, lazily turning in circles, one of them dropping flares behind them, red ones this time. Must be telling their gunners to shift their range, thought Edwards, and again marvelled at the application of science to the business of killing people. One day we'll have a gun that will knock those bastards down. Especially if the Hun works out a way of raining down darts on us poor sods down below.'

Two wounded Manchesters, with field dressings loosely applied to their heads and their caps perched askew like stage drunks, now came down from the right. They had been with their Vickers team and gabbled about the boche in the valley. 'We shot the fuckers but they kept on coming until we ran out of ammo. There's thousands of them. It's a miracle we're here; all the others have gone west. It's every man for himself back there. Good luck, chum.'

Any more of these 'good lucks' and I'm going to feel too lucky by half.

The Royal Welch were moving back now, in artillery formation. Shells were falling around them and in the rear, but bursting high, and the steel balls were fizzing around like angry insects but causing mostly superficial wounds. The men instinctively drew their heads into their shoulders, giving them an ape-like appearance. One man had his cap knocked off by a fizzing shrapnel-ball and counted himself the luckiest man in the Battalion. Edwards could see a large body of men, well spaced out, marching on the far side of the Roman road: they must be the Cameronians, the Scottish Rifles, our fellow rear-guard. There'll be no time to dig in, we'll just have to hug the ground and use our knapsacks to rest our rifles on, just like on the ranges. We can stop a brigade if the men will stick it. And we've got our Vickers with us now.

The men organised themselves into a line to the east of the road, platoon by platoon, extending about six hundred yards. It was a sugar-beet-field, with leaf cover at knee height so that a man had to go on one knee to get a firing position but could lie flat without being seen. The officers got into a huddle up by the road and Four Eyes went with them. The road was still being shelled intermittently and the officers all crouched down in the ditch beside the road. A car approached from the north. Edwards could see that it was an important person; Christ, it's the Corps Commander, things must be coming to a pretty pass if we've got the top brass up here. That's twice in two days I've seen him, we're getting to be quite like old chums. I'll be going round to his HQ for tea if I don't watch out and swapping stories about the North-West Frontier.

Edwards watched the Corps Commander talking to his Battalion officers, using his baton to point up and down the road. The strange thing was that the General was standing up and the battalion officers were still crouching in the ditch. The battalion officers seemed to realise that they were looking ridiculous in the ditch and then stood up. There was a lot of saluting and then the General did a surprising thing: he got on his horse and rode off towards the west, going at a fair canter. He was alone.

Buffy was alongside Edwards. 'Wake me up when the fun starts, Eddie, I'm just having a bo-peep but don't let Four Eyes see me.'

'You go ahead, Buffy. I expect we'll be here a while yet. I don't expect anything good to come from the Corps Commander's little visit.'

Nothing much was happening. True, there was the angry sound of battle all around them, the shrapnel fire now passing over their heads in a scream of rage as it searched for the retreating infantry on the Roman road, fire adding to the misery and fear of men who had already reached their limits. True, there was still a stream of men coming off the hill, the last to pass, half a company of kilted jocks led by a captain, all in good order and passing with yet another 'Good luck, chum'. Their relief in getting out was obvious, but half a company told its own story. Edwards noted the absence of the farming lads, all gone to fritz chokey if they were lucky. If they were still up there they were not coming back and they had sacrificed themselves for the rest of the Division. But those who go into prison camp don't get medals.

The light was fading although it was only about 4.00 p.m; the sky grew overcast and a slight drizzle began to fall. The GS wagons on the road were slipping and sliding as the surface turned to a greasy film, their drivers whipping the horses without mercy. The Lieutenant-General's car had turned down to St. Quentin. A Morris lorry with 'SELFRIDGES' still painted on its side lay abandoned by the road. From his one visit to London, Edwards could remember Oxford Street and the department stores as big as the troop-ship in which he had travelled to India. He remembered going to a cafe in Soho, with Buffy this was, and there being a German waiter; now in a beet-field in northern France he wondered whether that fritz was over the other side of the hill. And of course Edwards remembered the tart he had had; she had said to him the old familiar phrase 'Fancy a nice time, soldier-boy?' and in front of Buffy Edwards had said 'Let's be 'aving you', in his sergeant-major's voice which made the girl giggle. He had the girl in a shabby gas-lit room just around the corner, trying not to look at her yellow teeth, while Buffy smoked a couple of Woodbines in the street outside. He had finished before Buffy had smoked his second cigarette. 'She comes from Swansea and she's only a miner's daughter, but she's honest', was all Edwards had said about her. He never even saw her tits but she held on to his buttocks with eagerness as he got into her, she must keep it well oiled and all. Edwards had taken longer getting his boots and puttees off and on than the actual fucking.

Then there was a shout and Buffy woke with a start and Edwards could see movement on the right at about eight hundred yards, cavalry for sure but whose? Someone shouted 'Uhlans!' and Four Eyes took up the call and shouted 'Enemy Cavalry Eight Hundred Yards Half Right!' and twenty shots were fired from the line, the first shots fired on this day by the Royal Welch. Edwards didn't fire; he wasn't sure about the target; it seemed to him that the cavalry were wearing capes, they were shiny in the rain and he was sure that capes like that were a Lancer thing; he had seen them wear them often in parades and besides Four Eyes probably had rain on his glasses and binoculars, the silly sod. Several horses were knocked over and the rest of the troop got into some dead ground but it made Edwards uneasy.

They stayed in the beet-field for another hour until Four Eyes was called over for another Officers' chin-wag and came back announcing that the Battalion would move back another two thousand yards, to a line between Maurois and Honnechy, to counter a threat from the right. It was suspected that a strong boche patrol or even a brigade might be trying to get round on that flank and the 1st Duke of Cornwall's Light Infantry needed reinforcing.

All this time Mr. Moore had been quiet.

'What would your Mr. Russell have made of this then, Sir? The Suffolks stopped them on the hill and that's a fact, eh?'

'A journalist can't be everywhere and I might as well be here, with you as my guide, my dear Edwards. When I get to Amiens I will be able to send a wire that will tell the truth, even if it is only the truth about a certain beet-field in France. But the truth about this beet-field is as important as the official communiqué from GHQ. That's something I learned from reading Tolstoy's *War and Peace*. When battle is joined, a Field Marshal is about as much use as bottle of wine without a corkscrew; but at least you can knock the head off the bottle with your bayonet. In a battle, a general knows as much as the ordinary soldier and can do less, because when battle starts a general's work is done.'

'And did your Mr. Russell know your Mr. Tolstoy? It seems they had a lot in common.'

'If they met I am sure they would have had a lot to talk about.'

'I'd like to meet your Mr. Tolstoy; he could help me if I ever come to write about these times.'

'Alas, he's dead.'

'Did he get shot?'

'No, he died of a broken heart.'

'Poor fucker.'

For the fourth time that day the 2nd Royal Welch prepared to move off in artillery formation, this time with twenty of their comrades wounded on the field, all from the effects of shrapnel. The wounded were put on to GS wagons, which had been standing by on the road. The Battalion avoided the Roman road which was still under fire and went out due south, the officers leading the men in artillery formation through the stubble. The Scottish Rifles on the other side of the road did likewise and came out in tandem. The two battalions were joined by stragglers, stray signallers who had lost their sections, gunners without guns to serve, grooms without horses and various men from the HQs at Reumont whose normal batman duties were now redundant. Those without rifles, those deemed to be non-combatant, were sent on their way. A party of 1st Dorsets also joined them as did some more stray Scottish Borderers, who were cheerful despite maintaining that they were the sole survivors of their Battalion. This combined force, now tired, hungry and frustrated at being denied a fair crack at the foe, was the main force standing between the bulk of the retreating 5th Division and the best part of three German divisions who had just overwhelmed its right flank, massed infantry offering perfect targets on the Cambrai Road for the few 5th Division guns still firing.

If ever a chance existed for an army to put another to rout, this was it.

But these two battalions had their cohesion, their machine-guns, their rifles and the knowledge that they were not defeated. This was the moment most feared by Lieutenant-General Dorrien-Smith: the enemy must be pausing for breath and would soon use the remaining three hours of daylight to finish their task. But for the legions of the Kaiser it was a question of will, the will needed to overcome the natural instinct to gather up, to survive the day, to recover breath, to eat and drink, to exchange tales of survival, to sleep, to tend the wounded. Besides, they had no particular objective to reach; with the British quitting the field their task was done, although the determination of individual regimental commanders would decide how far the Germans would push on. They would have to do this without artillery support, having pushed on beyond their forward controllers. Dorrien-Smith could congratulate himself: it is not the matter of numbers that is the overriding factor; it is how that number is handled that counts in the ebb and flow of battle.

The British all along the twelve mile front had to get away, they had no choice, but the German divisions, both Reserve and Active, had to overcome the inbuilt inertia which comes to all men at the end of the day. But all the men of IV Army Corps commanded by Sixt von Armin on the British right were tired; they had marched thirty-eight kilometres the previous day and there was no such thing as a fresh regiment. And they were learning greater respect for the British; or to put it another way, fear was now an obstacle to their progress; fear of the khaki men who hid themselves in the fields and fired on them before they could be seen, firing what they were certain was specially adapted snub-nosed ammunition, adapted contrary to the rules of war.

The two BEF battalions, the Scotsmen and the Welsh, about fifteen hundred men and officers, together with the odds and sods, were moving back now, well spaced out. Discarded equipment lay round about, most of the fleeing men having discarded their haversacks. The Big Boys, the 60-pounders, were firing off the last of their ammunition at the far side of the hill where von Armin's men were still massed. Their draught horses had been taken out from their corral. One of the 60-pounders, in the haste to get away, became stuck in a ditch and couldn't be brought out. It had to be adandoned, after its firing mechanism was destroyed. Unbelievably, the two howitzers so recently rescued by the intrepid horse-teams were back in action and firing with fresh ammunition, obtained from God knows where, and firing blind into the brown, onto the Cambrai Road, without observers, Edwards hoping that there no captured British on the receiving end. The Scottish Rifles and the 2nd Royal Welch marched through Maurois again, the chocolate-seller still at her stall, and turned south-east, out toward open country. There was transport of all descriptions in the town, but mostly GS wagons driven by men of the Army Service Corps carrying boxed ammunition. The two battalions took up a new position, facing north-east, between Honnechy and Maurois and prepared for the third time to face an enemy who they were told was coming down from St Benin to the north-east. They were relieving a much reduced Company of the Argyll and Sutherland Highlanders, kilties, who were happy to move off, having more than done their bit up on the hill. They went off, led by their Lieutenant-Colonel, Moulton-Barrett, who had been up to the hill and back with his men. A Company of the Duke of Cornwall's Light Infantry, who had formed a part of the line east of the Selle valley but who had been driven off earlier that morning, moved off with them. There was no banter between the men, except for one kiltie who muttered something about having had his fill of fritzes for one day.

Buffy, Frank Edwards and Mr. Moore arranged themselves alongside each other in the stubble-field. There were good fields of fire for about five hundred yards to the north and east, the direction from which the enemy were expected to come. They could see the white puffs of shrapnel air-bursts to their left, up by the Cambrai road. A solitary plane lazily flew along the road-line, probably German, although it was too far away to see its markings. Great plumes of smoke were rising from Caudry to the north-west and from Le Cateau and Reumont to the north. They settled down to wait again in the fading light, gathering the straw around them as cover and putting straw in their caps as camouflage. Some of them went to sleep. Some munched on hard biscuits, although it was technically an offence to break out the hard tack without permission from an officer. Some men had chocolate and cheese acquired the day before in Le Cateau, the 'unexpired portion' of the previous night's meal. No smoking was allowed. They passed their water bottles around. They spoke only in hushed voices. If Fritz comes it would be good if he came as cavalry, as Uhlans, for they make good targets.

'Do you think they are going to come this time, Eddie?' Buffy wondered.

The answer came in a shout from an officer on the right: 'Enemy Infantry Five Hundred Yards! Fire at Will!'

Edwards could see them, shadowy grey figures in the half-light. Must be at least a battalion of them, emerging from God knows where. Silly fuckers even have a flag or some sort of standard on a pole, I mean what sort of game is that? No doubt about who they are this time.

Edwards set his fore-sight and worked his bolt, putting another clip in the magazine. He then realised that his bayonet was still fixed, and he removed it and replaced it in its scabbard. He was now firing from a kneeling position and able to see the enemy line faltering, as if they were on a Sunday walk and were not sure of the way to go. The banner or whatever it was still flew. Shoot the mad fucker who's carrying it, they won't like that.

Edwards could not, of course, know that the enemy infantry in the stubble were part of the 165th Regiment of the 7th Division of IV Corps, Reservists called back to the colours only two weeks ago, very much like Edwards himself, and like the Welsh drawn from the west of their country. They, again like him, had marched through Le Cateau and had noticed the Café de Paris, but had not of course enjoyed the luxury of going inside. By that time they had had fours sleep in the previous twenty-four, had marched ten miles through the Forest of Mormal, and had very little idea of where they were; their officers told them little, other than that they would soon be fighting British and not French soldiers. One soldier had said that if that was the Café de Paris it must mean that Paris was just around the corner. All day they had been fired at by an enemy they had never seen, an enemy that seemed to be the same colour as the ground he hid in, unlike the French whose blue and red so tellingly marked them out. And now they were in the vanguard of their Corps, a place that according to the textbooks should have been occupied by fresh troops. Their commander, Oberst von Quadt, had insisted that the regimental colours be carried into battle, thinking it good for their morale. His full name was Freiherr von Quadt-Wykradt-Hütchenbruck, who spoke impeccable English, acquired while he was up at Balliol.

Buffy was letting off rounds one after the other and so were another hundred of the Welch. Both Buffy and Edwards could see fritzes going down, whether shot or not was hard to say. The Vickers was still silent. The fritz officers were trying to rally their men and drive them forwards and they became the targets of now more than three hundred Lee-Enfields. The grey infantry were now firing back and bullets cracked through the air, a few finding their targets, but these was lucky shots and Edwards felt not in any way in danger of his life; the Welch could see the grey infantry in the field but their own straw cover concealed them from the enemy. Edwards could keep this up for hours. The enemy were going to ground and were reluctant to come on. They were on slightly lower ground than the Warwicks and this added to their tendency to shoot high. Some of them were seeking shelter from behind their knapsacks, which they used as a firing platform. The Vickers opened up, both of them, firing short bursts. He kept firing at where he thought the fritzes must be lying in the stubble, but he chose as targets the ones who had the courage to reveal themselves by firing from a kneeling position. There became less and less of the kneeling ones and Edwards found himself muttering 'On your knees you bastards, on your knees. Get on your knees and die.' The fritzes had advanced without machine-gun or field-gun support and were paying for it. Some of them were bobbing about like game-cocks, looking for shelter in the stooks, but others were staying on the ground, behind their knapsacks. The banner was no longer upright. But they were still coming on in small numbers. Edwards fired at one knapsack five times.

'This is a bobby's job, eh, Mr. Moore? Keep your Panama down just in case one of these fritz bullets has got your number on it.'

'In my experience, my dear Edwards, callers are always getting the wrong number and I don't think the boche will be any different.'

'Fire Low! Fire At Their Feet!' Four Eyes was right of course but old soldiers like Buffy and Edwards didn't need to be told this. Edwards was almost half-upright now in his eagerness to kill the grey figures; he thought he could even see the spikes on their helmets and thought of them as targets on the range. He put another clip in the magazine. Barrel getting hot now, no problem, got some oil on the old pull-through. This is what we get paid for. This is tray bon. He pushed his cap back. He adjusted his sight. He wanted his whack of the boche.

Then he felt the whoosh of pain as he was hit in the side by a bullet which knocked him back. Actually, he first put his hand to his side, examined it, looked at the blood already oozing from his lower right torso, said 'Fuck!' the first word that came to him, realised almost at once that it was not going to be his last word on earth, said 'Buffy, the bastards have got me', quite calmly, and then fell back, all in that order.

Buffy and Mr. Moore went to him at once. Buffy opened up his tunic and saw both the exit and entry wound. A good sign; in and out told him a lot. He called for a stretcher to take him to the rear. The word was passed along the line and surprisingly quickly two RAMC privates appeared with a folding canvas stretcher. They did another examination of the wound, put some iodine on from a phial which made Edwards wince a bit more, applied a dressing, put him on the stretcher and went off back to the forward aid post, with Mr. Moore and Buffy taking one end and the privates the other, all of them keeping their heads down as low as they could. Edwards kept up a steady flow of 'Fuck!' for the duration of the journey to the post, which was at Battalion HQ. The MO, Captain Dunn, saw him within a minute and pronounced the wound 'Debilitating but not serious'. Clearly, no vital organ had been hit and there was no need for morphine. All this had lasted perhaps fifteen minutes; Edwards had lost about a pint of blood but no artery had been severed. The bleeding was now largely staunched. It was an honourable wound. It was clean, swabbed and all traces of material from Edwards' tunic removed.

Mr. Moore and Buffy stayed for half an hour at the post; both were able to be of service as more wounded came in and the MO was glad of their help, particularly Mr. Moore, who turned out to have a steady hand with scissors and gauze, and was promptly named 'Florence' by the RAMC orderlies. Buffy laid a hand on his friend's arm and said 'We'll be back jildi'. As they left the post they heard Edwards saying to an orderly, 'I'll take my gold watch with me when I go if you don't mind', which they took to be a joke.

By the time Buffy and Mr. Moore got back to the line the German battalion had retired, and were seen to be dragging their wounded with them, back to the dead ground they had emerged from. Von Quadt had recalled the survivors from his regiment by sending a runner from his position in the dead ground, from where it was quite clear that the attack was faltering and there was nothing to be gained by pressing on. The Welch held their fire when they saw that they were attending to their injured. They were no longer a threat. The Fusiliers lay down their rifles, some of whch had begun to seize up from the constant working of the bolts. The two Lieutenant-Colonels of the Royal Welch and the Scottish Rifles had a pow-wow and agreed that unless further orders were received they would retire in the direction of St. Quentin, starting in half an hour when it got dark. The men had a strong desire to go over to the German position and count the fritz dead, but the officers would have none of it. The British officers could not know it but this was the limit of the German advance on this evening of battle, the commanders of von Armin's IV Corps realising that their enemy was not in full flight and that it was time to call a halt and tend their wounded. Buffy, with new-found confidence, addressed the journalist:

'I don't know about you Mr. Moore but I think we should go back to Eddie just to see that the old bugger is all right. I told him that we would be back. Can you square it with the Lieutenant?'

'I'll see Mr. Bosanquet and come with you.'

'You'll have seen enough to write a book now. How long was that War and Peace book you were talking about?'

'About six hundred pages'

'Fuck me. Just give me the peace bits.'

Chapter 19

Captain Johnson

Johnson looked up at the sky, looked at his watch, muttered 'Walk on' to the piebald mare and reckoned on getting to Bertry in less than an hour. He had a good FS map in its case if he needed to consult it. From Bertry he could go across to the Roman road at Honnechy and turn down it towards St. Quentin. His plan was to get some distance between himself and the enemy, get his wounds seen to and rejoin the Battalion in due course. He was not in a fit state to take up full duties at the moment; his wounds to his back and leg were a constant pain but at least the bleeding had stopped. Surely the Corps would make another stand soon, perhaps the other side of St. Quentin on the far bank of the Somme after blowing the bridges. The Somme would be a much more formidable barrier than the Mons Canal to fight behind and if the French 5th Army could bring itself to fight alongside, the combined force would stop the boche right wing before they threatened Paris.

He remembered an exercise in '09 when his battalion had had to defend a river against an 'invader'. The Colonel had put in a request for barbed wire but had been told that there wasn't any to be had. They were then told that they could 'imagine' it was there. There won't be much imagination needed now, he thought.

It was perhaps unfortunate for the two Entente armies on the north-west flank at this time that they were led by Sir John French and Charles Lanrezac rather than Henry Johnson, Old Wykehamist cricketer and signals captain in the Worcestershire Regiment. But they were stuck for the moment with the leaders they had. Johnson continued to ponder on these weighty matters. He remembered from his history at Winchester how Wellington had placed his finger on the map at the Richmonds' ball and told his friend Richmond 'We will fight him here', putting his thumb on the cross-roads of Mont St. Jean. That's what we need now, a Wellington with his thumb on the right place of the map, he thought.

His mind wondered back to the image of Phoebe, Phoebe in her straw hat with the ribbons, Phoebe whom Simon's mother had written was missing him terribly, Phoebe with those nipples erect in their corset.... Poor Simon. Phoebe and I will keep his memory alive. I will write soon to Simon's parents. And if Phoebe should seek to enrol in the nursing yeomanry, the FANY, then she would have my support. That reminds me, I wonder where Bertie Altham is at the moment. I seem to remember he's still on the 3rd Div staff so he can't be far, their HQ is at Bertry I think, perhaps I'll find him there. That'll be a turn-up for the books, he'll be busy of course but a brief word would be nice. Bertie with his Latin quips; well, he's not in arcadia now.

He thought of de Salis and the rest of the Battalion. Colonel Bird of the Irish Rifles was a good man and would bring them out; he knew they would not go without a fight. But he shuddered at the difficulty of the task ahead of them; retreats were more difficult than advances in so many ways. They should think of it as an advance in another direction, a fighting manoeuvre.

He rode on. If I come across those frogs with our horses I will use the Webley on them. I wonder what field regulations would say about the treatment to be handed out; probably have to hand them over to some French official; I say shoot first and officials be damned.

The sound of artillery fire to the north was almost constant and he marvelled at the ability of the enemy to keep up such a rate of fire. This war can't last long, he thought, if our side and theirs are going to keep up this sort of fire for much longer. There just won't be enough shells in the world to feed the guns, let alone money to pay for them. That's what we'll do, he thought with some certainty, go over the Somme and wait for the boche to run out of shells; they are a good way from their supply base after all. The Belgians have destroyed the railways in that Godforsaken country we are meant to be fighting for, which should play havoc with the German supply trains. It might take some time, at least until next spring, but the facts of economic geography would tell against the Germans in the long run, fighting as they are on two fronts. All in all, he felt in his slightly feverish state that he had got the war half won when he noticed that he was approaching Second Corps and 3rd Div HQs at Bertry. It's time I had a rest anyway, I'll just stop and get some water for the mare and maybe something for myself. And see if Bertie is there.

He went into the town and found the square, which was common to all towns in this part of France. The Union Jack was flying from the two main buildings, together with the 3rd Division flag and what must be the Corps flag. He hitched the mare to a post outside the 3rd Division building along with other horses and motor cars, and limped inside, returning the salute of the private on duty at the entrance. Inside, all was bustle, with signallers busy at telegraph transmitters set up in the hall. He asked for Captain Altham; he was shown to a room off the hall. Johnson went in. Altham was sitting at a desk.

'Et tu Henry! Ecco!' My God you look done in. Let me arrange some refreshment for you.'

'I've got a couple of slight wounds, a small chunk out of my leg and a blow to my back but if someone could see to my mare I would be grateful. I'm afraid to say that Simon Brett is dead, killed by a sniper, just by my side.'

'I'm terribly sorry to hear that. Phoebe's brother. I remember him well. But tell me how things are up there. No, I've got a better idea. My chief is busy but since you are straight from the fighting the Corps Commander himself would I am sure be grateful for a report. You know how these top generals are always saying that they never get to hear direct from the fighting troops, well, here's your chance to tell the chief how things are going. Captain Bowley, his ADC, is a friend of mine. I'll take you across. Righto? Certe et Recte as the old motto has it. Right up your whatsit. But we haven't got much time; the whole of Bertry HQ will be gone in little more than an hour and a half. This was always going to be a tip-and-run show and then double-quick back to the pavilion, if you get my meaning.'

'I can assure you it's not a cricket match up there, Bertie.'

'No, of course not, silly of me. But nil desperandum. Exeunt omnes, as they say.'

In the event Henry Johnson didn't blurt out his strategic theories about how to stop the Germans on the Somme. He realised that it wasn't his place as a junior officer to tell a Lieutenant-General how to win the war. In any case it was properly a matter for Sir John French and that was a military layer far beyond him. He confined himself to his immediate experience. He then looked in again on Harry Altham.

'You won't believe this Henry but I've got a request here from the Quartermaster of 5th Div artillery who wants me to look into the proper care and cleaning of the brasses on his draught horses' bridles. These chaps must think this show is some kind of gymkhana. I think I may well put that one in a pending file; but I'd better take it with me when we leave; we can't have the enemy finding out valuable intelligence, can we?'

After which Johnson was back on the piebald mare, both of them suitably refreshed, and heading east for the Roman road at Honnechy.

Shells were falling now in Bertry as he left the town and he could see Reumont to the north-east in flames. Stragglers were drifting back from the front lines, some wounded, but there were men who were looking a bit dubious. They were not from his Battalion so he had no business confronting them. He probably looked a bit dubious himself. He came to the Roman road and was instantly plunged into a mass of khaki humanity, most walking, officers riding, wagons of all descriptions, ambulances, all the vehicles of an army in full flight. Some were clearly desperate to get away. One excitable Service Corps private driving a GS wagon was raving about Uhlans just behind them, but he was told to put a sock in it by his mates. Everyone was looking utterly dejected, tired, some stumbling and walking like drunks from sheer fatigue. Other men, men from the better regiments he noticed, men who had stayed at least with their platoons, were more cheerful, or if not exactly cheerful were smoking their pipes and looking more like a crowd coming away from a cricket match at the end of the day. He stopped to talk to a 2nd Lieutenant in the KOSB.

'We had to leave a platoon behind up by the Cambrai road. At first it was the shelling that was bad, then their infantry came on but we lacked our Vickers. We got back to the sunken lane and fought from there but our Colonel was hit and the mens morale collapsed. We're lucky any of us got out. The gunners have lost as heavily as us. I saw them fire point-blank at a platoon of boche and the whole lot went down under a hail of shrapnel; bits of bodies everywhere. Magnificent sight. But the gunners were being sniped at the guns. Keep an eye out for Uhlans.'

Was this how Napoleon's army looked as it came back from Moscow? No, not that bad, not in France in August, don't be bloody ridiculous. Perhaps a Via Dolorosa would be a better description, a Vale of Tears. But at least it looks like the boche haven't broken through, although God knows there's nothing much to stop them. I wouldn't like to try and form a fighting line out of this dejected mass.

He rode on. Then a strange sight: a man in a Panama, a gentleman by the look of him, something familiar about him, walking along with two private soldiers, one wounded in the side of the body, judging by the bandage wrapped around him. Both Royal Welch. He stopped the mare.

'Can I help?'

The gentleman answered.

'This is my invaluable guide, Private Edwards and this is Buffy. I must get to Amiens to file a dispatch to *The Times*. My name is Moore. Edwards is wounded but has already given up his place on a GS wagon to someone in greater need than himself.'

'Then Private Edwards shall ride this mare and I will walk alongside you. I remember talking to you in Le Cateau last night.'

It was done. Buffy led the piebald mare and Johnson limped alongside.

'You're wounded, Sir' said Buffy.

'I'll be alright. There are many on this road who are suffering.'

More than three hundred men up on the hill lay dead and more than a thousand men and officers - Suffolks, Manchesters, Yorkshire Light Infantry, Scottish Borderers, and gunners - were even now being corralled into captivity, many of them wounded. They were to be led back into the same barn that the Suffolks had so recently and so fleetingly slept in, the officers led off to a separate building and told by their captors that any attempt at escape would result in the execution of them all. They were the lucky ones; they had lost their freedom, they faced an unkown future but they had lived through the greatest ordeal of their lives. And they had fought the boche to a standstill.

Johnson and his new companions trudged on, knowing there would be no rest before nightfall.

Chapter 20

Lieutenant Penfold

Just to the south east of Caudry, a town that had changed hands more than once during the course of the day, being first in British hands, then German, then British and now German again, stood the last men and officers of the 1st Battalion, the Warwickshire Regiment, to remain in the front line, the main body of the battalion having got away, under the command of Lieutenant Watkins. Now commanded by Lieutenant Bernard Montgomery, with Lieutenant Stephen Penfold as his Second-in-Command, it occupied the farmhouse know as Le Coquelet and a line of four hundred yards to its left. The two senior officers with the force were Major Haddow, who was badly wounded in the shoulder and effectively hors de combat, and Captain Nolan the Battalion doctor, who was of course a non-combatant. The position of the King's Own on their right, that is to say their east side, and the Lancashire Fusiliers on their left was not certain. The 3rd Worcesters, who had fought in and out of the town, were disengaging. The Warwickshire's orders, which had not changed since this morning, were to 'Stand and Fight'. The enemy on their front were for the moment quiet, but this situation was not expected to last.

At 5.30 p.m., with at most three more hours of daylight left, the force consisted of thirty men and officers, and forty wounded. Shells continued to fall both to the west and east of them, but so far the boche gunners had not identified the farmhouse as a target. The shelling the Warwicks had experienced since the last attack had been merely harassing fire. It was certain that the enemy was not far away, but probably waiting for reinforcements to come up before launching another attack. Penfold was convinced that the boche were also working around them, probably with the machine-gun which he knew to be out there somewhere. They probably thought that the British force consisted of more than just thirty able-bodied men. Montgomery and Penfold intended to lead the able-bodied out back to the British lines after dark, but to leave the wounded to the mercy of the Germans. Captain Nolan would stay with the wounded. Montgomery assumed that the doctor would be treated as a non-combatant and given the respect properly due to his office.

The two officers set about getting the wounded into the shelter of the house. Once that was done they could start to organise a system of all-round defence of the farm and its buildings. The farm consisted of the two-storey main house, a yard surrounded by a wall about ten feet high, and a free-standing barn situated to the west, about twenty yards from the house. All were of brick and stone construction. The house had windows on all sides, all with shutters which were closed. The entire structure would be impervious to shrapnel fire, but every soldier knew that a direct hit from a 5.9 salvo on the house would be fatal for most of the occupants. To that extent, it was more risky to go into the farmhouse than stay out in the field. It was impossible to assess the risk, but so far they had not seen any evidence of directed fire by heavy HE guns, although they had been in action earlier in the day against Caudry.

They started to move the wounded, moving four men at a time, all the rest of the men alert for any sign of enemy activity. It was an anxious time for the wounded, the orderlies and the men on alert. A barrage of shrapnel fell forty yards behind them, everyone ducking and throwing themselves down. Did this herald something more serious, an infantry attack? Penfold waved the carrying party on; better to carry on as quickly as possible now that the move had started. He took some comfort from the fact that they had not seen a boche plane for quite a while; he was convinced that they had ways of communicating with their gunners that were fiendishly clever, not only flares but wireless messaging as well.

By 6.30 p.m. everyone was in the farm buildings. The front door had not been locked, the owners presumably knowing that a locked door would only invite forcible entry. The orderlies immediately set about arranging the downstairs rooms of the house as a makeshift hospital, tearing up all the sheets they could find into strips to use as bandages to replace the blood-soaked ones on the wounded. There was a good supply of fresh water. There were candles in holders and oil lamps. Penfold looked around the house. There was an upright piano in the main room, although it was hardly the time for a sing-song. Above the fireplace there was a photograph of a young man in an officer's uniform, presumably the son of the farmer and his wife. Penfold guessed he had been a Reserve officer and was now at the front. He wondered how they were going to manage the farm now that the son had gone. The boy's parents must have fled quite recently and clearly meant to return once the fighting had moved on, in the manner of small farmers everywhere. They had left everything ready for their return, including the woman's knitting. But there was no food to speak of.

They placed Major Haddow on a settee in the living room and propped up his shattered arm with a cushion. Penfold paid him a visit.

'Major, we will do everything we can do to make the wounded as comfortable as possible. Captain Nolan is busy seeing to all that. We will break out some time tonight and make south-west in search of friendly territory. Do you think you are in a fit state to come out with us? You are the best judge of that.'

'I think I may be too much of a burden and will only slow you down and endanger the lives of the whole group. I must stay; you may have at least ten miles to go before you can find friends. You will not be able to carry me that distance and I don't think I could walk that far. Can I ask one favour?'

'Of course.'

'Will you make sure that my wife gets this ring? You can send it to the barracks in Warwick. She will keep it safe until my return.'

‘I will see to it’.

‘Lieutenant, have you heard of Colonel Travis?’

‘No, Sir, I don’t think I have. Somebody in the Regiment?’

‘No. Eighty-odd years ago in a Godforsaken part of what is now Texas, a group of Texans held out in a mission station against the Mexican army. This Colonel Travis was sick or wounded I forget which, but he was put in a room in the back of the building. He had a percussion pistol, or maybe two. He resolved to kill the first Mexican who came through his door. I have six bullets in the chamber of my Webley. I can kill six times as many of the enemy as Colonel Travis could. I intend to use them’.

‘I’m afraid Major I must point out that under the rules of war agreed at The Hague and Geneva, we are not permitted to use a hospital building as a place to fight from. This is a place of treatment for wounded so it must be regarded as a hospital. We are showing the Geneva Cross. Can we move you into the yard on this couch where you can of course fire away at all comers?’

The Major thought for a bit. He had another spasm of pain.

‘I agree, although you are being a bit on the legalistic side. Move me out if you will be so kind.’

Penfold ordered two of Captain Nolan’s men to move the couch and the Major out to the yard; it was done and he was made comfortable in a corner facing the gate which was on the north side of the yard, with the town of Caudry twelve hundred yards away. To the south-west the church spire of Ligny was just visible through the loopholes. Under Montgomery’s orders, the five-bar gate was being buttressed and reinforced with wood taken from a store in the barn, but still capable of being opened with the latch. The hedge through which they had come early in the morning lay six hundred yards west. There was a small orchard to the south of the farmhouse, no more than a few rather poorly fruit trees, with a vegetable patch in a corner. Some orderlies were lifting carrots, good nourishment for the men who had had no food except hard tack all day. A heifer was tied to one of the fruit trees. The barn which was used to store sugar-beet was situated twenty yards away on the east side and was now being occupied by a squad of men, under a sergeant, who were even now busy pulling out bricks to make loopholes for their rifles. All in all there were fields of fire extending at least six hundred yards in every direction. Sergeant Fox was in the yard organising the construction of more loopholes for the dozen men under his command. The yard wall offered good protection from fire, so much so that men could move freely about inside without being seen from outside. A door in the wall led to the barn. Penfold was impressed, as he always was, with these Birmingham men, not farming men but men from the squalid backstreets of the city, who could seemingly turn their hands to tasks that Penfold had to admit would not come naturally to him.

The Major had another word with Penfold.

'It's presumptuous of me I know, but I think Admiral Nelson had to use his left hand after losing his right. I'm going to do the same, and make a start with my revolver. If you know your history, Stephen, at Hougoumont the Coldstream had some close-quarter fighting at the farm gates; so we will be in good company if it comes to it.'

'If it comes to it, we will all have to use the steel.'

'I think our men went in with the steel this morning in Caudry and the boche ran like hares. I could hear the cries of a close-quarter attack from eight hundred yards.'

Penfold walked around the yard, inspecting the mens' work. Sergeant Fox was by the gate.

'Still got you rosary, Sarn't?'

'That bit of Roman idolatry has become part of me now.'

'There are German Catholics as well as French ones.'

'And the Pope's an Italian, an' all, Sir, so what side is he on when he's at home? It was simpler when the enemy were 'eathens like up on the

Frontier.'

'What's the state of the men, Sarn't? Morale holding up?'

'I've no worries on that score; but let's just say that with Prescott the last five years as a barman hasn't improved his military bearing.'

'Hang on Sergeant, I think Mr. Montgomery wants to have a few words with the men.'

Monty was getting the men to gather round. He cleared his throat, fingered his sword in its scabbard, wiped his beaky nose with the back of his hand and told the men to stand easy. Major Haddow could hear from his couch in the corner of the yard.

'I just want to say that for the moment the boche are keeping their distance but we don't expect this to last. There are two more hours of daylight. I know that some of you have taken up arms again from the dressing station. I salute you. We will need all the rifles we have. We expect the enemy to respect the hospital and give the wounded all the succour that we would do in similar circumstances. For the rest of us we will break out when we think, Lieutenant Penfold and I, that the time is right. Captain Nolan will stay behind. That is all; now to your posts.'

Stephen Penfold thought again of his toy castle, his lead soldiers and the words of the hymn, *Fight the good fight, With all thy might*. There's comfort in that certainty, to be sure, if one could take it literally. His father had no doubts about the Church Militant.

There were now twenty men at the loopholes in the barn and the walls of the yard. They had no firing positions in the house out of deference to the Hague conventions. A Geneva Cross had been put up above the house, mounted alongside the chimney. Penfold doubted whether it would make any difference; after all, they were taking up firing positions only yards from the infirmary and it was hard to make a distinction between the infirmary and the yard which abutted it.

Penfold sought out Monty.

'Do you think they will come at us before dark?'

'I think their commander is unsure of us. He might think that we all went back with Watkins' party. If so he would hardly bother with one farmhouse, unless he wants it to provide accommodation for the night; in which case he is going to be disappointed. But their artillery is still active, which puzzles me. Why bother with all that shelling if he thinks we have packed it in? They are still shelling all along the line'.

'Well you know what they say about Teutonic thoroughness; they never know when to stop, like those Wagner operas. *Lohengrin* was a world without end as I seem to remember.'

'Ah, the Germans and their 'Kultur'. They make a lot of fuss about it, like one of Dr. Freud's patients with an inferiority complex. The problem with the Germans is that they are a *nouveau riche* country, with no bottom.'

'I didn't know you were so well up on these things, Monty.'

'I know things that might surprise you, Stephen.'

Penfold had another anxious moment at the mention of his Christian name. He couldn't manage 'Bernard' and 'Bernie' was unthinkable. He found not for the first time that Monty's preternatural air of calmness, combined with his supercilious manner, both reassuring and irritating. And as if to confirm Penfold's anxiety there was a shout from the barn of 'They're coming' and a fusillade of shots almost immediately afterwards.

'Hardly a very informative shout. No numbers and no range. But I'll go over and have a look.' Monty took off for the barn through the door in the yard-wall that led out to the barn. He had to cross the few yards of open space, which he did at a crouching walk-run.

Penfold stayed in the yard. He said to Sergeant Fox,

'It would appear that they know we are here. At any rate we have declared our hand. I fear we are in for a hot time.'

The two men remained in the yard. The shooting from the barn soon ceased and there was no shooting from the men at the loopholes in the yard. Penfold asked one of the men peering through his firing-slit,

'Can you make anything out?'

'No, Sir. I thought I saw movement on the right but whoever it was has gone to ground. It was there that I thought the Maxim was earlier but .....wait a moment, what's that over there...can't be...come and have a look, Sir, for yourself.'

Penfold got his binoculars out of their leather case. He peered through them in the direction that the man had pointed. There was no mistaking a body of men at about seven hundred yards, clearly visible as German, marching along in close order, perhaps as many as five hundred, two complete companies, in four columns. It was an amazing sight, given that firing had just broken out to the right, and an opportunity not to be missed. The body of men seemed completely unaware that there were hostile troops in the area. He couldn't let them march on and he had no hesitation in stepping back and saying to the private, 'I shall give the order to fire to all who can bring a rifle to bear on the target.' What was even better was that the enemy were against the evening sky, now overcast but suffused with light. Rain looked imminent but was holding off.

The trouble from the Warwickshire's point of view was that only seven rifles could be brought to fire on the target; these seven men responded immediately to Penfold's command and managed to get off a dozen rounds before the enemy column went to ground. At seven hundred yards a body of infantry alerted to the hostile fire in the farmhouse becomes a serious threat and no longer a target. The first seven shots claimed what looked like seven hits. At seven hundred yards nearly all British infantry in 1914 could hit a target the size of a man. But what they needed now was a Vickers. True, there was very little cover for the enemy in the field but even the stubble could conceal a man and there were dips and folds in the ground, not previously apparent to the men in the farmyard, which made their targets harder to make out. Penfold thought of hornets' nests. This wasn't what happened when he shot down the enemy approaching his wooden castle; they formed up in column and attacked. The French in the young Penfold's war-game never understood that a column made a better target and at the same time only enabled the leading soldiers to fire. These field-grey soldiers didn't do that. He knew they were deploying in extended order, were manoeuvring, were recovering their poise, were even now firing back. And there was still at least an hour of daylight left. Simple arithmetic told him that the farmhouse garrison was doomed. And Penfold's stock of courage was being rapidy depleted. Opening fire on the columns now seemed a very rash thing to have done, revealing their position.

Monty came rushing back to the yard. The barn and the space between the two buildings was out of the line of sight of the enemy to the west.

'The Maxim on the right made an appearance, but it has been dealt with for the moment. And the men had great sport in shooting at a small troop of cavalry at twelve hundred yards. The Uhlans couldn't understand where our fire was coming from. What is the situation here?'

'We have opened fire at a large body of men at seven hundred yards or so. They are still out there and are likely to mount an attack. They are using fieldcraft and are firing back.'

Even as he spoke bullets were hitting the brick walls of the yard with a violence and a zapping noise that made the men instinctively duck. But the men at the loopholes continued to fire into the place where they could see the boche and where they had to be. They couldn't be anywhere else. He found himself shouting,

'Fire at the officers! Look for the swords! Fire at the stooks! Fire at will!' Kill them all! I know that my Redeemer liveth! Onward Christian soldiers!'

Monty gave Penfold a worried look. Perhaps Sergeant Fox will keep an eye on him, he thought. Monty made a mental note to have a word with the padre about Penfold.

Every now and again a grey figure out in the stubble would leap up for a few seconds and run back, disappear and then another would do the same. Penfold was watching through a loophole and could see plainly enough that others were working their way forward and spreading out. He took up a rifle and joined in the shooting. The men were vying with each other now and calling out their score; 'That one was mine!' 'No, mine.' 'Eight!' 'Nine!' It was a fairground shoot and the enemy were being knocked over one after the other. But some of them could be seen to be going back to the shelter of the hedge, from where they could build up a fire-base.

Penfold made out one grey figure, crouched in the stubble, his head-gear visible through the binoculars, and clearly an officer. Penfold estimated the range at six hundred yards, a small target but a shootable one. The man had no pack on his back, another sign that he was an officer. But Penfold laid his binoculars on the ground, called for Sergeant Fox and said quietly, 'I think this is one for you, Sarn't.'

Fox took his time; resting the barrel of the Lee-Enfield, he fired one shot and merely said to his officer, 'That'll do, Mr. Penfold.'

The only hope for the garrison, which they all knew in their hearts, was that when the enemy commander realised that there only a small number of occupants in the farm he would leave them alone as not constituting a threat and not worth the lives of his men. He might calculate that the garrison would surrender in due course and could be left to wither on the vine until they did. There was still an hour of light left in the day.

A few of the more lightly wounded men were reloading the magazines of the Lee Enfields and passing the re-loaded guns to the men at the loopholes; one man was using an oily pull-through on a rifle that was getting too hot. Other men brought drinking water in pails from the pump in the yard at the urgent request of Sergeant Fox. But nothing the men could do could hide the fact that there were at most a dozen men against the best part of five hundred. Major Haddow got up from his couch and with his shattered arm in a sling was urging the men on. 'Well done the 6th! That's my boys!'

The wall was getting a pounding from the German fire, bullets pattering against the stone and brick, and some of the Warwicks were getting hurt by flying shards of brick from around the loopholes, and one of them had been killed by a bullet coming right through the hole. Monty's men were firing again from the barn, which was an ominous sign. The enemy were now on two sides of the farm: the west and the east and the exits from the town of Caudry were only twelve hundred yards away. Caudry had been in German hands since the late morning and troops were surely massing there for a break-out. British shrapnel fire was still falling on the southern part of the town, to the great satisfaction of the Warwickshiremen.

Then came the scream of 77mm shells from three thousand yards north of the Cambrai road as a German battery commander, Hauptman Bonner, finally realised he had a useful target in the shape of an easily identifiable farm. It was on his map but so far no-one had told him that it was an enemy stronghold, and in the absence of orders he had refrained from firing on it. Now he was in receipt of a message brought by runner from the Company Commander of the dismounted Hussar Regiment 15, which was engaged with British forces to the south of Caudry. The message identified the farm clearly enough and was signed Oberleutnant Graf von Westerholt. The gunner had a great respect for these aristocratic cavalry officers and he was more than happy to oblige him with several salvos of shrapnel. He fired five salvos from the map, got through to his observer on the telephone and then waited for a reply from him, in his position to the west of Caudry.

Hauptman Bonner had been in and around this position since early in the morning. He had had to shift his position twice when British counter-battery fire became particularly troublesome, especially from some 13-pounder guns in front of Caudry at 6.30 a.m. He had received a salvo of well-directed fire with HE from a howitzer battery which had knocked out two of his guns, but that particular British battery had been driven off. He had used up all his HE on Caudry itself and then on the village of Audencourt and now he had only shrapnel to fire at the farmhouse.

'Good shooting,' came the voice of his forward observer. 'You have straddled.'

'Fusing good?'

'Yes.'

'That should please the Oberleutnant', Bonner said to his leutnant. 'He can go for his brandy now. Battery fire five rounds!' Thirty more 77mm shells straddled the farmhouse. 'Cease Fire!'

Back at the farmhouse the men thought the salvos would never end. They came in with the air-bursts almost simultaneous with the approaching shell-scream; the men ducked behind what little shelter the wall provided, but three of them were hurt in the yard. So far the men in the barn were unhurt, and nor were the wounded in the house any further affected. Tiles were knocked about on the roof but no serious damage was done to the structure of either building. And then the barrage was over; stillness returned.

Sergeant Fox looked across the yard at Lieutenant Penfold. Penfold was beginning to give cause for concern. He was sitting down on a small pile of dung in the corner, staring at the ground. He was muttering about his Redeemer, but that was nothing new. Fox decided to have a word.

'The men are alert and on their posts, Sir. No serious casualties. But the cow in the orchard has been killed.'

Penfold didn't seem to hear him. But then he stiffened:

'Prepare to receive cavalry! If the infantry form column shoot them down! Shoot the columns! Shoot the leaders! The Lord is my shepherd!'

Out in the field eight hundred yards away, in the hedge that the Warwicks had charged through twice already today, Graf von Westerholt, Oberleutnant in the 15th Hussars in the 2nd Cavalry Division of the Imperial German Army of Kaiser Wilheim II, was pleased. He was pleased for two reasons. The first reason was that his request for an artillery shoot had been carried out so successfully. An immense feeling of power came over the young officer; he was not only in command of one hundred men, but he could also call down fire merely by sending a runner. But the main reason that he was so pleased with the successful shoot, although it wouldn't have killed the occupants of the farm, was that now the target had been hit he need no longer lead his men into a fruitless and dangerous assault. He could tell his commanding officer, Oberst von Salis, that the farmhouse had been 'neutralised' and that no further action tonight need be taken, but the occupants could be rounded up in the morning. In any case, he told himself, it was not the business of dismounted Hussars to conduct infantry assaults. They had been on their way to collect their mounts, left in the care of the grooms to the west of the town, when unexpected rifle fire broke out and they could now go back to collect their horses and get on with doing what cavalry did, which was to pursue a defeated enemy. This ancient and honourable cavalry task did not include attacking infantry in fortified emplacements. That was a different job altogether; he might have added that it was a job for the foot-soldier, who throughout history has been the social inferior of the mounted soldier. There were plenty of German infantry about from the IV Reserve Corps and among the Jaeger battalions. Von Westerholt was very definitely not going to do their job for them. Indeed he doubted very much whether even if he led an attack his men would follow with much enthusiasm. He was conscious that his troops' cavalry carbines were no match for the rifles of the British infantry; indeed the farmhouse was at the extreme edge of their carbines' range. His encounter with British infantry near Beauvois early this morning had cost his Troop thirteen men, cut down by fire from the village, catching his mounted Hussars in the open. Some of his Hussars had fired back from behind their mounts lying prone on the stubble. He was learning to have great respect for the marksmanship of the British Tommy. And they shot his chargers without mercy, knowing that without their horses his men were quite undone.

The re-occupation of Caudry by Kurassier and Hussar troops had created a salient of German territory, leaving the 1st Gordon Highlanders and 2nd Royal Irish on the east side of the town to their own devices. There was no contact possible between the Gordons and the Irish and the Warwickshires; they belonged, in any case, to different divisions, the 3rd and the 4th respectively, always a problem in the British Army when it came to communications. The Warwicks knew from the amount of shelling and small arms fire to their north-east, that these battalions were still in action, but there could be no mutual help. As far as the King's Own and the Lancashire Fusiliers were concerned, they might have been five miles away, instead of the fifteen hundred yards or so that they actually were, or at least had been. The 3rd Worcesters, led by Colonel Stuart, had left their position to the south of Caudry an hour ago, in the direction of Montigny, leaving in small groups, covering each other as they went, under the orders of Colonel Bird who had taken over command of 7 Brigade. The disabled ambulance near Audencourt was still stuck in the sunken lane, leaving its wounded occupants with no alternative but to stay in it until captured, tended by the two orderlies. The guns (XXIII Battery) seen by Captain Johnson from the ambulance had been ordered back a thousand yards, retiring at the same time as the infantry. Johnson himself was now in the great caravan of khaki humanity on the Roman road to the south.

Lieutenant Montgomery could of course know nothing of the thinking of von Westerholt. All he knew when he looked through a loophole to the north-west was that small groups of grey-clad soldiers, their ridiculous pickelhaube just visible in the evening light, could be seen leaving the field in the direction of Caudry. He ordered a final five rounds rapid fire and went to sit by Lieutenant Penfold.

'I think the threat has passed; the enemy are slinking away. We will be free to choose the time of our break-out.'

Penfold went on staring at the ground. He wanted to sleep; he wanted everything, the boche, the shelling, the enemy who were now gathering all around him in the encroaching gloom, to go away so that he could lie down and sleep. So some boche went away; there were always more and more of them and they would never leave him alone. They would snipe him, they would come through the corn, their airplanes would seek him out and their guns would shell him. It was quite obvious that the enemy had worked around the farmhouse so that they were an islet in a hostile sea. Penfold, a landsman, had always had a fear of the sea and now he saw the farmhouse not as a place of refuge to be defended, but as a storm-lashed toe-hold, a place surrounded by terror, things too ghastly to behold that lurked in caverns forever unlit by the sun. The men would always expect him to know what to do; he was expected to be a leader of men. The truth was though, that he didn't know what to do. It was all so terribly shameful and unfair; it shouldn't be the BEF that was running away. The image of the soldier with his jaw shot away came back to him; where was the man now? He hoped he had been able to go back with Watkins' party.

'*I will lift up my eyes to the hills*
From whence cometh my help.'

'That's it, Stephen, that's where the help is coming from. We will go over the hills and seek out our friends.'

Monty the practical officer knew then that Stephen Penfold was a bit touched, but would shake himself down and come with him on the long journey to find friends in safe territory. They would have to wait several hours until darkness was their ally. Then they would head south and west, towards Amiens, all the way if need be; surely that British base would still be in our hands. There were many things to do before they set off but they would get through, Monty had no doubt, although he did admit to himself that things might get a bit tricky when they went off their map, as they were bound to do. But there was still firing to the north-east and the south-west and Monty wanted to wait until things had quietened down.

At about 5.30 p.m. the garrison in the farmhouse was greatly cheered when five salvos of 18-pounder shells screamed over their heads and exploded in angry white bursts nine hundred yards to their north, at the outskirts of Caudry, catching Westerholt's dismounted cavalry in a most satisfactory straddle. But although the two subalterns could not know it, this was the remaining two guns of XXXI RFA Battery using up the last of their ammunition, firing from just north of Haucourt, where they had been placed by General Snow early in the morning. It was lucky shooting. The guns and limbers were then hitched up to the horses and the two teams pulled away. The garrison at Le Coquelet was now on its own, the bulk of the remaining 4th and 3rd Division troops on both sides of them moving off, platoon by platoon, back to Ligny where a further stand was made, on the rise of ground identified earlier in the day by General Smith-Dorrien. But no new orders were received at the farmhouse because no staff officer could have got through to them even if it had been known that they were there. The fate of Watkins and the bulk of the Battalion was not known to the officers in the farmhouse. All over the 4th Division area the battalions were fighting their own battles, with Lieutenant-Colonels, Majors and even subalterns like Lieutenant Montgomery acting on their own initiative. Montgomery knew from the moment the shelling had started that morning that this was going to be a soldiers' battle.

Chapter 21

Lieutenant-General Smith-Dorrien

Lieutenant-General Smith-Dorrien was sitting in the back of the open Rolls alongside his Chief of Staff, Brigadier George Forrestier-Walker. Captain Bowley was in the front seat. Both the Brigadier and the Captain wore their swords and their Webleys were in their holsters. The General carried only his baton. The driver, Corporal Clegg, was a skilled mechanic and so far his most frequent job on the car had been replacing punctured tyres. He had had to do it four times in the past three days. The General's groom was riding just behind the car, which was doing about fifteen miles an hour on the road from Bertry to Maurois, which lies on the Roman road to St. Quentin, south of Reumont. The groom, a private soldier, carried a Lee Enfield in a leather holster but the General had no further armed escort.

Shells, mostly shrapnel but also HE, were now falling on Reumont, further up the road in the direction of Le Cateau. The town was partly in flames. General Fergusson's 5th Division HQ was in the process of packing up, bundling up files into leather trunks and batmen pressed into service as clerks were carrying them the short distance between the schoolhouse and the parked vehicles. The Union Jack had been taken down from its masthead on the roof.

'I think, George, that we should go north of Reumont to see for ourselves how things are going up there. 14 Brigade should be getting away and I would like to have a word with some of their officers.'

'Yes of course Horace; we'll find a farm track around the town and come in on the north side. Hold on to your hat, it might get a little noisy. But I fear that we might lose the greater part of 14 Brigade.'

'A shell burst in front of my car just before the battle at Mons; I don't think much of this German shrapnel. I just hope ours is a bit better.'

'Try telling the gunners that their shells are no good. They won't take that from an infantryman.'

The car, with its horse escort, skirted the town of Reumont using what was little more than a farm track and was approaching the Roman road when it became apparent that the shell-fire falling on the road was almost a constant rain of shells and the General was persuaded to halt the car five hundred yards short of it. They stayed in the car in the hope that the shelling would ease up a little. A group of KOSB came past, saluted correctly and hovered around; they had no officer. Captain Bowley spoke to one of the men, a corporal, the senior man with the group. The man's Borders accent was strong enough so as to be hard to grasp the sense in what he was saying. Captain Bowley translated for the General.

'It would appear that the Suffolks have all been rolled up, with most of the KOYLI. This man claims to be among the sole survivors of his Battalion, but in my experience they all tend to say that.'

'It may well be that the Retreat order did not get through to them. I think, George, that it would be best if we re-joined the road further back. Tell the men they have done well and they should carry on.'

Much to the relief of the other passengers of the Rolls, Clegg turned it around and went back around Reumont. The shelling was not reaching as far south as Maurois, lying as it does four miles from Le Cateau, and they got back onto the tarmac and cobbled road. There were ditches on both sides of the road which the General noticed could be used if the enemy lengthened their range. Captain Bowley then noticed a group of officers crouched in a ditch beside the road and ordered Corporal Clegg to stop the car. The Captain got out and went over to talk to them. He made way for a ragged convoy of GS wagons, carrying a mixed cargo of ammunition, both small arms and machine gun bandoliers, with some wounded men looking very uncomfortable perched on the wooden cases.

Captain Bowley realised at once that the officers in the ditch were the ones he had ordered to form the rear-guard, as the General had instructed him.

'Good afternoon, Gentlemen, the Corps Commander would like a word.'

The officers, who included a Scottish Rifles Major and the Lieutenant-Colonel of the Royal Welch, looked a bit sheepish at being caught huddled in a ditch when there was no actual shelling. The General and Brigadier Forrestier-Walker stepped down from the car and everyone stood up and saluted.

The Royal Welch Lieutenant-Colonel said,

'Sir, my Battalion is spread out on the east side of the road with the Scottish Rifles on the west. We will stay as rear-guard until dark, as ordered. We expect a possible enemy encroachment from the east, from the Selle, and we are confident of stopping it. We are in receipt of your orders, Sir, to this effect.'

'Indeed yes, Colonel. Very good. I understand that the enemy have been held up by the valiant 14 Brigade but they may yet come on. You are the first line of defence; I expect you to hold here and let 14 Brigade come through you. Carry on, Colonel.' The General used his baton to indicate the direction from which he expected the enemy to make their advance.

Everyone saluted. Smith-Dorrien then turned to Forrestier-Walker and said,

'I would like to ride out a way to the west. I may go as far as Clary. You take the car down to Maretz and I will join you there.'

In fact, although the Royal Welch and the Scottish Rifles could not know it, they were not the only rear-guard that day and were not exactly the first or last line of defence against a German break-through. All along the line of retreating 5th and 3rd Division battalions, small groups of men, often with only one officer and sometimes not even one, were staying back to guard the retreat of other groups, as they came out of the line in small parties. These groups came out in co-ordinated movements, as the Infantry Manual had taught them. There was no mass movement of men, which would have provided the enemy gunners with perfect targets. All were dog-tired, all eager to get away from the relentless enemy but craving above all sleep and nourishment. The time for killing was done; the time for escape had come. The professionalism of the Army asserted itself and 3rd Division, holding the centre and of the three infantry divisions engaged on this day the one least threatened, came out of the line with their brigades more or less intact as fighting formations.

At places these rear-guards had been ordered by Generals such as the Lieutenant-General himself. At other places deputised captains, acting as staff officers on behalf of senior officers, stopped bodies of men and attempted to form them into rear-guards. Some of these captains received dusty answers from men and officers unwilling to halt their flight to the rear. One captain, when requesting a colonel to turn about got merely a stare of incomprehension. Other parties of retreating infantry, sometimes consisting of men from different units, willingly obeyed orders to coalesce into fighting groups. The lines of retreating soldiers never became a rout. They brought their wounded out with them, as far as this was possible. Corporal Holmes of the Yorkshire Light Infantry near Suffolk Hill carried a wounded man back to an aid post, then went back into the beaten zone to rescue a wounded gunner lying beside his stricken horse-team. Holmes brought him out with the surviving horses, although he knew nothing about handling horses himself, let alone ones hysterical with fear; he was awarded the VC, one of five on this day. And there were those like the rump of the 1st Warwicks and 1st Gordons near Caudry who did not retreat at the appointed time because they did not receive their orders to do so. Others, like the 1st Rifle Brigade at Fontaine to the west of Caudry, commanded by a company commander, Major

Salmon, fought until the Jaegers were almost on top of them before fleeing for their lives, leaving their wounded behind in the care of their doctor and a ring of dead Jaeger infantrymen around their position. At Ligny, toward dusk, two guns on the forward slope were abandoned when enemy infantry got within two hundred yards and it became too dangerous to hitch up the horses; the gunners ran back to the town but two of them were shot in the back as they fled.

Lieutenant-General Smith-Dorrien rode out to the west in the direction of Clary. He wanted this ride to see for himself the way things were going. He felt the burden of command. He knew what it was like to run away from an enemy intent on killing him; as a young man he had fled on horse-back, on foot, and finally by swimming across a river, away from the Zulu warriors with their assegais. That was down towards Rorke's Drift; he had shot a Zulu point-blank in the face and had not forgotten the way the revolver bullet had blown out the back of the man's skull. He could recall every detail of that face, even after thirty-five years; it had been two days before his twenty-first birthday. The flared nostrils, the bared teeth, the steel point of the spear, the animal skin around the man's black mid-riff, all was clear in his mind. They had been brave warriors those Zulus, no doubt about it.

The sun was low and obscured by cloud and a light rain was falling. His horse was a fine gelding from the stables of the Quartermaster General. They trotted along a farm track now serving as a road between Clary and Bertry, not much more than a dirt path, normally used by farm carts and driven cattle, the General rising easily in the saddle. The sound of the guns in the north was audible but strangely muffled by the rain. Soon this road would be used by men of the 3rd Division coming back from the area round Caudry and Audencourt, a little over a mile to the north. They would be tired and dejected, he knew, but he no longer feared a rout. After them would come, at first, Uhlans hunting down the British, men on horses with spears. At least the Zulus had no horses in '79. The back of an Uhlan's head would explode just like a Zulu's, he supposed.

Then he heard a different gun-rumble, this time coming from the west. It must be at least four or five miles away, carried by the westerly wind; not British guns, that was certain; a sharp crack and then another only two seconds later. Then more, followed by more but always in quick succession, almost drum-fire. An ambulance passed him; Smith-Dorrien pulling the gelding over to the side of the track to make room for it. He listened again to the guns from the west. Ah, of course, they must be French 75's; Sordet must have cavalry guns just like our RHA's 13-pounders. That means the west flank is secure and Sordet is standing his ground just as I asked for. Why couldn't that fool French have told me this instead of his unnecessary wire about retreating, reminding me of what I already knew? Perhaps I should have ordered 14 Brigade out before I did. But they wouldn't have got the order anyway in all likelihood. Retreats are damn difficult to do in the midst of battle; even French knows that. But no doubt he will hold me accountable for the losses in 14 Brigade; it will give him ammunition against me.

He passed a cottage with the two inhabitants outside in their cabbage patch, an old man and his wife, both wearing clogs, and tipped his cap with his baton. They made the barest acknowledgement. For a fleeting moment the Lieutenant-General and the peasant farmer looked into each others' eyes. He should perhaps tell them of the nearness of the enemy but lacked the language. Allemands, they would understand that; sale boche. The Allemands might buy their cabbages but more than likely just take them. But where would these two old people go? They will stay here like peasant farmers the world over and the invaders will live off the land in the way that they have done since Caesar's time. Sir Horace was not accustomed to thinking of the fate of French farmers. But the business of moving thousands, hundreds of thousands of men, of feeding them and quartering them in a foreign land, a conquered land, that was the sort of business his mind was able to grapple with. He knew that the men who do this business, the men who come after the fighting men, requisition-men, were not men of honour, with a military code that he could understand. And he knew that however many cabbages these peasants might grow, they couldn't feed the German invader as well as themselves.

He turned the gelding back towards Maretz and spurred him into a trot. A couple of miles and he would be back on the Roman road and then he would find the car and have his meeting with French in St. Quentin, if the man hadn't already upped sticks for Noyon. Probably in a funk, but at least he should have left some officers behind to look after things. Damn cavalry-men never understand about the details of supply and organisation; it's all dash and glory with them. You can't have a modern war run by cavalrymen. Quartermasters, they're the key to modern war, even if most of them are just jumped-up clerks. Quartermasters will always follow orders, unlike cavalrymen who always think they know best. Damn fool French wasn't at a proper school like Harrow, spent his youth climbing up the rigging of sailing-ships for God's sake. Calls himself a student of warfare just because he's read a couple of books, but soldiering was never about reading books. It's about the eye for ground and a hundred other things but not books.

At the Maretz cross-roads all was confusion again; the Red Caps were doing their best, and staff officers were trying to get men sorted out into their brigades or even divisions. One staff Major was standing at the cross-roads chanting out '5th Division to the right, 3rd Division to the left'. Smith-Dorrien went almost unnoticed by the throng of exhausted soldiery; he looked around for the Rolls and then saw it underneath a tree by the church. He looked at his watch: 6.30 p.m., time enough to get to St. Quentin in an hour if they could get through the log-jam of wagons.

Corporal Clegg was giving the Rolls a wipe down; chauffeurs seem to have an urge to get their shammy leathers out whatever the circumstances. Ah, good, Bowley and Forrestier-Walker are here as well.

The Sherwood Foresters penant proudly displayed, my first posting, the old 45th. The 2nd Battalion will be out soon, must look them up.

Smith-Dorrien acknowledged the salutes of his officers. He handed the gelding over to his groom. He told them that from the noise of the guns to the west he had every confidence that the French were holding there. Forrestier-Walker said,

'We are fairly sure that it is only on the extreme right that the Corps is seriously threatened and the threat is contained. We have given von Kluck a smashing blow, there is no doubt about it. But I fear many of the field guns are lost, machine-guns as well, which may be due to confusion over your orders at dawn, Horace. I have to tell you that General Drummond of 19 Brigade has been badly wounded in the shelling at Reumont. Reumont has been abandoned.'

'We will lose many a good man before this business is done. Come, I have an appointment at GHQ.'

They set off down the road to the south-west. They went straight ahead at the first cross-roads, where Red Caps were directing the traffic, again separating the wagons and men by division. The Rolls was waved on with a smart salute, pennants fluttering, Clegg using the centre of the pavé. Rain was now falling more heavily and darkness was not far away, but there was time enough to get to St. Quentin before dark. Clegg was using the claxon of the Rolls constantly, the columns of men walking on both sides of the road taking little interest in the car. There was no traffic coming up the road.

'Henry V crossed the Somme near Ham on his way back to Calais in 1415,' Captain Bowley, an Old Harrovian, knew his history. 'He was said to have ten thousand horses and fifteen thousand infantry and archers.'

'And our riflemen are the longbowmen of our time, but as for ten thousand horses, I don't believe a word of it. Just think of the forage and the commissariat required,' replied the General, and lapsed into sleep. It was the night of the 22nd that he had last had a night's sleep, in the farmhouse at Sars.

The General was woken by the car swerving to avoid some small-arms ammunition boxes in the middle of the road. A convoy of GS wagons ahead had jettisoned the boxes, in an apparent attempt to lighten their load. Corporal Clegg increased speed to twenty miles an hour and caught up with the leading wagon, with an Army Service Corps Captain in command. He was flagged down and summoned over to the car. He was visibly shaking, but he mustered the best salute he could.

'Uhlans are reported to be coming on and the safety of my convoy is paramount, Sir'. He was addressing the occupants of the car as a whole.

'Nonsense, Captain, Uhlans my foot. Go back and collect the boxes. If we had time I would report you to your senior officer.' This was Forrestier-Walker. The captain looked relieved, as well he might. It was his bad luck to be caught out by the Corps Commander himself. Without the pressing business of the moment he would certainly have been put on a charge.

The car drove on and reached the outskirts of St. Quentin. Civilian traffic was thick now, refugees mostly but the locals were out and about. Shops were still doing business and French cavalry were riding in, clearly from Sordet's divisions. Their big horses looked blown; they did not have the look of horsemen returning from a successful engagement. Smith-Dorrien decided there was very little to be gained in talking to them. In his experience the first out from a battle are the most unreliable and they appeared in any case to be officer-less. So far there were very few British troops, just the sort of quartermaster ASC wagons to be expected at a rail-head in the rear of an army, soon to become a front-line position, so fast were military developments proceeding. The Rolls was now about four hours ahead of the nearest troops of Second Corps, the vast bulk of whom had, of course, to walk. Smith-Dorrien spoke to Forrestier-Walker,

'George, French can wait. We have more pressing business. Let's go first to the station and find the senior RTO. I have a feeling that things are not as they should be.'

At the station things were as he had feared. There was rolling stock, passenger wagons, in the station, enough for two trains by the look of it, but there was only one engine and the railway workers that he could see were hanging about uselessly. Some French cavalry troopers, unhorsed, were sitting on the down platform, clearly the worse for drink. Royal Field Artillery kit lay all over the place: wheels for the guns, signallers' wire, limbers with boxed ammunition. A 3rd Division RAMC ambulance was arriving at that very minute. He sent Forrestier-Walker off to find the senior British officer. He came back shortly with a Major Nye, Quartermaster and acting RTO.

'Major, this is not good. You must make up two trains, and I don't care how you do it, but find another engine and get these railwaymen to look sharp. Commandeer the whole lot if you have to, don't be afraid to get out a revolver to make your point. Say you are under the direct orders of the Corps Commander and that they are now under British Military discipline. Get the wounded out as a priority and have another train as a back-up. Even an old shunting engine would do. All this kit has got to go down the line to Noyon but we will use road transport as well. This place will be in German hands by this time tomorrow. Do I make myself clear?'

Major Nye gave his smartest salute and assured the General that he and his staff would see to it. He hurried off.

'George, we still have things to do here. Get a convoy of wagons back up to Le Cateau with provisions, biscuits, bully, jam. And water. Get an armed escort ready to go with it. There is no time to lose. Over there, get me that sergeant with the wagons and horses.'

The man came over from the other side of the station fore-court, handling his two horses with skill. He brought the wagon to a halt and saluted.

'Sergeant, this equipment has got to go down to Noyon,' pointing to the gunnery equipment. Get a convoy ready and don't stop for anything or anybody. The trains are for the wounded and the wagons are for equipment. Have you got that? I am making you responsible for the safe delivery of this equipment to the RFA at Noyon.'

'Yes, Sir.'

'And now George we will go and find Sir John French.'

But Captain Bowley had already been to the Mairie.

'GHQ have already packed up and gone. They finished their lunch with Joffre at 2.30 p.m. and took a train. That explains why there is only one engine left in St. Quentin. They are setting up shop in Noyon, twenty-five miles down to the south-west.'

Smith-Dorrien was not surprised but not pleased at this news.

'In that case I have no alternative but to go down there and report to Sir John. And then I will have to come all the way back again. My place is here with the Corps. Gentlemen, I suggest you both stay here and sort the men out into billets as they come in. They will be exhausted and will need food and shelter; some will have to bivouac wherever they find themselves. You will need to get hold of the civil authorities. Commandeer what you can in the way of forage. There is much to be done. There is a long night ahead of us.'

Chapter 22

Captain Johnson and Private Edwards

If someone had told Henry Johnson a day ago that he would be sharing his horse with a private soldier, that he would be conversing with him, and that he would be limping along a road in the company of a man in a Panama hat and another private soldier, he would not have believed it. Such things were simply not done in the Army, in the same way that his intercourse with the servants at the house in Broadway was of a perfunctory nature, confined to the weather and perhaps cricket-matches. Servants undoubtedly had lives of their own, had spouses and children, went to the sea-side on their annual holiday, but he was only dimly aware of them. They were known by their surnames and the servants of visitors to the house were given the surnames of their masters. But it was a gentleman's duty to look after his servants, in the same way that he looked after the men in his platoon. His familiarity with the lower social orders, or rather the lower middle-classes, came more from reading the Grossmiths' *Diary of a Nobody* than actual social intercourse. Funniest thing he's ever read, that bit where Pooter paints his bath bright red.

But he was happier walking than riding and riding seemed to aggravate his leg wound. It would not look seemly in any case to be riding when so many were wounded and struggling to keep going. His own wounds were things to be borne. One must set an example to the men. And if someone had told Private Edwards that he would be hob-nobbing with officers on equal terms he would have been equally surprised. Edwards even saw an artillery driver with his arm around an exhausted infantry lieutenant beside him on the diving seat of an ammunition wagon; such a sight would have been unthinkable only two days ago. Edwards watched the lieutenant wake with a start and realising his position shake himself free. All around him men were staggering as if drunk but the truth was that they were beaten to the wide.

They were now in a convoy of struggling khaki humanity on the road down to Maretz, but a convoy without formation; wagons with wounded, walking wounded helping each other, but not one had abandoned his weapon. This was open country, big fields of stubble, freshly cut wheat, neat stooks, but no human habitation to be seen, no salient natural features. The sky was overcast, with speckles of rain. There was still the drum-fire of artillery in the north. A single insolent Taube was flying north at five thousand feet, its engine unhurried, helped by upcurrents of warm air. No-one bothered with it. Darkness was approaching. This straggling convoy was not the confident, proud Army that had gone up to Mons from Mauberge singing *Tipperary* and grateful for the gifts of food and wine lavished on them by the Belgians, even if they had to swig the wine out of sight of the officers. It was not even the same Army that had reeled back to Bavai after the battle on the Mons canal, with the enemy in close pursuit. There was no singing now. It was difficult to see how this incoherent mass could be reformed into its fighting components. Johnson was walking alongside an artillery lieutenant whose battery had lost five of their guns up on the hill. The gunner officer was without his cap. Their one remaining gun was being pulled by only four horses instead of the usual six. Two exhausted gunners were riding the horses, or rather clinging on to them, another two were riding on the limber. And for now they were without any ammunition. The officer was dejected but bearing up. Johnson wanted to have a word with him.

'Captain Johnson, Signals, 3rd Worcesters. And you?'

'Lieutenant Hodgson, 80 Battery, XV Brigade. I don't know how we are going to recover from this. We should never have been placed on that hill. Probably all due to the confusion over the last-minute orders, whether we were going to make a stand or not. But anyway we couldn't get the resupply wagons up to us, although a few got through, only due to the bravery of the drivers. When we did get good targets it was too late, but we managed to knock over a fair number of them up on the hill over the road. Towards the end we were firing at fuze zero; battery fire was not possible but we kept our last two guns firing to the end. By that time they had got machine-guns on to us and our men were getting hit while serving the guns. And we couldn't fire back at the boche Maxims without hitting our own men. Slaughter it was. In the end we had to smash the sights of the remaining guns and take the breaches with us. No time to put a charge down the muzzle and blow it with the lanyard. It was a miracle that we even got one gun out. The poor Suffolks, well, all they could do was stay down in their little holes. The rest of my gunners are behind me somewhere or maybe ahead, but I'm damned if I know how many got off the hill. I don't really know where anyone is, for that matter. My brother is in 120 Battery who were on the left of the road and I think he got away but I'm not sure. I saw them firing point-blank at the enemy who were coming on in platoons. They were brave those boche, no doubt about it, and they were torn to shreds.'

Johnson listened to this account with mounting anger. He knew as a signals officer that there was no need to have guns up forward, not with modern signalling. We are going to have to clear out some of the old officers in this army, he thought, but kept it to himself. 'Old School' meant old fool more often than not. He passed Hodgson his flask and invited him to drink but the young officer refused.

Edwards thought of Gunner Major who they had helped into the Forward Hospital at Reumont earlier in the day. Reumont would be in German hands by now and that can only mean that all the wounded would be prisoners already. Poor buggers; shelled, wounded, shelled again, then captured.

'Could I ask you, Sir, was Gunner Major, a corporal, in your battery? Only, me and the gentleman here helped him down the hill earlier.'

'Yes, Private. On Number 2 gun in fact. He insisted on going back alone when he was wounded; said we couldn't spare any men to help him. When we came through Reumont just now we hadn't got time to stop at the hospital with the place under fire as it was. There was nothing anybody could do to save the men there. We thought of stopping and using our gun against the enemy from Reumont but we had no ammunition. The boche must be in Reumont by now.'

There was a lot that Lieutenant Hodgson didn't know and couldn't know. How the horse-team of Captain Reynolds towing the two rescued howitzers had halted two thousand yards back from the hill, stopped a passing ammunition wagon, found that it contained 4.5 inch HE, unlimbered and were back in action within minutes, shelling the Cambrai road. How Major Yate of the KOYLI had charged the enemy who were coming down the hill shoulder to shoulder, and how all nineteen of his platoon had charged with him, getting out of their trench as the enemy closed in. How Major Yate lay gravely wounded on the field of battle, tended by Sergeant Atkinson, also wounded, who had charged with the words 'God Give Us Strength', his gun-metal hot in his hands, his bayonet now glistening with blood. How their German foe, respecting their courage, had spared their lives. How Captain Bruce of the Argylls, a descendent of the Scottish patriot, had continued firing a rifle at the encroaching enemy until shot down in a storm of Mauser bullets. How up until the end, he and his friend Captain Maclean had vied with each other in shooting more boche than the other, shouting out the tally to all and sundry, Captain Maclean surviving thanks to a German officer who decided on a whim to spare his life. How a certain Lieutenant Sherwin of the KOSB, with a brother in the Dubliners, returning groggily from unconsciousness, and finding himself surrounded by Germans, had grabbed a Red Cross armband and attempted to put it on in the belief that it would secure his safe passage. The Germans spared his life also, recognising that he was not in a rational state of mind.

The five men struggled on: Buffy, Edwards, Mr. Moore, Lieutenant Hodgson and Captain Johnson. Edwards suggested that someone else should have a turn on the mare and that should be the wounded Johnson. For once Johnson did not demur. They swapped places, although Edwards said that there was room on the horse for two. Edwards cupped his hands to assist the captain into the saddle, Buffy holding the mare's bridle, Mr. Moore giving Johnson an extra hand.

They passed through Maretz, now well clear of the German shelling. Some of the inhabitants had clearly decided that the boche would not be far behind and many of them were loading up their carts for escape. Others were looking forlorn, resigned to their new fate, the older ones with memories of a previous generation of German-speaking invaders who had passed this way. Johnson thought how, in a mere matter of hours, the boche were going to have the pick of the most salubrious accommodation and perhaps even the co-operation of the more complaisant locals. He knew as a matter of fact that a large proportion of these people were not exactly pro-British. They would not understand the military necessity of the retirement; to them it might appear like running away. After all, had we not been historic enemies for as long as anyone could remember; only forming an alliance when threatened by a common enemy? The priest he could see across the road, hadn't all his education in the seminary been directed by Catholic certainty about the true faith and the abomination of the English Reformation? At least the Belgians had a proper hatred of the boche; Johnson had heard of a German soldier who had been killed by slow decapitation, the Belgian partisans using a band saw for the purpose. It had been common knowledge when they had been up at Mons. But for every German killed by Belgians, the Germans killed fifty Belgians. As far as Johnson was concerned, and his knowledge of Belgian history was as sketchy as most Englishmen's,

Belgium was an unfortunate country that just happened to have been placed in the wrong place, between France and Germany. But he had never actually met a Belgian, to talk to that is, until last night in the restaurant in Le Cateau, which is odd considering they are a Kingdom and our near neighbour. And now he was fighting for them and they were talked about as the plucky Belgians. Of course, an Englishman always has sympathy for the underdog; unlike the Germans who would as soon kick a man when he's down.

Buffy and Edwards were having a conversation about the war.

'I tell you, Buffy, the froggies cannot win this war without us for one reason. They have a rifle, called a label or something like that, you've seen them with the froggie troops in Le Catoo, awkward long buggers, the rifles I mean, anyway this rifle can only fire one round at a time. The bolt won't put the round up the spout from the magazine when the rifle gets hot so they feed in the rounds by hand, just like we did in South Africa. Where would we have been just now when fritz was coming at us up there if we had to put in the rounds like that? Up the fucking Khyber Pass, that's where. Then think of a million froggies doing it by hand if you get my meaning and they're stonkered.'

Mr. Moore was enjoying this discussion; it reminded him of Bardolph, Pistol and Nym in *Henry V*. He asked Buffy if he had any ideas about how to defeat the Germans. Buffy took his Woodbine out of his mouth.

'Yes, and it's a very simple one, Sir. The frog government is going to go down to Bordeaux. Good; then we won't have to defend Paris. Declare it an Open City, let the Germans march in; all the fritzes will go off to the Follies Bergeres and have a bon time with the girls. They will get drunk on the vin blanc and refuse to fight. La Guerre Finie.'

Just then a wagon clattered by, with men hanging on to boxes of supplies stencilled with the words 'APPLE AND PLUM JAM. WD.' 'Some blokes get all the plum jobs', said Edwards. He noticed that one of the men on the wagon was an RFC pilot, his goggles hanging loosely around his neck.

Henry Johnson wondered whether to make his contribution to the debate by enunciating his plan to do battle on the Somme, using its defensive qualities, buttressed by barbed-wire fortifications, to stop the boche. But he wondered if that would be enough; the British would be left holding on to a useless stretch of river, the boche would be left holding on to the north of France and no Guerre Finie. In any case, discussing military strategy with private soldiers was faintly absurd.

The five of them went on in the gathering gloom, Johnson having to use his heels to keep the poor mare from stopping to eat grass by the side of the road. Johnson heard a man say 'Thank God we've got a Navy!' and wasn't quite sure whether this was meant in jest, or indicated a cry of despair. But it became clearer when a chant went up of 'Hands across the sea!' repeated twice, followed by 'Hands across my bloody arse!' The spirit of the Army was not broken. Johnson knew then for an absolute certainty that the Army would recover from two defeats, that it would march on maybe for days or even to the gates of Paris, that the battalions now on the oceans in the care of the Navy would come back safely to the home islands, that in time new armies would be formed from the bank clerks and servant classes of the towns and cities of England and that the Kitchener volunteers now in training would bolster the vanguard now reeling from the onslaught of the Hun legions. But in truth there was not much banter, just the trudging of weary feet, as men put all their remaining strength into getting to a point where the officers would allow them to rest for a few hours before resuming the retreat which knew no end. And there was no singing now.

Edwards knew now that if he was going to survive this War he would go back to Le Cateau. Next year, or however long it was going to take to finish it, it would be his first destination. He could picture the street in his head. He would try out his French. At the moment he couldn't get beyond

'Allemands nix goot', which wasn't French anyway. He wondered what the French was for 'I'm back.' And then he thought 'San fairy ann'; they would go for a drink at the Café de Paris, Suzanne and Frank, after a bit more of the jig-a-jig. He might even take his socks off.

The group of five, by merely following the retreating mass of men and vehicles, came to the cross-roads in Estrées. A group of 5th Division staff officers stood by a car stopping every man who went past, the engine of the car kept running to keep its lights on. The group was addressed by a tired-looking red-tabbed major wearing a pith helmet.

'You can stop here for the night. Find your units in the morning. There is room for men and NCO's in a barn down there on the right. Lieutenant, you can go with your men and the gun down there and make yourself cosy,' pointing to what looked like an open green space. 'Officers over there in the café, where the owner has kindly fixed up some lovely feather beds, but I can't be sure about the linen sheets.'

They had little food but there was water. Edwards still had a small piece of bread in his tunic which he had scrounged back in Le Cateau, which he finished off. But all they wanted was sleep. The piebald mare went off with the artillery horses and the gunners to the small field, where at least there was grass with some moisture in it. Lieutenant Hodgson stayed with his men and the gun; on the night-march, survivors from the fighting up by the Cambrai road had been giving the gun grateful pats of thanks and Hodgson was not going to be parted from it now, not after all that they had been through; the only gun from the six of his battery that was salvaged from the disaster. Johnson and Mr. Moore went to the café and found a corner of the lounge to sleep in; all the bar tables and chairs were piled up on the pavement in front of the café, called optimistically the Café de la Paix. Buffy and Edwards went off to the barn which was packed with troops from at least five different 5th Division battalions, with the familiar smell of a hundred sweaty bodies, mingled with the smoke from Woodbine cigarettes. Even their wounds did not prevent

Edwards and Johnson from sleeping. Simon Brett and Puffing Billy and twelve hundred BEF men and officers lay dead on the field of battle.

Lieutenant-General Douglas Haig was tucked up in a farmhouse near Etreux twenty miles to the east, his stomach now recovered. He had enjoyed a meal of fricassé de lapin, cooked by the lady of the house. There had been a bottle of quite agreeable hock, shared between Captain Dawnay and the General. Dawnay had remarked that his wine merchant might have trouble getting hold of supplies of the '14 Neufchatel, which he knew the General was fond of. Haig, a taciturn man, had merely grunted. In fact he took little interest in wine. He would rather discuss the breeding of riding horses. He had no reason to change his orders for the morning, which were to continue the Retreat in the direction of Vadencourt/Guise. There was no communication possible with GHQ, a situation which suited him quite well. He was pleased with the progress his battalions had made on the roads south.

Mr. Moore, the William Howard Russell of the new century, had heard the voices of the fighting men and he had seen the blunders, the pity and the folly of war. He knew that many of the brigades were broken and scattered beyond recall. He had seen men fleeing for their lives. He had seen men blown to bits. But he knew that the spirit of the army was not broken.

Chapter 23

Lieutenant Penfold and Lieutenant Montgomery

When darkness came on the night of the 26th, Lieutenant Montgomery decided it would be best to let the men take turns in having a short sleep. He reasoned that it simply would not be humanly possible for men who had had no sleep for three days and nights to speak of, to set out on a dangerous night march unless they had the minimum of three hours sleep. His plan, such as it was, was to leave the farmhouse after midnight when there would still be five hours of darkness left. He planned to use that time to get as far as Selvigny, which he hoped to find in British hands, a distance of only five miles to the south-west on the map but, as he well knew, going across country in the dark was going to involve much more than five miles, but with his compass he was confident that he could do it. He planned to avoid all villages, especially Ligny and Clary. He was making the assumption that the enemy would occupy all the ground as far south as the line Bertry-Caullery, but would be billeted in the villages and would keep away from the country and isolated houses; after all, they were a hostile invading army and they must at all times be fearful of the local population. He was also making the assumption that there would be other wandering bands of British stragglers like his own abroad in the night. Under Field Regulations and the Manual of Military Law, both of which he was of course familiar with, he regarded the order to 'Stand and Fight' as no longer tenable, and it was his duty to lead his band of twenty-five men to a place of safety. He would rely on the humanity of the enemy, under the conventions of war, to provide medical treatment for his wounded, who would remain under the care of Captain Nolan in the farmhouse until such time as the enemy captured them. The Geneva Cross would of course be left flying from the roof of the farmhouse.

He must regard Stephen Penfold as an unreliable officer for the time being, although he must continue to treat him, at the same time, as a respected but subordinate colleague, which was going to present difficulties. He knew he could rely on Sergeant Fox. He decided to have a few words with Major Haddow and then get a couple of hours sleep himself. Rather worryingly, there was still shell-fire and outbursts of small-arms fire, seemingly in all directions. It was impossible to tell whether night actions were going on or whether it was just the result of nervous and jittery gunners and soldiers on both sides. The half-moon was going in and out of clouds. He said to himself again, as if for reassurance, 'darkness is our friend', but he wanted a little moon-light at least. He also said to himself, because his relationship with the Almighty was one whereby He was there to be drafted in when things looked a bit sticky, 'Oh God be with us and be my rod and my staff. Lord how numerous are my enemies; many are they that rise against me. But thou lord are about me as a shield.' The bible is not short of metaphors for those of a military frame of mind, but Monty was thinking more in terms of defence than smiting. He considered putting in a request to the Almighty for a bit more moon-light and a bit less cloud, these being sort of in His domain, but rejected it as being perhaps too close to presumption or even insubordination. It was to be a while yet before Monty would be able to address the Lord God of Hosts - His rank presumably above that of a Field Marshal - on anything like equal terms.

Monty outlined his plan to the Major, who was still reclining on his couch in his corner of the yard. He had his Webley by his side.

'I wish you luck and Godspeed, Monty. I will hold the fort here until you are safely away. My shoulder is a damn nuisance and it's not getting any better. The doc is nervous about gangrene but he's not telling me the truth. But don't forget what I said on the troopship.'

‘I’m sure it will be all right, Gerald, and that you will be in good hands.’

Monty found Penfold and Sergeant Fox together in the farmhouse, giving comfort and aid to the wounded. He addressed them both.

‘I should get a little sleep if I were you. I’m going to lie down for a couple of hours. You go first. Sarn’t, will you please get the men ready in the yard at midnight, with their kit ready. And I want all faces blackened; there must be some corks here somewhere. If not, use mud. Only essentials to be carried. I will say a few words before we set off. And I want each man to carry with him in his pack one carrot, not to be eaten until we get to our friends. I’m a simple soldier, Sergeant, and I believe in the stick and carrot. We have the carrots; you can think of me as the stick.’

Sergeant Fox didn’t know whether Mr. Montgomery was telling a joke. With Mr. Montgomery it was sometimes hard to tell but on the whole it was safer to assume that he was not.

‘Right you are Mr. Montgomery and carrots it is, Sir.’

Monty and Penfold synchronised their wrist-watches, both of which had luminous dials.

‘Oh, and one more thing, Sergeant. Do you speak any French, enough to converse a bit with a farmer?’

‘Our Minister used to take in French kids as a business, like, and I picked up a fair bit from them.’

‘Then you shall be our interpreter should the need arise.’

‘Do I get any extra pay, Mr. Montgomery?’

‘Only if you hit the bull’s eye, Sergeant.’

‘I will wake you just before midnight, Sir.’

Monty had a last word with Captain Nolan. Neither of them referred to the next few hours. There were things Monty wanted to say but couldn’t put into words and there were things he could say, but which shouldn’t be said. What he couldn’t leave unsaid was his concern over

Stephen Penfold,

'Doctor, Stephen is a bit touched, as the saying goes. He stares at the ground a lot. He seems to have lost his grip. Is there anything I should do?'

'Monty, I'm not one these new-fangled neurasthenic experts. I'm a simple flesh and bones man. I'm sure he'll be alright; don't ask too much of him, that's all I'd say. Most of medicine is common sense, but don't tell anyone I said that. The last forty-eight hours would test the nerves of a camel. People talk about 'taking courage', as if it was a commodity that you can help yourself to in a shop. Well, it isn't; it's a rare thing at the best of times and easily exhausted. And keep an eye on the youngsters; there's a bugler who's only sixteen years old although he won't admit to it.'

At midnight precisely the men were gathered in the yard. Half a dozen of the men had slight wounds, bandaged up by the orderlies, but Dr. Nolan was sure that their wounds would not slow them down. Monty spoke a few words in a matter-of-fact way. By the light of an oil light he told the men that he and Mr. Penfold would take them out to Selvigny, to the south-west, which he was confident would be in British hands. If it was found to be in the possession of the enemy they would push on to the south-west until they found friends. They would travel at night, aided by what moon light there was, and would hide up in the day if need be.

'Keep in close touch with the man in front of you. I will lead with our only electric torch, which I will use sparingly. Mr. Penfold will take the rear position. Sergeant Fox will be near me. Bayonets will not be fixed unless I give the order. We will eat our carrots when we find friends. Silence is essential. I don't want to hear mess-kit clattering around in your haversacks. Tie your spare socks around the kit. I trust your water-bottles are full so that they will not slosh around. Now we will go.'

At the word 'cawots' the men suppressed a laugh.

Unknown to the Warwickshire officers, two miles to the north-east of them, up by the Cambrai road and near the village of Audencourt, the 1st Gordon Highlanders and the 2nd Royal Scots, two 3rd Division battalions that had seen violent action at Mons, were still at 11.00 p.m. occupying their trenches, the trenches they had been fighting from all day. Like Lieutenant Montgomery, Lieutenant-Colonel Neish of the Gordons had received no order to withdraw and in the absence of such an order he had refused to move. At 11.15 p.m. he yielded to pressure from his fellow officers and gave the order. The Gordons, about five hundred of them, together with about fifty Royal Scots, moved south in the general direction of the Warwicks at Le Coquelet Farm, but slightly to the east of them. They moved in single file, each man keeping in touch with the man in front, making a line of about five hundred yards. Like the Warwicks, they were compelled to leave their wounded behind, although they made valiant, but largely unsuccessful, efforts to carry them.

South of Caudry, on the road to Montigny, the group became split up. A small group of Royal Scots, no more than a dozen, at the rear of the column, lost touch with their leaders and took a wrong turning, going off to the west. They had no compass and what moon there was went into a cloud. They went around in circles for a time, although they did not know it. They were becoming dispirited. The senior man was a corporal who would have liked to spend the rest of the night in a dry corner of a field; anything was preferable to going around in circles in the pitch dark. And the desire for sleep was almost overwhelming.

At their lowest ebb, when they had been walking around in the unfriendly darkness for three hours, they stumbled on to what seemed a deserted farmhouse. The corporal could discern a gate and a wall. He withdrew a few yards and had a whispered conversation with a Jock. They decided that they would go into this building, spend the rest of the night and the next day in it and try again to make an escape the following night. The word was passed down the line of men. There was no dissenting voice to this plan.

Inside the farmyard, lying on his couch, Major Gerald Haddow could hear whispering. To him it sounded like the whispering of guttural German. He put his left hand around the butt of his Mark V Webley pistol, its revolving magazine holding a .445 inch round in each of its six chambers. He put the safety catch to the 'off' position. His mind was absolutely clear; he would fire all six rounds at the Huns. They had to come through the gate, which was only ten yards from him. There was no other way in; he would sell his life dearly. He knew that his wound would kill him in any case. His only worry was that he was going to have to fire with his left hand and knowing the recoil that the Webley gave he doubted that he was going to be anywhere near as effective as he would have been had his right arm been serviceable.

The corporal found the latch to the gate and slowly opened it. The other Scotsmen were close behind him; one of them let out an oath, 'Ach, fookit', which again sounded like a German, at least to the ear of Major Haddow. At that moment he fired three .445 bullets in the direction of the gate, whose position in relation to his couch he was very familiar with. One of these three bullets found the chest of the unfortunate corporal, the other two going off into the night air in the general direction of Caudry. The Major did not get a chance to fire off any more rounds because the man behind the corporal fired his Lee Enfield at the gun flashes of the Webley, hitting the Major in the lower part of his chest. The Major was already dying when the rest of the farmhouse woke from their slumbers. The Royal Scots rushed over to the dying Major and in the darkness, and by the sound of his last words, realised the terrible truth of what had happened. The Major's last words sounded very much like 'Come on the 6th'. His greatest desire, to personally shoot a German officer, remained unfulfilled. The corporal, whose name was McNulty, would be dead within two hours. Captain Nolan could do nothing for him.

The group of twenty-five 1st Warwickshire men, led by Lieutenant Bernard Montgomery, had, by the time Major Haddow was killed, skirted the large village of Ligny to the east by finding what seemed in the dark to be animal tracks. The village was obviously in German hands, judging by the noises of celebration coming from the only bar in the village, which was brightly lit. The Germans did not seem to have posted any sentries, which was a great relief but not something that could be relied on. Montgomery flirted with the idea of creeping up on the estaminet, bursting in and killing the occupants, but instantly dismissed it. His job was to lead his group to safety and not indulge in heroics. A dog barked at them from the back garden of a small house, but no-one was paying it any attention. All his men were keeping a discipline of silence without having to be told to. They were evolving a method of staying in contact with each other by holding on to the rifle butt of the man in front. Their night-vision was as good as it was going to get. So far Montgomery had not used his electric torch more than once to find his way, although he was using it often to consult his map, doing so with the beam well shielded. His compass with the luminous dial was invaluable; he was keeping to a SW bearing. They had been walking for two hours or so when Montgomery called a halt beside the track. The men all gratefully sat down on the damp ground and Monty had a whispered conversation with Sergeant Fox.

'Sarn't, I calculate that we have covered half the distance to Selvigny. I don't propose to stop again until we reach the edge of it, when we will need to have a close look-see, although that's not exactly the right word. My map marks a forest the other side of it and we might have to make for it if the worst comes to the worst. But beyond that I can't tell you much because it is off the map. Pass the word down the line: 'No carrots yet.'

Sergeant Fox had an idea that the men might be making suggestions as to where Monty could put his carrots.

Monty's map showed that they would have to go round one more village, Caullery, before getting to Selvigny but he was now beginning to feel quite optimistic about their chances of getting there; he was beginning to feel less optimistic about the chances of Selvigny being in British hands. But what was reassuring was that the Germans were all seemingly concentrated in the villages and were avoiding the countryside altogether, as he had suspected they would. And they must all be as exhausted as his own men.

They went on. Just after by-passing Caullery, where they had the now-familiar dog barking, but which again was ignored by the local population, beyond a voice shouting 'Tais-toi', they saw a light in a small house, beside the track, perhaps a skilled artisan's dwelling. It was the first light they had seen and Monty brought the line to a halt. He wondered whether to get Penfold to come up for a discussion about what to do, but decided that on balance he was better off at the back. The inhabitants of the house must be able to tell them at least something of value about the Germans' whereabouts. Monty was sticking to his theory that there would be no Germans billeted this far from a village and he was making the assumption that all the locals would be friendly. In short, it seemed a fair bet that if they were to knock on the door they might learn something to their advantage. He decided to put Sergeant Fox's French language skills to the test.

'Sarnt, we'll knock on the door. Can you use your best French to find out whether any German soldiers have passed through here and if so in which direction?'

Monty knocked, not loudly. He put the beam of the electric torch on himself and the sergeant to identify themselves. A window was opened on the first floor and a male voice said, 'Qui est lá?' Fox said,

'Soldats Anglais.'

'Mon Dieu.'

'Les Allemands. Ils ont passė par ici?'

'Ils sont partout, les sale boches. Partout, je vous dit.' The window closed.

'Merci, Monsieur.'

That was as much information as they were going to get. It could mean the enemy had got as far as Selvigny or it could mean that they were stopped for the night short of the village. It seemed to Monty much the better course of action to steer clear of the place altogether. It was quite clear that the Frenchman couldn't know about enemy movements much beyond his house and it would be pointless to question him further. Monty decided to get Penfold to come up.

He told Penfold what the Frenchman had said. It was clear that Penfold was in no fit state to make decisions of any sort, but he seemed capable of going along with Monty's orders.

'I think we should now work on the assumption that the Germans are in Selvigny. We should by-pass the village and head into the forest to the south. It will be getting light in two hours. And I don't mind if one of your men strangles the next dog that we come across.'

They set off again. They gave Selvigny a wide berth, having to go through what seemed like a marsh, startling some ducks which cackled and flapped around but settled down again. Frogs gurgled and made their contented noises. They were getting used to the night noises of the country by now. Monty knew the men were mostly Birmingham men, to whom the noises of the trees and the soft groaning they made in the darkness would have held hidden fears, with the moon-light slanting through leafy branches in a gothic parody. There were more fences to negotiate here, coming upon them suddenly in the darkness, and causing the men to call out softly to each other 'Here's another one'. Fences meant livestock but where were the horses and cattle? They helped each other over obstacles and ditches. The men seemed to trust Monty more than Monty thought was justified. He was beginning to curse himself for the predicament they were in; he should have taken the whole rump of the battalion out at the same time as Watkins took his group back. It was foolish to stay on in the farmhouse, what use could they have ever been there beyond blindly following orders to 'stand and fight? He was going to get the whole group captured for no advantage. He was a fool and there were no two ways about it. The war was three days old and his part of this great enterprise was going to amount to practically nothing. And what with all these fences they can't be doing more than one mile an hour, and they would be in daylight before long, exposed in open country. If they came across a small patrol of boche they could perhaps fight their way out but any more than a platoon and they would have to surrender. He couldn't risk the lives of his men unnecessarily. And on top of all this fear and uncertainty was the terrible tiredness that was overcoming them all. For the first time, Bernard Montgomery was beginning to have doubts whether he could succeed in this mission to lead his men and an officer who was also dependent on him to a place of safety.

Monty was becoming intensely aware that twenty-five men carrying a variety of equipment, rifles, bayonets, packs, water bottles, entrenching tools slung from their belts, in fact the full panoply of the things they carried, made a lot of noise, even if they had stripped it down to a minimum. The men hated to be parted from their mess-tins. One man would make a lot of noise; twenty-five made a cacophony. Monty felt that they were advertising their presence to the night-world and he could do nothing about it.

Monty stopped to look at his compass. He planned to take the road south which ran alongside the forest. They would move off the road and walk parallel to it, but just inside the forest. They could take their bearings from the road which would be visible, but remain hidden in the trees. South of Selvigny they picked up the road and moved into the trees, which seemed to be a plantation of some sort. The half-moon gave a glimmer of light. Monty now felt they could make progress on this southerly route, which must at the very least be taking them further from the enemy and nearer Second Corps troops. They were now off the map.

Not much more than eight hours ago, there had been twenty thousand British troops on the left of the line only five or six miles to the north of where they were now; they can't have all vanished from the earth. How far back would they have gone? Six miles? Ten miles? And he was bemused at the total absence of French refugees. He thought that they must have all pushed on through the hours of darkness in their desperation to get away from the Teutonic invaders. But each step was taking his group of men nearer to safety.

Twigs, branches and all manner of vegetation lay underfoot and crunched and crackled as they blundered through the forest. Monty thought that they might as well walk along the road for all the difference it would make. At least on the road they would make faster progress.

Sergeant Fox grabbed his arm just as Monty was about to halt the column and move on to the road. Monty stopped. The whole line of twenty-five men stopped.

Monty listened. There was something moving ahead. There was no mistaking the fact that a creature, a deer, a human being or whatever it was, was moving through the forest. And coming closer, moving toward them from what seemed his left side, the eastern side, going toward the road. The sounds of movement grew louder; there was obviously more than one of whatever it was. There were sounds of metal on metal. Monty decided that it was human and that the human was British; why would Germans be hiding in a forest? Monty shouted out;

'1st Warwicks! 1st/6th!'

There was then the sound of twenty-five rifle-bolts putting twenty-five rounds into twenty-five chambers. An infantryman could work his bolt in darkness with his eyes blindfolded, something which they had had to do in training many times. An answer came out of the darkness;

'2nd Royal Scots!'

'Advance and be recognised! How else are you known?'

'Pontius Pilot's Bodyguard!'

There was then much hand-clasping and whispered greetings and general release of tension as the Warwicks and the wandering Royal Scots found each other. Monty switched on his electric torch. There were a dozen of the Scotsmen. One of them, a private, spoke in a lowland Scots accent;

'We are mighty glad to have found you. We lost touch with our column five miles back and have been trying to go south-west. We lost touch again with some of our men a while ago and we heard firing but know nothing. I am Private McCormack. Are we near Clary?'

Monty was quick to assert his authority. He said,

'You will come under my command. I am Lieutenant Montgomery. We are well met by moonlight. We are heading south; the daylight will come in a little over an hour and we will walk on the road until light when we will seek a place to hide for the hours of daylight. McCormack, I appoint you leader of your group; you will take your men to the middle of our line. There are twenty-five of us and Lieutenant Penfold is in command at the rear of the column. Sergeant Fox, you will stay with me at the head of the column. You will all keep in close touch with each other by holding on to the rifle of the man in front. We will halt again in one hour at my command.'

After one hour of marching on the road they were still a good way short of Elincourt, a small town of whose existence Monty could only guess at. They had had to move off swiftly into the trees when Monty heard the sound of approaching horses but it turned out to be nothing more than a lone farmer, carrying on in their time-honoured way. The Germans were strangely absent from the country.

They were rounding a bend in the road when they saw the lights. This time it was not a solitary farmhouse but a complex of buildings, a timber yard perhaps, with what looked like motor lorries parked by the side of the road. Motor lorries could only mean troops, and very definitely not British lorries. A horse whinnied; did that mean Uhlans? The whole column went to ground. Monty silently motioned to Sergeant Fox to get the men off the road to the right. He whispered to the Sergeant;

'This looks to me like a German outpost and my guess is that there will be at least a Company here; cavalry and infantry. It is too strong to attack. It will be getting light in half an hour. I think this must be the furthest that the Germans have come south. We must give this a wide berth and then we will be in open country. But if this is not an isolated post the boche will have other strongpoints nearby.' The last sentence came to him as an afterthought. He knew instinctively that to mount an attack now would be beyond what the men could reasonably do.

'Yes, Sir. I will pass the word along. Be ready to move.'

Monty was more worried about the situation than he had let on to the Sergeant. With only half an hour at most of darkness he was faced now with trying to get his band of stragglers through what might well be several interlocking enemy positions, with the dreaded Uhlans now deployed in their designated pursuit role. His tired brain thought of the alternative. He could abandon the attempt to break through for now and lay up for the day, observe the comings and goings of the enemy and make another attempt tonight. This was always part of his original plan in any case. The men still had some hard biscuit which would last them for twenty-four hours at least. They would share what food they had. The idea of finding a place to sleep now became irresistible. Everything would look better in daylight, as long as they could find a corner to hide in. His mind was made up: they would turn off the road to the west, and sleep. He gave the order to Sergeant Fox and the word was passed down the line. They would move to a temporary resting place.

As dawn broke on Thursday 27th August, Monty's stragglers found themselves exposed on the edge of a stubble-field but quickly moved off into a more sheltered place. There was a morning mist with the promise of sunshine. Those with bandaged wounds got their mates to attend to their dressings. McCormack saw the blackened face of Sergeant Fox for the first time in daylight and said, 'Ach, it's Jack Johnson'. Fox merely replied, 'Hairy Jocks, that's all we need; have you brought any haggis wi' you?'

Other bands of British stragglers unknown to each other were abroad in the alien corn; they came from many different regiments but all had one goal: to return to their friends. Some would head west for Boulogne, some north to Antwerp and some south to the Somme. Their chances of escape were dependent on many things: luck was to play its part and the Warwicks and the Royal Scots had the luck to have Lieutenant Bernard Montgomery, a future field marshal, as their officer. The platoon-sized force, which Monty now thought of as his Commando, fell into a welcome sleep, with two men ordered to stay on watch in rotation.

In the early morning light Sergeant Fox observed Lieutenant Penfold very thoroughly and deliberately brushing his teeth.

Chapter 24

Lieutenant-General Smith-Dorrien and Sir John French

Sir Horace Smith-Dorrien changed his mind; he did take his ADC Captain Tom Bowley with him in the car to Noyon. He was coming to rely on the young officer for his usefulness in getting things done as well as his sympathetic ear. It was no co-incidence that they were both Old Harrovians.

Corporal Clegg set the Rolls in motion at 10.30 p.m., Wednesday 26th August, and found the road out to the south-west without difficulty. The staff had given him a map, but it was a French one with the distances marked in kilometres which he found confusing. He was told that the Corps maps didn't cover this part of France and that he was 'off the maps', which was a bit alarming. 'So I'm going into unknown territory am I', he had asked the staff officer.

He had had time to study the map: a straight run down to a place called Ham; God knows how the froggies pronounced it. And then another straight run down to Noyon with only a few places of any size on the way. There might be a few refugees about at this time of night and perhaps some Service Corps wagons, but he didn't expect much traffic. A paved road the whole way. He had two spare tyres if they had a puncture and a full tank of petrol. Forty-five kilometres, which was only twenty-eight miles, shouldn't be more than a two hour drive. Should be a cake walk. One thing you could say about the frogs, they built straight roads, or should that be the Romans?

Corporal Clegg would have liked to get away a bit earlier but the General had wanted to go back to the station to reassure himself that the trains would be got out. Clegg knew that the General was a stickler for getting things done himself, and he would have a temper on him if things weren't done to his satisfaction. He could hear the General talking to Captain Bowley in the back of the Rolls.

'I couldn't find the mayor, perhaps he's done a bunk, not that he is any of my business but there is no Town Major yet and I don't trust these local French civilians. The mayor could easily throw a spanner in the works. I've told Forrestier-Walker to stiffen his backbone but even George has no authority over the civilian government; what we need is a reliable French liaison officer with authority over civilians. With GHQ going off it might look to the mayor that we're not prepared to fight. Sets a bad example. I'll mention it to Sir John but he won't like what I have to say. But since he didn't even leave a single staff officer in the town as far as I could see, he can hardly say he acted with discretion.'

The General ground his teeth as he thought of GHQ packing up even as the plates were cleared away from lunch. He knew how much Joffre and the French generals liked their lunch. These froggies make far too much fuss over their food. Why they can't just serve up a good lamb roast and be done with it I'll never know. Sir John has got time for lunch but no thought of the men coming back from battle.

'We will cross the Somme at Ham, Sir. You wanted me to remind you about the bridges.'

'Ay, yes. Tom, thank you. That's something I will need to talk to French about. If we are going to go on with the Retirement the other side of the Somme, we will need to get the Engineers ready with their charges. It's always a damn tricky business blowing bridges; too soon and our men get caught the wrong side. But better too soon than too late in my experience. If some of our cavalry get caught the wrong side they can always find another way across somewhere. But some of these bridges will be medieval masterpieces; we wouldn't like it if the French came over and blew the bridges at Henley and Marlow. And if it only inconveniences the enemy a small amount is it worth it? We may need to come back this way again one day, after all.' The General stroked his moustache for a while and then went on,

'But there still remains the possibility that we might fight on the Somme and use it as a moat. Of course that will depend on what Joffre has in mind. My guess is that we will go on down and defend the gates of Paris. There's nothing to galvanise an army so much as fighting for its capital, although of course Paris is not defensible in the way it was back in 1870.'

'I seem to remember John of Gaunt saying something about a stretch of water being used in the office of a moat, although that might have been the Channel. And the dungeon at Ham has had some famous inmates: Joan of Arc and Napoleon III, to name but two.'

'Everyone's always trying to give me a history lesson. Had enough of that at Harrow, as you should know, Tom. But if you want a history lesson from me, you can blame Napoleon III for this current War, with his disastrous loss of Alsace and Lorraine. We managed to stay out of that one. But forget about history for the moment and just remember the salient military truths: occupy the high ground and use the reverse slopes, you can't go far wrong if you can achieve that.'

Sir Horace dozed for a while as Corporal Clegg kept the big car at a steady fifteen miles per hour. The electric lamps pierced the night to a depth of twenty feet but Clegg was nervous of wagons and refugees. There were patches of fog and Clegg expected more when they came to the river valley. He was keeping the car on the crest of the road to avoid unseen objects or people on the verge. Clegg knew that he had to make a sharp left on the approach to Ham and then it was straight through to Noyon. He was through Ham by 11.30 p.m. and the General hadn't even woken up. Clegg noticed a great dump of rations at the cross-roads, proof that the Corps was expected down here before long. A Quartermaster private was guarding the dump, which consisted of big tins of bully, tins of jam and biscuits, jerry cans of water. A slight drizzle meant that Clegg stopped the car every now and again to wipe the windscreen with his shammy leather.

The car passed a convoy of heavy wagons pulled by draught horses; Captain Bowley could see that they were carrying a load of RFC stores and he knew from his brother, a pilot in No. 4 Squadron, that the squadrons were moving their bases every day. As the Rolls slowed down to pass the convoy he could hear the drivers talking in soft Somerset voices; they seemed to be talking to the big horses in conversational tones, the drivers and horses, harnesses jangling in that musical way, clearly enjoying an easy familiarity. 'Go you on, gently', he heard one of them say.

Horace woke up half an hour later. His mind was still very much on the battle and what he was going to say to his superior officer. He would be told no doubt that he had taken a great risk in offering battle; but when is a military campaign without risk? What real choice did I have anyway? And of course it is one of the most supremely difficult military operations to break off a battle and retreat. I had to do it at Mons and I have done it again today. Sir John was less than helpful on the night of Mons, keeping me waiting for five hours before the retreat order came through. Sending the order by motor, as if he had all the time in the world. That was a time to use the telephone or telegraph if ever there was one, and damn the eavesdroppers. And use the Gaelic, as I have urged. I'm going to have to watch my temper if French starts one of his puerile lectures on how to run a battle.

'And I'm going to push French if I can about Haig. It's possible that he had good reasons for absenting himself, but I'd like to know them. My bet is that French won't have any idea either but that he won't admit it. He'll make a great show of having a grand strategy but it will all be a bluff. Kitchener might have a strategy but he's in England and can't know the situation on the ground, which is changing all the time.

'Of course we won't get casualty returns which give a true picture for a little while. The first returns will be bad, I'm sure. They will show all the stragglers as casualties of course, in the same way as if they were lost for ever. French may make a play with that if he wants to make a point. But we know that the vast bulk of the three divisions made a good retirement and covered each other just like in the Manual. And there will be many men out there in the darkness even now trying to get back to their battalions and so on. But at least I'll be able to tell French that the bulk of the Corps is safely away.'

Captain Bowley stayed silent throughout this monologue, desperately trying to keep awake.

They were approaching Noyon now. Even at 12.30 p.m. there was a good deal of movement on the dark streets, which Corporal Clegg assumed was refugees, desperate to get as far away from the invaders as they could. The thought crossed his mind that amongst them there might be some who had been sent by the enemy to do harm. Who knows, there might be some among them who were armed and would be tempted to take a shot at a senior officer in a car with no escort. The corporal was nervous of getting caught in congested streets and took a turn off the main road when it looked by the gas lights that there was no clear passage through. He assumed that he would sooner or later find himself in the centre of town, where GHQ would be set up, presumably in the Town Hall.

But he rapidly became lost in a series of unlit back streets and it took ten minutes to regain the main road and find the Square. The General was beginning to get agitated. The Town Hall was clearly recognisable as GHQ by the Union Jack placed over the entrance; it stood by itself in the centre of the large square which was obviously a market place in peaceful times. There were cattle pens from a recent auction. There were two sentries on duty in front of the building. Corporal Clegg drew up to the steps; the sentries saluted and came to open the doors of the car. The

General entered the building, followed by the Captain. What followed was for Sir Horace Smith-Dorrien one of the most unpleasant interviews of his life although he hardly expected to be congratulated on a great feat of arms.

It began badly and got steadily worse. It was after all well past 12.30 p.m. and Sir John had been called from his bed. Sir Horace was kept pacing the vestibule for twenty minutes, slightly longer than he thought reasonable and long enough to be considered a deliberate insult, which is what it was. Sir Horace and Captain Bowley were both given a cup of tea by a corporal, who was told to attend to Corporal Clegg as well, who had stayed out by the Rolls. No officer had so far appeared. General Wilson was somewhere in the building but was not summoned, and nor was General Murray, which Horace thought odd. Horace was conscious of the fact that he was the second most senior soldier in the BEF and this delay was intolerable. Sir John French emerged in his uniform, but without a tunic, his shirt tieless and with his britches held up over his chubby middle by braces, in an attempt Horace thought to convey that he had had to be rushed but at the same time could not be bothered to dress properly. Horace was of course correctly dressed in his full uniform. The effect was to make Horace feel overdressed rather than at ease.

Sir John motioned for Horace to accompany him to the Mayor's office which served as the operations room. Maps were spread out on the desk, showing the whole of the front from Cambrai to the Sambre. Horace began,

'I was disappointed not to find you at St. Quentin, Field Marshal, but I understand the reasons for your move if not the fact that you left not even a skeleton staff behind.'

'The movements of GHQ are my affair, General.' The two men had known each other for more than twenty years and first names was their normal mode of address when they had to converse, but this time and place was not one for normal civilities.

'Indeed yes, Field Marshal', the title again phrased by Horace in an attempt to confer respect for the office, but at the same time giving it an inflexion to convey that Sir John was only its temporary occupant, the only worthy recipients of the rank being old Bobberty and Kitchener, Horace doubting whether this subtlety was appreciated by Sir John. 'I have left my chief of staff in St. Quentin to take charge of the arrangements for receiving the 5th and 3rd Division troops coming back from the front.'

'I am sure that the Divisional and Brigade staffs can cope adequately with all demands placed upon them.' The Field Marshal raised one of his eyebrows in an attempt, thought Horace, to undermine the role played by Second Corps staff. It was true that the Second Corps staff were a war-time creation and not used to working together and Sir John doubtless thought little of their work. Sir John left unsaid that General Plumer had been his prefered choice as field commander of Second Corps. He was certainly not going to give Sir Horace any allowance for being forced to fight two battles in his first week of arriving at the front. Horace, growing red in the face, wished he had Forrestier-Walker with him. He spoke up again:

'Let us not discuss staff matters. I will be returning to St. Quentin as soon as I am able,' implying that his presence here was interrupting important business. 'Forgive me if I tell you things with which you are already familiar. You know that my Corps was violently attacked soon after first light this morning on a front of twelve miles from Le Cateau to Esnes.' He pointed at the map spread out on the desk. 'The battalions were barely in their trenches when the artillery attacks began, and in some cases still on the march. It was simply not possible to turn our backs on the enemy and walk away. Allenby was firmly of the view that our best course was to fight and give the enemy a stopping blow; he was in any case out of touch with his Brigades. I am pleased to report that that is what my Corps has achieved; the enemy has come down as far as

Honnechy-Selvigny,' pointing at the map, 'but no further. I have just come back from there myself. The right flank - 14 Infantry Brigade and XV RFA - were the most seriously threatened and suffered greatly from the absence of Haig's 4th Guards Brigade. I fear that many of the guns have been lost. Haig's absence was a mystery to us all; but Sordet on my left flank stood his ground.'

During this short speech Sir John was growing increasingly agitated. It was his turn now:

'As you know General, Haig was forced to fight a night action at Landrecies last night and his troops were badly mauled and were in no fit state to move on Le Cateau. General Sordet responded to my wire, as I knew he would. But you say you are 'pleased'. Are you 'pleased' that you have lost most of 14 Brigade and most of XV RFA? You have fought a battle which should never have been fought and you have survived through luck rather than judgement. You have shattered the Corps. And I can't expect any help from Lanrezac, who has lost his nerve. I need hardly remind you that in the Navy captains go down with their ship when they bring about their own destruction.'

This was intolerable. Horace thought for a moment of his best means of counter-attack. Was the old fool implying that I, the Corps Commander, should have fallen on my sword like some Spartan? He decided on a counter-attack.

'You know as well as I do, that Field Regulations make the local commander the best judge of the situation. I had no choice but to offer battle and I need hardly remind you that it was on ground of your own choosing, using trenches dug under your orders. The men were magnificent and nothing you say can detract from that. They stood their ground all along the front and caught the enemy in the open and shot them down like rabbits.' He chose to ignore the ridiculous comment about captains going down with their ships. An appeal to the fighting quality of the men could always be guaranteed to get the old fool's eyes to mist over. 'And I can assure you, Field Marshal, that I stood by the road as the men came back and it was as if they were coming back from a race meeting.'

'Of course I know, General, that our men are the best soldiers in Europe and if I had a million of them I could throw the enemy out of France. But I have only the five infantry divisions, which has stripped the home islands bare. I cannot afford reckless generals who think they can fight their own battles, who choose to ignore my orders to retire. You have exceeded your authority, General, and you have no idea of the strategic situation. And furthermore, my information is that Allenby and Sordet saved your bacon. You can have nothing to be pleased about and your optimism is misplaced.'

Once again Smith-Dorrien chose to ignore some of French's remarks. If French thought that the cavalry had played the major role in the battle he was an even bigger fool than he took him for already. Just then General Sir Henry Wilson entered the room, full of apologies about not being called. The Sub-chief of Staff, at French's bidding, at once launched into a convoluted exposition of the new situation, now that Joffre was to create a *masse de manoeuvre* on the British left. He talked about Smith-Dorrien having narrowly avoided a Sedan, but that the Anglo-French Armies had yet to fight their Waterloo, but with *la main dans la main* they soon would, if necessary at the gates of Paris. He talked of the Schlieffen Plan, of which he claimed to have an intuitive knowledge, and of the wars between Hannibal and Scipio Africanus and of a battle at a place called Cannac. Smith-Dorrien thought Wilson was getting his wars all muddled up and was possibly a little mad. Wilson then talked of the stategical withdrawal into the interior of the country, as if these fancy words would add weight to his words. Horace found his voice, a peculiar grating sound, irritating. He felt suddenly very tired; he might be able to sleep with luck on the way back to St. Quentin. Wilson said something about optimism being a valuable commodity in a general but realism should govern military operations, as if he himself had a monopoly of it. He then went on about *réculer pour mieux sauter*, or some such phrase, as if saying it in French made it sound more impressive. He was contradicting himself now, at one moment preparing for a great counter-attack and the next preparing the whole BEF for a period of rest and recuperation, to abandon his beloved French allies. He finally said, as if it were a matter of fact, that BEF gunnery was much better than the enemy's, although where he got that from was a mystery. This was too much for Smith-Dorrien. If he stayed any longer he would get infected by the general malaise, pessimism, madness and wishful thinking that hung about the place. He decided on a Parthian shot.

'May I remind you, gentlemen, that wars cannot be won by retreats. But this Retreat is a fighting retreat and that is what we have just done, with your explicit approval, received by wire. My Corps is in no way 'shattered' and to call it so is....perverse. I will leave you now for St. Quentin, where I still have work to do. I assume that your orders for continuing the Retirement in the direction of Noyon still stand and that there will be no battle on the Somme.'

'You can be damn sure that I will not fight as long as that untrustworthy frog Lanrezac is on our left.'

The use of the word 'left' here indicated that French had his back to the German invader. But half the time Smith-Dorrien couldn't tell which way French was orientating himself, north or south. At one point he seemed to be saying that 14 Brigade on Suffolk Hill was on the left of the fighting line, which made no sense unless he regarded Haig's Corps as forming part of the line, which made even less sense. He wondered for a moment whether the old fool knew his left from his right. And you can't argue with a man whose mind is made up, who seems determined to believe only the worst...and yet at Mons he had been thinking of an advance across the canal, driving the enemy before us.

'One more thing, Field Marshal; will you be issuing an order regarding the setting of booby-traps? My Engineers have some ingenious people who can rig up some clever devices, I believe.'

'Booby-traps? What are you talking about? They are not the sort of thing that a gentleman should concern himself with. Your orders are to retire on the axis St. Quentin-Ham-Noyon. And this time you will follow them.'

Smith-Dorrien picked up his cap and stick and went back into the vestibule, where he found Clegg and Captain Bowley, both half-asleep on straight-backed chairs. 'Let us return to St. Quentin.' Sir John's last shot about booby-traps was another deliberate insult, but best ignored. The matter of the bridges remained unspoken; it would have to be left to the Corps and Division staff. He had completely forgotten to mention the German air-to-ground communication, which if Captain Johnson was right was a very worrying development. And he had forgotten to put in a request for a French Liaison Officer, one accredited with the proper authority. He swore to himself and ground his teeth.

Chapter 25

27th August: Lieutenant Montgomery and Lieutenant Penfold

The morning mist, which was restricting visibility to a hundred yards, cleared by 7.00 a.m. on the 27th and revealed that Monty's composite force of thirty-seven Warwickshires and Royal Scots, his Commando, was occupying a low-lying corner of a stubble-field some six hundred yards from the complex of farm buildings on the road south. The men had had two hours' sleep, Monty slightly less, having done fifty press-ups while the rest of the Commando was still asleep, watched by the two slightly bemused men on sentry-duty. They were now more or less alert, apart from Prescott who was complaining of stomach cramps.

It was obvious to Monty as he looked through his binoculars that the farm complex was being used as a temporary base for German cavalry and lorry-borne infantry, and that judging by the amount of movement already visible they were soon to become very active indeed. Already he could see Germans about, dressed in shirt-sleeves and braces, forage caps on their heads, lining up at what looked like a horse-drawn cooker. But as long as they weren't actually spotted there was no reason for the Germans to come out looking for him; their coffee and bread would keep them busy for a while yet. The thought of the fresh coffee made Monty's mouth water.

He decided it was time to involve Lieutenant Penfold in the command. Penfold came up to Monty, keeping his head well down. He looked tired but otherwise alert.

'Stephen, I would guess that our forces will have moved on down most of the way to St. Quentin by now; which means that the nearest troops, probably 4th Division men, will be at least five miles away and there will be boche-infested countryside between us and our salvation.' It was curious how words of a religious nature sprung to mind when Penfold was around. 'I have an idea which I want to put to you.'

'I'm all ears, Monty.'

'I don't think the whole Commando can get five miles through this open country without being detected and if it comes to a fight we would not want to take on more than a patrol of platoon-size. There simply aren't enough woods to enable us to travel undetected. And I'm worried about some of the young soldiers; they don't have the stamina for the long haul. I'm going to make an assumption: we will find a farm-house. They will have wagons. If we requisitioned a wagon we could put the weaker brethren on a wagon, hidden in a load of straw. They could have a sporting chance of getting through to St. Quentin. The rest of us would continue on foot and take the route across country to Estrées and down to the west of St. Quentin.' He knew that the St. Quentin Canal lay to the west and that it offered a sort of highway to the south. 'And then the drums will be calling us home.'

Monty could tell by the look of Penfold's face that he didn't like the idea of entrusting the fate of the young soldiers to such an uncertain venture. The men would be entirely at the mercy of a single boche road-block, who would be bound to be looking out for British stragglers trying to get back to their battalions. Both officers understood this, without having to spell it out, but Monty thought that if a wagon could be arranged the chance was worth taking. Monty signalled for Sergeant Fox to come to him.

Fox crawled up to Monty. Monty asked how the men were faring.

'Well, Sir, let's just say I don't think all of them can last another twenty-four hours on the run like this. It's the youngsters you see, Sir. Some of them are suffering with the feet. There's a couple that are lagging a good deal and need a bit of encouragement, like. A couple of the older Reservists have very bad feet as well, not to mention a couple of nasty flesh wounds. And there is one of them who has distinctly socialist tendencies, if you don't mind me saying, Sir. And then there is Private Prescott, who is a law unto himself.'

'We are going to go south-west and investigate the first likely farm we come across. We're going to get there by hook or by crook. My guess is that although the boche will control the roads, they won't yet have imposed martial law, so that the searching of individual wagons, if it occurs, will be very much a hit-or-miss affair. I propose to put the weakest of the men on a wagon, concealed with straw, for them to make a run for St. Quentin. That will give the rest of us a better chance of getting through. And pray to your Methodist God that the farmer is willing to help although I fear that patriotism will not be enough for a French farmer. But we have the power to requisition and with the help of a little money and a redeemable chit we might persuade him to part with a wagon and a couple of horses.'

'Yes, Sir, and with a little help from my rosary they might just make it.'

'The men hardly need reminding of the need for stealth. Get Sergeant McCormack to take up the rear with Lieutenant Penfold and you can walk with me.'

They set off in single file, Montgomery leading. The boche were still keeping to the roads and hadn't fanned out across country, so by hugging the hedges and going from one patch of cover to another Monty covered about half a mile in roughly the right direction in about an hour. For once there were no dogs about. He stopped the Commando for a rest in a poplar copse. There were some blackberries, which the men ate eagerly, although they were unripe. There were farm tracks which must lead to a farm-house. It was all reminiscent of Monty's days as a Boy Scout and all much easier in daylight.

They spotted a farm in another twenty minutes and settled down to observe any coming and goings. Monty got his binoculars onto it: a well-maintained set of buildings, brick and stone, solid shutters, no sagging in the roof, obviously a competent and industrious family, by no means simple peasant-farmers. It was a mere six hundred yards away, but that short distance would have to be crossed in the open, the farm being surrounded by pasture with the grass not close-cropped like it would be by sheep, but neither long enough to afford much possibility of concealment. There were no visible Germans of any sort around the farm, but the north-south road the other side of it was all too visible and horse-drawn traffic was passing every five minutes, mostly of a military nature and all too obviously German. There was no way round it. This had to be the farm where he was going to seek help. Monty called up Sergeant Fox.

'We'll do it on our bellies, Sarn't. I don't care if it takes two hours, it's the only way. See that wall? It is pretty obviously the farmyard wall and once we get into the yard we will be out of sight of the road and we'll be able to make ourselves known to the farmer.'

'Yes, Sir, I'll pass the word along.'

The men took off their haversacks and tied them to their rifles so as to make only one burden to carry. They soon got into a rhythm and within half an hour Monty was around the far side of the wall. A *grenier* stood the other side of a yard and there were two men in blue serge clothing stacking logs and, even better, there were two wagons standing in the yard, looking like hay-wagons in a Constable painting. There must be horses not far away thought Monty but he couldn't see any for the moment. So far he hadn't been spotted by the men in blue and he decided it would be best to stand up and show himself rather than startle them. He stood up and said, feeling rather foolish, 'Bon jour, messieurs, je suis officier Anglais.' The men merely stared at him but Monty advanced toward them, thinking that they might not know the difference between an English and a German uniform. He had used up most of his usable

French and gestured for Fox to join him. The two men walked toward the Frenchmen, the rest of the group saying behind the wall and out of sight of the road. Both men instinctively adopted postures showing that they came in peace, Fox lowering the point of his rifle. Monty was aware that he still had traces of blacking on his face. He noticed that the younger man had a withered arm, which would exempt him from the army. Both Monty and Fox gave a salute, intended as a courtesy, that they came as friendly soldiers.

Fox spoke the words he had been rehearsing: 'Nous voudrons aller á St. Quentin. Aidez-nous, si'l vous plait. Nous cherchons l'Armée Britanique. Nous avons de l'argent.'

The Frenchmen did not react immediately. The older of the two, who were probably father and son, said after a while,

'Vous êtes combien?'

'Trente-sept, monsieur'.

'Ah. Ça, alors, c'est pas simple. Les Allemands sont partout.'

Fox hadn't rehearsed any more sentences than the ones he had already used. He wanted to say something about concealment in wagons but couldn't find the word for 'hide' until he remembered playing hide and seek with the French boys at the Minister's house and the French boys calling it 'cache-cache'. So he said, simply,

'Cache-cache dans le wagon', remembering seeing 'wagons-lits' written on the side of railway coaches and remembering to pronounce the 'w' as 'v'.

The Frenchmen did not think that British soldiers wanted to play hide and seek in their wagons. They understood perfectly that a group of English soldiers wanted to be taken past suspicious boche soldiers all the way to St. Quentin, a journey of some thirty kilometres, hidden in a wagon. This needed some thinking about.

'Nous avons faim, monsieur.'

'Nous avons des legumes.'

'Tres bon, merci.'

Monty could understand that and thought that progress was being made. Like most Englishmen of his class he had a belief in the intrinsic goodness of men of the soil, but he was also imbued with a conviction that all Frenchmen were driven by a love of money, food and wine. His other conviction was that the streets of Paris were thronged with loose women, but that scarcely applied here in this rural corner of Picardy. Sergeant Fox had mentioned money so Monty started to fumble in his tunic pocket. At Shorncliffe, when he knew that he was going off to war, he had sewn five gold sovereigns into the pocket of his tunic. The Frenchmen watched him extract one of them. Monty was also fully prepared to write out a Requisition Order for a wagon, which the farmer could redeem for money at a later date, when the war was won.

Monty now felt sufficiently confident in the way things were going to motion for the rest of his group to come out from behind the wall. Lieutenant Penfold led them out into the yard; the father and son merely looked on as if this were a normal event, as if they saw thirty-odd men in British military uniforms with blackened faces every day of their lives, the men unshaven for two days and some of them clearly wounded. Again, to Monty, the Frenchmen's insouciance was a helpful sign; he motioned for Penfold to take the men into the barn, which was half-filled with corn. He said to Sergeant Fox, who was still standing by his side,

'I think we are getting somewhere. I will give them one gold sovereign for the food. Ask him if he will accept the coin. Can you negotiate some boiled potatoes and whatever else they have? And see what they think of going to St. Quentin with a wagon of straw hiding some of our men.'

Fox went off into a pow-wow with the two men, the father being the one who did the talking. Monty thought it was better to let Fox conduct the negotiation rather than have to have everything translated for him; he would join them when asked.

The discussion between Fox and the farmers went on for what was for Monty a frustratingly long time. It was obviously a question of the wagon that was the sticking point; the son went off to arrange for the boiled vegetables, leaving just the father and Fox in conversation. Fox came back to Monty to report.

'Sir, I think we have an understanding. We will need your approval of course, but the gist of it is that Monsieur Martin, the father, is willing to part with one wagon and two horses, on receipt of a Requisition Order from you. He will provide enough straw to conceal five men. He insists that one of your men drive the wagon, dressed in a smock over his uniform which he will give us. He wants no money for this but would accept money for food and would be grateful for the sovereign, which he will keep until peace comes when he will use it to buy champagne. He thinks that the wagon has a good chance of getting to St. Quentin, and wants them to set off right away. He knows a back-way which he will point out to us.'

'You have done well, Sarn't. Tell him that we are most grateful and I will write out the Order now. The offer of food is most welcome; I will give him the sovereign.'

The boiled vegetables were eaten hungrily by all the officers and men; even Prescott perked up a bit, although he was now complaining about a pain in his groin. While eating, the five volunteers for the wagon-ride were accepted by Penfold, one of the men agreeing to act as driver. He was told that in the event of being challenged by a German to act the simple farm-boy and say no more than 'Mon Dieu'. Three of the men chosen were youngsters, the other two being Reservists with particularly sore feet, both of them with shrapnel wounds that were painful and were going to need expert medical attention. Private Prescott was not among them. One of the youngsters was chosen as the driver, who also happened to have a slightly half-witted expression, but who claimed to know about horses, having worked briefly on a milk round. The driver was provided with a smock over his uniform.

The wagon was got ready, the four men got in beneath the piled straw, the horses harnessed up in the shafts and they set off at 10.30 a.m., with hopes of getting down to St. Quentin by 2.00 p.m. Monty wanted to leave with his group of twenty-five men and felt confident of making good progress now that the five weakest men were on their separate way.

Before leaving, Monty had another talk with M. Martin, aided by Sergeant Fox. They were advised that the route to take for St. Quentin that offered the most cover lay to the west; Martin was convinced, although Monty wasn't sure how he could know this, that the boche were pushing out only screens of cavalry to the west, their infantry moving south, the route to Paris. This made sense anyway. The Martins offered to act as look-outs to help the Commando in crossing the road, which was being used by German vehicles and troops. Monty gratefully accepted the offer, which he knew was dangerous for the two farmers.

Monty knew that the western route gave him a chance of bumping into French cavalry or Territorials, making south from Cambrai after their battle on the 26th and perhaps like themselves delayed for whatever reason on the march. Fortified by their food, and provided with cooked beets and turnips in their haversacks, Monty's Commando all solemnly shook hands with the Martins, both father and son, with expressions of goodwill on all sides. M. Martin clasped Monty's hand and said,

'Bonne chance, mon brave. Vive L'Entente. Vive La France et L'Angleterre. A la Victoire!'

Monty managed a salute and a 'Vive La France!' And for good measure a 'Vivat Rex!'

Penfold, shaking hands with the Martins, wanted to say something about his gratitude towards them and how in happier times he would come back and visit them. He lacked the words. He said nothing. He felt beset on all sides. He took up his position in the rear of the column. The men all made it safely across the road, with the assistance of the Martins.

Monty's plan now, on the advice of the Martins, who had furnished him with a sketch-map, was to head for Malincourt, avoid the town, then go due west across country to the St. Quentin Canal which he would follow down to St. Quentin itself, or to the west of it, although he knew that he would have to react to the lie of the land and whatever the fortunes of war threw up. He knew that this route would take at least six hours walking at a good pace, meaning that he could not hope to reach the latitude of St. Quentin before evening, the evening of the 27th, when he hoped to find the town still in British hands. In any case the further west he went the safer. He was clinging to a belief that the British and French would call a halt to the Retreat sooner rather than later and the Oise and the Somme, offering barriers for defence, would be the place for another defensive battle; that meant that French would call a halt somewhere on the line Ham-Peronne. He could not know that Sir John French's total refusal to co-operate with General Lanrezac to the east precluded such an eventuality, and that Lanrezac would fight his own battle on the 29th. He could not know that Sir John French had now lost all belief in his Second Corps as a fighting force and that he regarded its commander as a liability. Being only a 2nd Lieutenant and out of touch with the rest of the Division for the last twenty-four hours, he could not know that Sir John could not even co-ordinate the two halves of his own Army, let alone manage co-operation with his despised allies. He was quite prepared to spend another day lying low in a safe place before making another night-march. His self-confidence had returned.

If pressed he would have to admit that his best hope lay in coming across errant French cavalry, who might be persuaded into providing an escort. And that would depend on not stumbling on German cavalry who would provide an escort of a different kind. His men still carried their carrots in their packs. Lieutenant Penfold could be heard softly singing to himself, '*Wher'ere I walk...*' Lieutenant Montgomery put in a request to the Almighty for the continued presence of his guardian angel; in the circumstances he thought it was a pretty reasonable thing to ask for.

Chapter 26

The Day After the Battle; The Retreat Continues

Throughout the late evening and night of the 26th August, men and officers of 3rd and 5th Divisions had been coming in to St. Quentin, which lies on a bend on the Somme twenty-five miles south-west of Le Cateau. They came in carts and wagons, on limbers and in ambulances, they came on horse-back, but they came mostly on foot, all exhausted to the limits of human endurance. Many were wounded, like Private Edwards, who spent the night in a barn near Estrées, along with Buffy, while Mr. Moore and the wounded Captain Johnson slept fitfully on a pile of great-coats in the café near the cross-roads. Their wounds were dressed by Buffy and the indefatigable Mr. Moore, who added iodine to the dressing. The exodus from the battle continued the next morning, 'exodus' being a not inappropriate word for such a movement of thirty thousand men and animals on the Roman road, all fleeing from a force of three hundred thousand invaders. The Roman road was a 'Via Dolorosa', a road of sorrow and pity. It was a multitude of biblical dimensions. The exodus down the road continued throughout the morning and afternoon of the 27th. It was but one small part of a retreat that was being conducted by a million men in six Entente armies throughout northern France, a story of failure, misery and unutterable tiredness that would become known as the Battles of the Frontiers. But on the Via Dolorosa, each man was aware only of the small patch of road in front of him.

Lieutenant-General Smith-Dorrien may have likened the multitude to a crowd leaving a race-meeting, but it was not a comparison that would have been recognised by the men themselves. Nor would they have appreciated Brigadier Forrestier-Walker's comparison of the end of a day's battle with the end of a day's hunting. But 'exodus' implies deliverance, and a deliverance it was from the threat of destruction by the four German army corps commanded by Generaloberst Alexander von Kluck. By the evening of the 26th, he had no fresh pursuit troops to put into the field to attack the rear-guards so hastily improvised by the British. Those troops that did attack the Royal Welch Fusiliers and other rearguard battalions on the evening of the 26th did not come on with the determination of fresh troops. Von Kluck believed at first in any case that he had destroyed the bulk of the 'contemptible' BEF and that the way was now clear for his descent on Paris. He believed that all he had to do was keep up the forward momentum. But for the second time in three days Second Corps of the BEF, on the 26th, had survived its attempted annihilation and had inflicted losses on their enemy greater than their own, which were already nearly fourteen thousand men and officers, their casualties since lining the banks of the Mons Canal on the 22nd.

At 6.00 a.m. on the 27th August, Smith-Dorrien was woken as usual by Captain Bowley. The General had been sleeping on his campaign bed in an annexe of the Mairie, the same folding bed that he had used in the Transvaal. For a man who still had had no more than four hours sleep a night for the past four nights, the General was remarkably alert. He said at once to Bowley;

'I will spend no more than six hours here in St. Quentin; it is not the Corps Commander's job to organize the convoys. In any case St. Quentin is only a place to pass through. We will set up our next HQ at Ham, on the Somme. But I have a feeling that we shall not be staying long there.'

'I was not planning to get any change-of-address cards printed, Sir.'

Somewhat earlier in the morning, eight miles to the north of St Quentin, Private Edwards had woken with severe pain in his side from the bullet wound he had received the previous day. The bullet had passed through, leaving torn flesh, muscle and tissue, but no vital damage to any organ. It was clean, having been swabbed and given several treatments with iodine, so that the bandage was now as yellow as a banana. Captain Johnson was similarly bandaged and swabbed, weak from loss of blood but able to mount the mare and continue south, and in full expectation of finding his 3rd Worcesters somewhere along the road, or at least news of them. Johnson and Mr. Moore, with the piebald mare, stuck together in the throng of soldiery, as did Edwards and Buffy, who managed to scrounge a good chunk of biscuit and bully for both of them from a dump of supplies left at the crossroads by GHQ Quartermasters. Both wounded men had managed to start the day off with full canteens of water, to fight off their great enemy, thirst.

Major Tom Bridges of the 4th Dragoons had spent the night of the 26/27th in a bivouac with his Commando north of St. Quentin, near Walincourt, was up at dawn and by 8.00 a.m. on the 27th was on the high ground north of St. Quentin. Like all Cavalry officers and troopers, Major Bridges carried a groundsheet behind his saddle.

To anticipate events for a moment, Lieutenant Montgomery and Lieutenant Penfold, with their twenty-five man Commando, spent the night of the 27th/28th near the St. Quentin Canal, about eight miles north of the town and about three miles west of the Martins' farm. It had taken the rest of the 27th to travel the three miles from the farm to the canal, moving gingerly from cover to cover, by which time the bulk of the BEF was well south of them; Monty's plan of getting down to the latitude of St. Quentin by the evening of the 27th now abandoned. On the morning of the 28th they had a hearty breakfast of the boiled vegetables from the Martins' farm and by 6.00 a.m. were moving south down the canal in the direction of St. Quentin, now left to the mercy of the enemy by the

British, although Monty could not of course know this. Although Monty would never admit it, he was greatly enjoying the escapade, which was coming to resemble more and more a Boy Scout exercise, with an added whiff of danger. He had regained his self-confidence, never in his case in short supply. So far only distant patrols of enemy cavalry had been spotted, which Monty had easily avoided. Later in the day, the 28th, they came across two wandering German quartermaster soldiers, probably deserters, who were filling their water bottles from the canal. Two Royal Scots soldiers, under orders from Sergeant Fox, fixed bayonets and killed both of them, although they had shown clear signs of wanting to surrender. ('Camerad?' He's no my camerad.') It was tacitly agreed that the killing of the two Germans would not be mentioned outside their group, or at least not the precise circumstances. Their bodies were left in a thicket of reeds. But crossing the next five miles would need all Monty's stealth and cunning to get through the German-occupied countryside.

The Gordon Highlanders, together with about twenty Royal Scots - like Monty's Commando, adrift in the night looking for a way through to friendly territory - had stumbled into a German stronghold in Clary in the early hours of the 27th and after a brief firefight had laid down their arms. Five hundred of them went into captivity, their kilts providing the Germans with endless amusement. Two Gordon officers had crept up on a group of Germans carousing in a bar in Clary and had shot the lot of them with their Webleys, which the Germans accepted as a legitimate act of war.

Lieutenant-General Smith-Dorrien again made the St. Quentin railway station his first port of call on the morning of the 27th. This time he found a satisfactory Quartermaster major who seemed to have a firm grip on things, although the French railway employees would still not take orders direct from an English officer. A train left, loaded with three hundred wounded in the care of the RAMC, leaving one short train in the station at 10.00 a.m. This short train, three carriages with Red Cross markings, was intended for RAMC use. A depleted company of the Argyll and Sutherland Highlanders, with Captain Hyslop and Lieutenant Stewart at their head, arrived at the station at 10.30 a.m., almost drunk with fatigue. They had fought on the hill with the Suffolks and the Manchesters and had walked back to St. Quentin, with a sleep in the open for four hours. When the men saw the train seemingly ready to leave, they sat down in the second class carriage seats. There was no joking, no banter; the men simply went to sleep, the sleep of men who had gone beyond reason. The Quartermaster major was disregarded. The Argyll officers realised that it was going to be hard to shift the men and ordered the train driver to get going for Noyon, which was, after all, where the Battalion was under orders to proceed to; when he showed some reluctance to proceed without further orders, Captain Hyslop showed him the business end of his Webley, which was sufficient authority. The train was requisitioned. It steamed out for Noyon with its exhausted human cargo.

Sir Horace Smith-Dorrien missed the Argylls' requisitioning of the train because by that time he gone to find the mayor, who was holed up in a corner of the Mairie. He was preparing to go down to the Mairie's cellar at the first fall of German shells. Captain Bowley had tracked him down and recognised at once that the mayor was in a funk. Who could blame him? He was convinced, and not without reason, that the Germans would shell the town with or without the presence of the British, but purely as part of their normal frightfulness. They would then take him hostage, along with the rest of the town burghers, all of whom would be held accountable for the behaviour of the citizens of St.Quentin. He did not regard being put up against a wall and shot as part of his mayoral duties. He took the perhaps inconsistent view that the Germans, although proponents of beastliness as official policy, would respect the wishes of a civil Mayor and refrain from shelling his town and furthermore refrain from raping and otherwise abusing its fair citizens once they were presented with the Mayoral Document. He also took the view that the British should pass through his town as quickly as possible while he got on with the business of surrendering to the first German officer who should appear over the horizon. To this end he had had his staff prepare a surrender document, on which the ink was still wet and that he could show the English General if he wished to see it. This document declared the city of St. Quentin to be an Open City, cited various legal and historic precedents, and generally raised the ancient city to the cultural, civic and architectural importance of Reims; it was not and never had been a garrison town or a town of any military importance whatsoever beyond being a communications hub on the river Somme. Its destruction would serve no military purpose. The Mayor would very much like to see the signature of a senior British officer appended to the document.

All this the inestimable Captain Bowley translated for his chief, or at least the gist of it, his French being just good enough for the purpose. But it was not hard to grasp what the Mayor was up to.

The General did not want anything to do with such a document. There had been a good deal of teeth-grinding while all this was being made clear to him and he quickly decided that he wished to hear no more of this nonsense.

'Tell the Mayor that the Germans do not respect pieces of paper, which is one reason why they invaded Belgium in the first place.' He did not add, because he could not know it, that the German 2nd Army was about to shell mercilessly the city of Reims, especially targeting its cathedral, a fact that would hardly reassure the Mayor. 'But you can tell the Mayor that the refugees are greatly hampering my Corps and restricting its ability to manoeuvre.' At this the Mayor merely shrugged his shoulders.

And with that, the General and Captain Bowley went out into the square and found Corporal Clegg and the Rolls-Royce, the pennant of the Sherwood Foresters, the General's old Regiment, hanging limply on its pole on the front mud-guard.

'I suppose the lily-livered fool can't do much harm with his ridiculous piece of paper; we'll all be gone by the time he makes contact with the enemy.'

'Yes, Sir.'

Privately Tom Bowley thought that the Mayor should be locked up in his funk-hole until our troops had passed through, but let it rest.

'We can do nothing useful here now. Lanrezac may fight on the Oise and the Sambre canal but that will be Haig's concern. I would guess that French means what he says and that he will have nothing to do with it if it happens, and Haig will stand idly by like he did yesterday. It's a case of 'do-as-you-would-be-done-by'; Lanrezac left our right in the air at Mons and now will get no help from French. I think K of K should put on his Field Marshal's uniform and come over and take charge at GHQ, then we might all be able to pull together. As it is, French is sulking like a school-girl. Come, we must press on to Ham.'

Smith-Dorrien climbed into the back of the open Rolls-Royce, Bowley by his side. He had every confidence in Colonel Rycroft AQMG of his own staff, who would stay behind at St. Quentin and liaise with General Robertson's staff at GHQ; the telephone lines were operating between St. Quentin and GHQ at Noyon and the town hall at Ham, although Haig was still out of touch as far as Smith-Dorrien was concerned. Smith-Dorrien had ordered Rycroft to ensure that Engineers would be the last to leave St. Quentin, keeping the telephone-line open until the last BEF men had quit the town, before cutting the lines. The Second Corps division generals, Hamilton, Fergusson, Snow and Allenby were reachable, but only with difficulty, all of them being on the move; mounted officers, motor cars, telephone, telegraph, despatch riders on motor-cycles, even the RFC, were all used at various times. It was by any standards a situation that was taxing more than just the overstretched signals engineers. The Duke of Westminster was motoring back and forth between various headquarters like a shuttlecock, his sporting rifle fixed to the bonnet of the car, his chauffeur fixing three inner-tube punctures a day. The Duke was having the time of his life.

Smith-Dorrien was still fuming from his nocturnal encounter with Sir John French. The nerve of the man, implying that I was in breach of my orders yesterday. The trouble with French, when he was in one of his pessimistic moods, was that nothing a man could say would shift him from his black humour. To the pessimist any bearer of good news is anathema. Of course things were bleak at the moment, with the Corps, and now 4th Division as well, reeling back from two battles with a vastly superior force bent on its destruction. But what the stubborn fool doesn't recognise is that the men, standing firm in their companies, with the gunners of the RHA and the RFA with them, have shot the enemy down time and again, and time and again have got away in the face of the enemy. All French can do is wring his hands and deride their valour and treat me like a man who doesn't know his business. It's damnable. And of course men are straggling back, they can't be present at roll-calls, it's what you would expect in a retreat. But I've seen the men on the roads and they are not a beaten army. Exhausted yes, beaten, not. And the enemy are extending their lines of communication by the hour.

Smith-Dorrien remembered now seeing a document marked 'Top Secret' in the War Office a couple of years ago which predicted 75% casualties in a British Expeditionary Force in the opening months of a European campaign against the German Armies. That sort of document couldn't be openly discussed but it was a thorough piece of work by some staff colonel, which had looked at the Russo-Japanese War and the effect of modern weapons on conscript armies and made for some alarming reading. Of course the main difference between the British and the Continental armies was, and remains, the fact that the British army was an all-professional force, trained to the highest standard, each man serving at least seven years in the colours, whereas continental conscripts had two or at the most three years of training. But what were the British to do when that Army was gone? A citizen Army trained by Kitchener was the only answer, now that K of K had rejected the wholesale deployment of the Territorials on the Western Front. To give French credit, he understood the need to keep our only army in the field, just as Wellington had in the Peninsula; but an army has to fight sooner or later. What would old Roberts do at a time like this, that's the question. Like Kitchener, Smith-Dorrien held a poor view of the fighting qualities of the Territorial Force battalions, who had been raised purely for home defence.

The Rolls, with Corporal Clegg at the wheel, left St. Quentin at noon by the old south-west gate, skirted the Somme, and was soon reduced to walking pace as the river of men and wagons filled up the pavé. Poplars lined the road as the mean houses gave way to open fields. Men of many different regiments shuffled along, still dog-tired, their NCO's chivvying them, the officers for the most part riding, but Bowley could see numerous officers walking alongside the men, having given up their horses for a wounded man. The wagons carried a multitude of supplies, with men often holding on to the ropes securing the boxed ammunition. Bowley stopped the Rolls to put up the roof, thinking it preferable that the men should not see their commander in person, thus avoiding any necessity for saluting; a man is not obliged to salute a car, even with the penant flying, although many did in fact do so. Smith-Dorrien dozed; Bowley didn't have that luxury. Order and discipline hadn't broken down, but men and officers were being thrown together in ways that threw the established order, the military codes of conduct - enforced by law evolved over centuries - into temporary abeyance. One Highland sergeant was seen wearing a new tartan kilt, wrapped around his substantial middle and secured with a safety pin; it was in fact a travel rug whose previous owner had been a Rifle Brigade officer, the rug jettisoned by the road to lighten the load of the transport. The officer's mother, at home in her manor house near Twyford, would no doubt have said 'I'm sure it's gone to a good home'. The RB officer, like the rest of his battalion, was somewhere between Estrées and Bellenglise, still to the north of St. Quentin and the battalion was still split up into three separate groups, reeling from the onslaught at the Quarry near Fontaine, where their second-in-command Major Rickman had been killed. It would be three days and nights before the battalion was to be re-united.

Two miles to the north-east of St. Quentin, not far from the source of the river Somme, a name that as yet held no particular resonance with the British, marched Frank Edwards and his mate Buffy, of the 2nd Royal Welch Fusiliers. In fact their progress was more in the nature of a series of staggering and faltering steps, but progress it was. Frank Edwards had now grown accustomed to his wound, which needed to be kept clean, the bandage checked, but as long as he didn't knock it or strain it he could carry on, provided his feet didn't give up on him. His canteen was now empty. A drink of water would be a fine thing; even in the parched land around Quetta there was usually a pahni-wallah to be found, which is more than you can say for these froggies who are all over you one minute and doing a vanishing trick the next. All this bully is giving me a terrible thirst. If he had given any thought to his comrades in the 1st Battalion, it would not have improved his equanimity; they were still sunning themselves in Malta. They passed an abandoned lorry, a brick transport from Kidderminster, which prompted thoughts of the squire and the manor house near Shrewsbury where Frank's mother was still in service.

They came to a cross-roads at Remaucourt, where a booted and spurred staff major from 3rd Division told them that the rest of their Battalion had passed through only half an hour ago and if they got a move on they would find them at St. Quentin. He then informed Edwards that his puttees were a mess and one was missing altogether and he should smarten himself up or he would be a disgrace to his Regiment. He used his swagger stick to indicate his scorn for the missing puttee.

Edwards could only just put one foot in front of another. He and Buffy were clinging on to each other like shipwrecked sailors. His puttee had been used as a makeshift bandage. His uniform was splattered with his own blood and the blood of the wounded gunner. Buffy was carrying both rifles, one in each hand, gripped around the trigger-guard. They both had their haversacks on their backs, having been parted from their big packs since the night of the 25th, at Le Cateau. God knows when they would see them again.

But he managed a painful if half-hearted salute and even managed a verse of *If You Were The Only Girl In The World* as he tramped on. He thought again of his teacher, as he now liked to think of her, an educated person, able to speak two languages. Buffy's supply of Woodbines was still holding out, Frank being that rare thing in the Army, a non-smoker.

'Get a move on? What sort of joker is that? George Robey? I wouldn't want to be his batman; he would want china tea and scones as if he was at the Ritz. It's not my fault if I look like the wild man of Borneo.'

Just behind them and alternately riding the piebald mare were the dejected figures of Captain Henry Johnson of the Worcester Regiment and Mr. Arthur Moore of *The Times*, his linen suit rumpled and torn beyond repair, his Panama hat stained with sweat and mud. Johnson's uniform was blood-stained from his wounds and caked with grime; he had been wearing it constantly for five days and nights, his three pips almost obscured by dirt. Mud from the foul ditch outside Caudry still clung to his boots and his britches, which were held together by a safety pin from where the RAMC orderlies had cut through the cloth to get at his wounds. He smelt abominably, even to himself. He was unshaven. The mare was visibly weakening and beginning to falter, her head drooping. They too were confronted by the staff major who was much more considerate, even solicitous after their welfare, more so when Johnson mentioned his friend Harry Altham, also of the 3rd Division staff. But the major knew nothing of the whereabouts of the 3rd Worcesters ('Have seen neither hair or hide of 'em'). He did, however, offer them a drink of water and told them that the source of the Somme was just down the road and would provide the horse with ample to drink. 'You might even manage a wash and brush-up' he added helpfully. The temperature was rising again; it was going to be a long and thirsty day. The two men spoke little as they went along, Johnson for the moment riding and Mr. Moore, being unwounded, walking. Johnson said,

'Do you notice anything unusual, Arthur?'

'Not particularly, Henry. You presumably don't mean the damnable heat, the presence of so much suffering, the fact that this fine Army is enduring its fourth day of ignominy, or that that staff officer was unnaturally and almost offensively well-groomed. Shakespeare would have recognised that chap, 'fresh as a bridegroom and perfumed like a milliner.'

'No; have you noticed the silence, the absence of gun-fire? This is the first time since the 22nd that I haven't been within earshot of the guns and it's a strange feeling. Today is the 27th isn't it? I seem to have lost all sense of time.'

Unknown to Captain Johnson, at that moment fifteen miles to the east the Connaught Rangers were fighting to the last man, pinned down in an orchard near Etreux and forming square like their ancestors at Waterloo. But they were of course out of earshot of the two gentlemen. Nearer the two gentlemen, the 1st Hampshires had been attacked that morning by German field guns and infantry, their Colonel wounded and captured. But everywhere German infantry were discovering a new respect for the musketry of British riflemen. They would not attack without the support of guns. And their cavalry were equally wary.

Johnson and Moore then came upon a couple of men, a corporal and a private, both 13 Brigade Signals men. They had a Maltese Cart with two large pigeon baskets strapped on; they were lying down by the road and were clearly in want of orders. They recognised Johnson's shoulder flashes marking him out as a Signals Officer and they stood up and came to attention. The corporal addressed the Captain;

'Sir, the poor little bleeders are all dead, if you'll pardon me, Sir, but we've carted the little chaps from Solesmes to Le Cateau to Reumont and down to here, and they never did get a chance to serve their country, seeing as how they hexpired before we got a chance to release them. What should we do Sir? The rest of our unit and our officer are nowhere to be found, Sir.'

'Throw the pigeons into the field and carry on down to St. Quentin where you will get word of your Brigade, I'm sure. Carry on, corporal.'

Johnson rode on, using the soft ground beside the road, Mr. Moore walking alongside, the mare not even flinching when they passed a dead horse, flies buzzing around its nostrils and eyes. Johnson assumed the horse had died of exhaustion, there being no sign of injury. He took off his cap to wipe the sweat from his brow and took a look around.

'Here's something reassuring which I can see from here; there's a troop of our cavalry on that hill to the east, or at least I presume it's ours. And it looks like they've got infantry with them, French by the look of them.' He pointed across the Somme to a low hill, on the top of which riders could be seen against the sky, contrary to the normal practice when the enemy were expected. Every soldier knows to avoid the sky-line.

It was in fact the 4th Dragoon Guards, one hundred and fifty of them, led again now by Major Tom Bridges, assisted by the intrepid Lieutenant Hornby, the officer who had killed the first German of the war by running him through with his sabre. They were under orders from Brigadier de Lisle to hold the high ground to the north-east of St. Quentin. In this task they were to enlist the help of a battalion of French Territorials, red-trousered infantry led by a Lieutenant-Colonel named de Sorbier, a man of well over fifty years and in whom Bridges had very little faith. Bridges had met him that morning at 10.00 a.m. and after the usual pleasantries and courtesies the conversation had gone roughly as follows:

'Mon colonel, General de Lisle has ordered me to hold this ground until six o'clock this evening when all the Le Cateau troops are expected to have passed through. As you know, cavalry do not hold ground in the same way as infantry. He has asked me to request that you will hold this hill until 4.00 p.m., when you will fall back through the town. I know that you have only one machine-gun ('mitrailleuse') but your men should dig in and face north and east.'

'Oui, mon commandant, bien sur. On fera le devoir.'

Bridges noted that they appeared to be very under strength, two companies at most, and they had no rations that he could see. If he knew anything about these sorts of units they would probably send out foraging parties to the nearby farms. He could anyway do no more, although he would come back later in the day and check up on them. He fully expected them to run at the first whiff of shrapnel. Their digging tools did not look up to the job, although they were no more inadequate than the British issue. Infantry had to be made to dig in, a task more uncongenial when they know that they will vacate the position in a matter of hours. The Frenchmen had put down their huge packs and Bridges expected them to use them as cover and a firing platform, which they would probably consider as obviating the need to dig in. From de Sorbier's position a line of bedraggled British infantry and vehicles could be seen snaking down the Bohain road. Poor bloody infantry; it was to avoid marching that Bridges had joined the cavalry. He knew the infantry were at the limits of their endurance.

While Bridges was talking to de Sorbier he was brought word by Lieutenant Hornby that a mysterious car had appeared on the high ground to the north-east, about three quarters of a mile away.

'Why mysterious?'

'Well, Sir, it is a Benz, or appears so through the glasses, but the occupants, and there are four of them, are all wearing what looks like black bonnets trimmed with lace. And they are using a pair of binoculars.'

'So it's a German staff car filled with widows; mysterious indeed. Send a patrol out to investigate and if necessary apprehend them.'

'I'll go myself with a sergeant and five men.'

Bridges watched the seven horsemen canter across the stubble, jump over a stream and fan out into a line abreast as they went up the slope. Hornby had his revolver in his right hand. When they were within a couple of hundred yards of the car it reversed, did a smart turn-about and disappeared over the horizon in a blue cloud of exhaust-smoke. Hornby galloped back to Bridges to report that the 'ladies' had been observing them through binoculars and if they were ladies then he was a Dutchman.

'The wily Hun will stop at nothing Lieutenant; they come as refugees, they come as women in motor-cars and no doubt they will come as nuns. I'd as soon face a troop of Uhlans.'

Bridges divided his squadrons into three groups and positioned them so that they could observe the main approaches from the north, but kept for himself the bridge over the Somme at Morcourt, where he also placed a machine-gun. A couple of 13-pounders would be useful but he was fairly sure that the guns were the other side of S. Quentin by now. He arranged for patrols to be pushed out to keep touch with the enemy. He then settled down to wait. His squadrons, or sub-divisions of them, could keep in touch using bugles and flags or if necessary gallopers. The horses were sent back a hundred yards in the care of the grooms. It was midday, a heat-haze shimmering over the fields. His orders were to hold this ground for six hours and then retire on St. Quentin when the last of the infantry should have passed through; de Lisle's words still echoed in his ears:

'Tom, we are in a very tight corner and the infantry are on their last legs. You are the rear-guard commander and if necessary you must fight it out and die like gentlemen.'

Bridges knew that he was in a tight corner when he went back to the French Territorials at 2.00 p.m. and saw not a single pair of red trousers. It was as if they had never existed.

Is that what they call doing their duty? It is as well to remember that Marianne is a woman and unpredictable; and these amateur soldiers in spite of a fierce appearance with beards like pirates keep one guessing; for all I know they have gone for le dejeuner.

At 4.45 p.m. Captain Johnson and Mr. Moore crossed the Somme at Remaucourt, now guarded by Major Bridges' Dragoons, the major himself being on a tour of inspection of his outposts. The piebald mare refused to drink from the river, but Johnson let her eat some good grass. He noticed her girth needed tightening and pulled the saddle-belt in a couple of notches.

Mr. Moore paused to have a word with the lieutenant commanding the troop; there was as yet no sign of the enemy, either horsed or infantry, but the lieutenant was prepared to stay at the bridge for three hours at least, or until the last of the stragglers should have come through from Le Cateau. There was no question apparently of blowing the bridge, a fine eighteenth century structure, which Mr. Moore was secretly pleased about. It would be a sad loss and would not delay the Germans more than a few hours or so. As the two gentlemen looked down on the gently flowing river Mr. Moore turned to the Captain and said,

'It's a pity we have no time for a bathe; it would do your injuries a world of good, old man.'

'Yes, but we must push on, Arthur. And in happier times you must come to Broadway and play tennis and bathe and eat ice cream.'

'Ice cream....something I've been dreaming about these past hours.'

'Yes, Arthur. And do you by chance know those lines of Housman's that go something like…

> *Come you home a hero,*
> *Or come home not at all,*
> *The lads you leave will mind you*
> *Till Ludlow tower shall fall….*
> *And make the foes of England*
> *Be sorry you were born.*

'I do indeed, Henry. Curious how the scholar-poet claims an understanding of soldiers, and could write *dead or living, drunk or dry, Soldier, I wish you well.* And yet could urge that soldier to *stand and fight…And take the bullet in your brain* without any sense of pathos.'

'Quite right. I wouldn't want AE for my sergeant. And certainly not as my general. Come to think of it. I don't think he understood that running away is not a shameful thing; it means living to fight another day. Or rather, he knew that of course but could not countenance it. We should not listen to these armchair warriors, not even if they are the Poet Laureate, who know nothing of a soldier's life. Shakespeare, whoever he was, was a soldier, I am certain of it. Tolstoy as well, as we know. The truest lines Housman ever wrote were *when the journey's over There'll be time enough to sleep.* Those are my watch-words. But the journey will be a long one.'

The two gentlemen passed through St. Quentin, pausing only to water the piebald mare from the fountain in the square, now eager for water in the unpredictable way that horses have. They had a drink and a welcome splash-down themselves and Johnson took the opportunity to have a look at his dressings. He decided to leave them as they were. Red Caps were directing the mingled and bedraggled battalions on towards the south and making no attempt to sort them out; all that would come later. The Retreat must go on. The two gentlemen, Johnson riding the mare, were a little perturbed to see a white flag hoisted on the town hall, but were too tired to bother themselves with it. They gratefully accepted a gift of apples from a black-clad woman tending her stall. They gave one to the mare. Mr. Moore had his mind firmly set on getting to Amiens.

They joined the caravan of khaki on the road to Ham. They did not go near the railway station and so saw nothing of any troops who were refusing to obey orders. The whereabouts of 7 Brigade was still a bit of a mystery and Johnson was already reconciled to never seeing his personal kit again. His leg wound was throbbing but he knew this was to be expected. He began to compose in his mind the letter he would write to Simon's parents. He knew what was grieving him the most; it was the fact that he had not been able to lay Simon's body to rest. But he would write of their green and carefree times together in India, their salad days, and playing cricket by the water-meadows of the Itchen, for *death, he taketh all away, but them he cannot take*. Johnson was pleased he could remember that line, but he was damned if he could remember who wrote it.

Chapter 27

27th August, Late Afternoon St. Quentin

The Mayor of St. Quentin was still in his mayoral ante-chamber at 3.00 p.m. when word was brought to him that two British Lieutenant-Colonels were willing to see him. He had spent the last half-hour in a state of febrile torpor, tugging at his moustaches and watching from his window the columns of BEF soldiery passing his Mairie. To the Mayor every soldier had defeat written on his face. He knew that behind the defeated English would come the Prussians, eager for the spoils of victory. No woman under the age of fifty would be safe from ravishment. His own cellar of fine Burgundy vintages would be guzzled like beer. Drunken German soldiery would roam the streets displaying the arrogance that Prussians have made uniquely their own.

But at this latest news the Mayor brightened considerably; he still hadn't given up hope that his document, if backed up by written British assurances that they would not fight for the town if attacked, would save St. Quentin from bombardment. There remained the matter of finding the right German hands in which to place the document, but the Mayor was sanguine about his prospects of doing so. He had a car with a white flag ready just outside the Mairie; indeed, the two battalion commanders cannot have missed it. He was quite prepared to drive out himself on the road north and put himself at the mercy of the first German officer he came across. He would be the saviour of St. Quentin. There was also the matter of his own personal safety; if he could show his usefulness to the German command he would surely be treated with the respect and deference that his office was owed. The Mayor would be keeping very quiet about one thing: the fact that he had been born in Alsace might arouse fury in the Germans who would regard him as a traitor to the German cause, his family having decided not to live under German rule.

The two Lieutenant-Colonels were led into the mayoral presence, one being entirely without any hair on his head or face and the other having the regulation military appearance of parted hair and generous moustaches; the former being Monty's commanding officer Lieutenant-Colonel Elkington and the latter being the Lieutenant-Colonel of the Royal Dublin Fusiliers, both of 10 Brigade. They shook hands with the Mayor, who had donned the sash of the tricoleur; he was after all the local representative of the Third Republic, duly elected by the eligible voters of St. Quentin and appointed by the President of that Republic, and the Mayor claimed to be speaking in his name.

The Mayor gave more or less the same speech that he had made earlier to Lieutenant-General Smith-Dorrien. This time he received a much more favourable response, the two Colonels able to get the gist of the Mayor's plea that his town should be spared bombardment. The two officers had come from the central Place where the remnants of their two battalions were lying on the ground, utterly exhausted, and refusing to leave the town unless provided with a train to take them; they had heard rumours that other battalions, and the Argylls were mentioned, had already been provided with trains for their convenience. Some of the men had gone into houses recently vacated by their owners, and men and NCO's were now lying on beds, having ransacked the kitchens in search of food and drink. Some had found wine which they were even now drinking, opening the bottles with blows from their bayonets. They reasoned, and not without a certain epicurean logic, that all this plenty would be available to the whole of von Kluck's Army by this time tomorrow and now was a good time to enjoy it. They did not entertain the thought that an epicurean defence would not be a sufficient plea against a charge of looting, the penalty for which included the death penalty. Some of the men fired their rifles in the air to get rid of the last of their ammunition.

It was in short, a situation not far short of a mutiny. For some unaccountable reason therc were no Red Caps in the town and the Warwickshires and the Dubliners were in no mood to obey orders from Colonel Rycroft of the Quartermasters, the senior officer in the town at the time, to resume the march. The men had piled arms in the Place and had effectively disarmed themselves, although some of the Dubliners had already abandoned their arms in the mad scramble to get away from Haucourt. Lieutenant Watkins had led his company-sized band of Warwickshires all the way from the front-line south-west of Caudry, where he had parted from Monty and Penfold late the previous afternoon. They had been on the move continuously since they had arrived at Le Cateau on the 24th, arriving at St. Quentin around 4.00 p.m. on the 27th, by way of Beaurevoir, and now they had had enough. They came in at the tail-end of the retreating mass of infantry. They had marched up and down, back and forth, for more than fifty miles in four days. Most of their officers had been killed in the insane attack yesterday, Major Haddow throwing his life away, and that of the Royal Scot, in his act of wilful sacrifice in the farmhouse, although the men could not of course know this. The men were still muttering about French spies hiding behind the shutters of the cottages in Cattenieres. Lieutenant Watkins was still almost unknown to them, having been with the Battalion a matter of weeks. He was not in any case a man with a commanding presence.

The 2nd Battalion of the Royal Dublin Fusiliers, like the 1st Warwickshires, had been at Haucourt early on the 26th. The Dubliners were already a good deal scattered about before the action started. Both the Dubliners and the Warwicks had men straggling back from the fighting on the 26th, in separate parts of the country, Monty's Commando now on the St. Quentin Canal. Major Sherwin of the Dubliners was now striking west making for Boulogne, where he was eventually to lead eighty men and officers to safety after an odyssey of a hundred miles, losing twenty men killed and wounded in clashes with Germans on their way. Two companies of the 2nd Dubliners had formed a rear-guard at Haucourt and had come out in tandem with Watkins' A Company at the end of the day. It was these men, Irishmen from Dublin and Warwickshire men from the large cities of the Midlands, that now made up the bulk of the disaffected troops in the Place at St. Quentin. By 5.00 p.m. almost all the other troops of the three divisions had passed through the town, or had moved south on other routes.

The two Lieutenant-Colonels took a decision which was in the circumstances the worst decision they could have made. Being very much aware of the condition of their men, they signed the document put under their noses that declared that they would not fight for the town but would lay down their arms if the Germans attacked. It is possible, but unlikely, that they did not know what they were signing, or thought it of little consequence. They were both very tired, having had no sleep to speak of for three nights. They shook the Mayor's hand. The men quickly learned of the existence of this document and not unnaturally found this an additional reason for refusing to march, to march on to fight again. All this was happening at the same time as Major Bridges' discovery that the French Territorials had abandoned their position. To make matters worse, several troops of French cavalry from General Sordet's Divisions appeared in the town at this point, without officers, their horses blown and the men all swearing that they were the sole survivors of a disastrous rout on the British left, and that Uhlans were not far behind and that the women and children of the town would soon witness and experience acts of gross violation that should never be seen in a Christian country. Although the BEF soldiers could not understand any of this torrent of French, ('Sove ki pur? What's all that about?'), they understood very well the gesture of drawing an imaginary knife across the throat. And they could understand the meaning of a pelvic thrust.

Curiously this apparent certainty of imminent mass rape and pillage did not stiffen any lingering resolve in the exhausted soldiery lying around the Place to get to their feet and quit the town; it merely seemed to confirm their belief that any further resistance to the German onslaught was pointless and they would rather stay put and surrender. As one of the Dubliners said to his mate, 'We're fucked if we stay and we're fucked if we go, so we might as well stay.' The men, about four hundred in number, did however move the short distance from the Place to the railway station, where they sat down on the down platform, from where trains to Paris would normally stop. Lieutenant Watkins, the son of a phosphate trader and still an unknown quantity to the men, went with them but had given up trying to exercise authority. He told the men that there were no trains to be had, but the men would not listen to reason. One man was heard to mutter 'Well, you'll just have to go and find one, then.' Some of the men remained in the houses, where they were presumably asleep or drunk, or both.

None of this collapse of morale was known to Lieutenant-General Smith-Dorrien who had by 2.00 p.m. reached what had become his new Corps HQ at Ham. Nor was it known to Captain Johnson or Mr. Moore who were south-west of St. Quentin on the Ham road, as were Buffy and Frank Edwards and the vast majority of the exhausted Second Corps survivors. Lieutenant Montgomery was still leading his Commando of twenty Royal Scots and Warwicks in the Uhlan-infested farmland around Riqueval to the north of St. Quentin. If Monty had known of the decision taken by his commanding officer in St. Quentin to surrender to the enemy on the say-so of a French civilian, he would have been horrified but not totally surprised, given that he had decided as far back as the 25th that Elkington was not fit to command men: the abandonment of the high ground around Solesmes, the disorderly night march, the failed attack on the 26th were all the work of an incompetent command. Lieutenant-

Colonel Elkington's abrupt departure from the field of battle was all of a piece with these disasters. If Monty had known of the near-mutinous state of the Warwickshiremen he would have put it down to poor leadership. The situation in St. Quentin did however become known to Major Bridges up by the bridge on the Somme to the north of the town. At 3.00 p.m. he had dispatched Captain Harrison, a fluent French speaker, into the town to find out if the infantry were clear, as apart from the occasional lame duck, the stream of survivors coming down the Le Cateau road was now no more than a trickle. If there were no more to come down from the north and if the town was clear of British troops, there was no longer any point in forming a rear-guard, there being so far no sign of the enemy.

At 5.00 p.m. Captain Harrison returned to the bridge, bringing news of the mutinous troops at the railway station, the signing of the surrender document by the two Lieutenant-Colonels and the presence of a white flag outside the Mairie. Bridges now decided to act.

'Captain, I am leaving the machine-gun and two troops here at the bridge. The enemy may be slow in coming on but come on they will. If I had some Royal Engineers here with some charges I would blow the bridge, but you can't have everything. The rest of the force are to fall back into the town. God knows where the French infantry have gone. Please accompany me to the Mairie where I will need your help in dealing with the civil authorities. We may have to be a bit firm with both the Mayor and our troops but it will call for a bit of diplomacy.'

'Yes, Major, and we had better have some strong men as additional persuasion.'

They rode into town, arriving at about 6.00 p.m., to find the Warwicks and the Dubliners still camped at the station, the junior officers having given up trying to get them on to their feet. The two Lieutenant-Colonels were nowhere to be seen. The mass of tired, filthy and dispirited men made a pathetic sight, but Bridges quickly came to the conclusion that this was not a full-scale mutiny, more the result of extreme exhaustion and the lack of competent officers. There was no sign of any drunkenness; if he knew anything about quartermasters it was pretty certain that the battalion rum jars would be kept well out of harm's way.

'Captain, please go to the Mairie. I don't care how you do it but get that document into your hands and bring it to me. Get the authorities there to provide some rations, bread and cheese and the like, beer too if they can get it, and put it out in the square. I will get the men to the square; a bit of food and I'm sure they will be more responsive. And we must get them to clean themselves up.'

At the station Bridges decided to address the men. He was helped by his height of well over six foot and the fact that he was an officer who seemed to know exactly what he was about. He knew instinctively, like Lieutenant Montgomery and Captain Johnson and indeed Lieutenant-General Smith-Dorrien, what men can and will do. The men sat up, but were still in no mood to stand up. The station was quiet, the only sound coming from an RFC Avro flying over St. Quentin at five thousand feet. Bridges waited until he thought he had the attention of most of the men sprawled on the south-bound platform. He cleared his throut and spoke as loudly as he could, the accoustics of the station giving his words resonance. He was standing outside the porters' cubby-hole, beside a large poster featuring a raped and naked woman, with soldiers in spiked helmets in the background. In place of her left breast the woman had a bloody wound. Another poster featuring the Michelin Man and La Bonne Route gave Bridges a memory of happier times.

'I know you have had little or no sleep for four days and that you have had very little to eat or drink. I have arranged for rations to be provided outside the town hall, where you will now go. Further dumps of rations have been placed on the road to Ham. For those of you not fit to walk for whatever reason I will find carts to take you on to Ham. Otherwise you will walk-march. I have been ordered by Brigadier-General de Lisle to form the rear-guard here at St. Quentin and I can assure you that I will leave no British soldier alive in the town when I withdraw.'

At this point Bridges paused to observe the effect of his words on the men. That's about as far as I can go with threats. Now for some straight talk. He had their attention and there was no back-chat. He continued,

'Your orders are to continue the Retirement, and in this Army orders are not subjects for discussion.' He was pleased with this phrase. He continued standing on the platform for a minute and then joined Lieutenant Watkins and a small knot of officers, wanting to keep a distance between himself and the sullen semi-prone soldiery. The presence of so many NCO's worried him, athough he couldn't see any sergeants amongst them. He was aware that his uniform was dusty, his boots begrimed with Picardy dirt, his face badly bruised and swollen, and knew that this counted in his favour in the eyes of the men; a red-tabbed and red-faced HQ staff officer would meet only derision. Staff officers would start talking about mutiny, which wouldn't help matters at all. And he knew that a cavalry officer cut a more dashing figure than an officer of line infantry.

The men muttered amongst themselves. They did not appear to have appointed a leader but after an interval of ten minutes in which they seemed to weigh the Major's words they began to shuffle the half-mile back to the Place. The idea of staying in the town and submitting themselves to the doubtful mercies of the Germans was becoming less attractive. There they were joined by men emerging from the houses, some of them the worse for drink. The officers decided to ignore the more obviously drunk men, but kept a watchful eye on them. Captain Harrison had with him some hefty cavalry farriers who could lift the front end of a charger and were not easily intimidated by a drunk Irishman. Captain Harrison, Major Bridges, Colonel Rycroft and Lieutenant Watkins stood on the steps of the Mairie while the men had a good feed from the bread and cheese and weak beer provided as if by magic by the

Mayor, now meekly taking orders from British cavalry officers. The white flag which had been so much in evidence on the Mairie had been taken down, on the orders of Captain Harrison. Major Bridges was acutely conscious that he was outranked by the two renegade Lieutenant-Colonels, one of whom, Elkington, he knew well. Both of them were nowhere to be seen; they might already have left for Ham as far as anyone knew. They would have to be dealt with later by the Provost Marshal and in due course handed over to the Adjutant-General and probably cashiered. He himself would probably have to give evidence in any future court of inquiry. Now was the time for diplomacy and judgement. It was not, in any case, a straightforward matter for a cavalry major to issue marching orders to infantry battalions. But Major Bridges was not a man who suffered from lack of self-confidence; and he was a man who knew what had to be done. He knew his Dryden and he spoke the familiar words to Lieutenant Watkins:

> *This hour's the very crisis of your fate;*
> *Your good or ill; your infamy or fame,*
> *And all the colour of your life depends*
> *On this important now.*

The men were however still far from ready to form up in fours and march out of the town. In fact, the cheese provided by the town burghers seemed to have assuaged their hunger but not given them an appetite for marching. The life seemed to have been sucked out of them. The adrenalin rush they had experienced in their first battle up at Haucourt had long since expired. In any case for most of them there had been no direct contact with the enemy; few of them had had the intense satisfaction of meting out death to their enemy from the barrels of their Lee-Enfields. The early morning attack against the invisible enemy had left the Warwicks profoundly shocked: they had, after all, left many of their friends dead on the Picardy stubble. All of them had been shot at and shelled, had marched and counter-marched and had been let down by their commanding officers and were now led by callow subalterns, most of the company commanders having been killed or wounded. In leading A Company of the Warwicks out of Haucourt, Lieutenant Watkins had insisted on following his orders from Brigadier Haldane to the letter, which were to take the road to Ligny even though this road was being heavily shelled and there were plenty of alternative routes he could have taken, although he had no map. The men had had to run the gauntlet of the shelling, which they did in short rushes, trying to time their rushes between salvos. They had had nine men wounded, who were taken back to the church in Haucourt, where they were captured by the Germans when they took the village at about 8.00 p.m., along with the other wounded who could not be moved, the village priest being led away at bayonet-point. Watkins' men had bivouacked and slept for a few hours by the Cambrai-Bohain road, a little south of Esnes, during the night of the 26/27th, not far from where Monty's Commando was to pass twelve hours later, a corner of a field they shared with a company of the Rifle Brigade, much reduced after their battle at Fontaine.

It was at this point, that is to say about 7.00 p.m. on the 27th, that Major Bridges had an inspired idea.

'Captain, do you see that shop over there on the other side of the Place? The one with the hoops and the toy prams? 'Jouets de St. Quentin', the sign says. It also has some drums and other musical instruments. Could you please find the owner, borrow a drum, a mouth organ and a pipe? Requisition them if need be. The bandsmen's instruments are scattered God knows where. I've got an urge to form a band. I think the men might just respond to a bit of music.'

Harrison did as he was bidden. The men continued to lounge about in a sullen manner. Lieutenant Watkins and a couple of the other subalterns managed to get them re-united with their rifles, which gave them at least a more soldierly appearance. Harrison emerged from the toy-shop with the instruments necessary for the improvised band.

Both Captain Harrison and Major Bridges were able to play a tune on a mouth organ and a musical pipe. It wasn't too difficult to find a third member of the band to keep a rhythm with the drum. The trio struck up with *Tipperary*, probably because they thought it would appeal to the Dubliners. It did. They then went into *The British Grenadiers*, a stirring tune with good marching qualities. The trio, led by Major Bridges, marched around the Place and were soon joined by a throng of men, now eager to join the innocent fun. A man in a bowler hat appeared from nowhere and joined the band, doing a Charlie Chaplin routine with his bowler and a passable imitation of the shuffling gait. Everyone started to laugh and cheer. Soon the band was swollen by men following it round the fountain in the middle of the Place, now eager to follow their new leader. Some of them splashed each other like children. A mongrel dog wanted to join in. The Major was becoming the Pied Piper of St. Quentin, as he led the crocodile of men down the road to Ham, in search of their regiments and the rest of the Corps, the men marching in the shadows of the poplar trees as the sun went down over Albert to the west. The men formed up in ranks and were soldiers again; they had their rifles and packs. Their sergeants had reappeared, as if from nowhere, looking a little sheepish, having decided to keep their heads down. Horse-drawn carts carrying those who professed themselves unable to march followed behind. Major Bridges, accompanied by Captain Harrison, rode back to St. Quentin in the gathering gloom, with child-like cries of 'Don't leave us, Sir,' ringing in his ears. They then started singing *It's a Long Way To Tipperary*.

The 4th Dragoons rear-guard came in to St. Quentin and the last British soldier quit the town by 10.00 p.m. Major Bridges saw to it that the telephone wires to the town hall were cut and the equipment smashed. The switching gear in the signal box at the station was disabled but the bridges remained intact, for want of orders. The man in the bowler hat had been seen getting in to the back of a large de Dion motor car driven by a smartly dressed middle-aged gentleman, driving goggles on his forehead, with his wife alongside him, her straw hat held in place with a silk scarf. The driver of the de Dion had earlier been seen siphoning the petrol out of a broken down Selfridges lorry. The Mayor went back to his funk-hole and there were no German officers to surrender to. But just before quitting the town at 10.20 p.m., Tom Bridges decided on one last gesture. He went back to the Mairie, entered the vacant Mayoral office and using the Mayor's fountain pen and note-paper wrote;

'To the German Command.
Please respect this ancient town and all who reside here. We shall return'.
(signed) Thomas Bridges,
Major, 4th Dragoon Guards, Cavalry Division, BEF. August 27th 1914.

Major Bridges and Lieutenant Hornby rode out of the town together, having satisfied themselves that there were no stragglers left behind, letting their horses find their own way on the pavé, there being just enough light from the half-moon to enable man and beast, now equally tired, to make out the road. They didn't speak; it was all they could do to remain upright in their saddles, before they found a lit farmhouse and a half-troop of Dragoons bivouacked in the lee of a barn. A trooper took their chargers and they spread their groundsheets on the ground and slept until dawn. There were oats and water for the chargers and hard biscuit for men and officers. Bridges dreamt of black-clad Uhlans, of airplanes as black as crows and a black dog frolicking at the heels of men who remained impassive, staring with a look of utter despair.

German cavalry rode into St. Quentin in the morning of the 28th August.

Bridges' note was seen by Oberleutnant von Westerholt of the 15th Hussars, who remarked to a fellow officer,

'Arrogant Englishman! As if I needed to be told to behave like a gentleman. We do not make war on women and children.'

Chapter 28

Arthur Moore at Amiens and Afterwards

Mr. Moore and Captain Johnson reached Ham at 6.00 p.m. on Thursday 27th August. Captain Johnson was delighted to find his friend Bertie Altham, of 3rd Division staff, in the town hall, along with Second Corps staff officers. As far as two military Old Wykehamists are able to, they greeted each other with gestures of genuine warmth, Bertie's 'Ecce Homo' accompanied by hand-clasping and a pat on the back. He called Henry 'My man from Ubique'. Henry Johnson introduced Arthur Moore to Altham.

'What would be the best way for Mr. Moore to get to Amiens? You and I know that he will have the devil's own job of getting his dispatch past the censor but there is an office of the Press Bureau in Amiens with couriers standing by, and Arthur must get his dispatch into the hand of a courier by tomorrow if it is to be published by *The Times* on Sunday.'

Johnson turned to Mr. Moore. Moore added, addressing Bertie Altham, 'Henry is right. I don't trust the wires or the telephone. The copy would get mangled beyond repair once it gets into the hands of the Post Office, let alone what would happen to it were it to go through military channels. A Press Bureau courier is the only way and that means Amiens for me by tomorrow.'

Altham knew what had to be done: 'The trains are not running between Ham and Amiens, or at least not today, but first thing tomorrow there will be a motor-lorry convoy leaving for the rail-head at Amiens, carrying wounded bound for Le Mans. There will be a cavalry escort. I can get you a place in a lorry and you will be there by lunch-time tomorrow, the 28th, by way of Peronne.

'I cannot thank you enough, Captain Altham. I will never forget my time with the Welch Fusiliers and Captain Johnson of the Worcesters. I will leave you now to prepare my dispatch. What I have seen over the last two days will enable me to bring the official communiqués into a closer approximation with the truth.'

Johnson wished Mr. Moore Godspeed. 'And we will eat ice-cream in Broadway, where I have a promise to keep with a certain lady.'

Captain Johnson and Arthur Moore were found camp beds in the Mairie, where they had their first decent night's sleep for four nights. They availed themselves of the primitive washing facilities, but remained in the same clothes they had been wearing for four days and nights. Johnson reached Noyon on the 28th from where he was taken by train to the base hospital at Le Mans, where he made a full recovery from his wounds. There was time enough to sleep.

The Times of London received the copy by special courier late on Saturday evening, the 29th August. Arthur Moore was able to help himself to a typewriter in Amiens, where he put the finishing touches to his dispatch. He had addressed it to the Chief of the Foreign Department who immediately agreed with the Editor that the article as written bore all the hallmarks of truth but that it was highly improbable that the authorities would allow it to be published as it stood. They submitted it to the Censor who retained it for two hours, and the Editor was fully prepared to publish the Sunday edition without the Dispatch.

They were astonished however when it returned from the Censor at 11.30 p.m., carefully edited for publication, but retaining the essential thrust of the original. The Head of the Press Bureau added a memorandum urging the Editor to publish it in the form in which it had been returned. There was just time to insert the article for publication in the Special Sunday edition; it was also made available by cable to the *New York Times*.

FIRING NEAR AMIENS

Heard There Yesterday – How the British Fought at Mons

Special Cable to THE NEW YORK TIMES

LONDON, Sunday, Aug 30th. – An Amiens dispatch to The London Times, dated Saturday, gives a connected account of the fighting in Northern France. It says:

"First let it be said our honour is bright. Among all the straggling units seen, the flotsam and jetsam, of the fiercest fight in history, I saw fear in no man's face. It was not an army of hunted men, nor in all the plain tales of officers, non-commissioned officers and men did a single story of the white feather reach me.

"No one could answer for every man, but every British regiment and every battery of which any one had knowledge has done its duty, and never has duty been more terrible.

"Since Monday morning last the German advance has been one of almost incredible rapidity. The British force engaged in a terrible fight which may be called the action of Mons. Although it covered a big front on Sunday, the German attack was withstood to the utmost limit. A whole division was flung into the fight at the end of a long march, and had not even time to dig trenches.

"The French supporters who were expected do not seem to have been in touch, although whether they were many hours late I cannot say. Further to the right the French, after a long day's gallant fighting, broke. Namur fell, and Gen. Joffre was forced to order a retreat along the whole line.

The Germans, fulfilling one of the best of all precepts in war, never gave the retreating army one single moment's rest.

"Pursuit was immediate, relentless, and unresting. Aeroplanes, Zeppelins, armoured motors, and cavalry were loosed and served at once to harass retiring columns and to keep the German staff fully informed of the movements of the allied forces.

"The British force fell back. Desperate fighting took place southward continually. The army fought its way desperately, with many stands, but was forced backward by the sheer unconquerable numbers of the enemy, who were prepared to throw away three or four men for the life of every British soldier.

"Tonight I write to the sound of guns. All the afternoon the guns were going on the eastern roads. A German aeroplane flew over us this morning and was brought crashing down. A Royal Engineer chauffeur told me that the axle of his car was broken and he had to abandon it. He had no more than left it when it was blown up.

"Losses are great. I have seen broken bits of many regiments. Let me repeat that there was no failure in discipline, no panic, no throwing up of the sponge. Every one's temper is sweet; nerves do not show.

"A group of men, it may be a dozen less or more, arrives under command of whoever is entitled to command it. Men are worn with marching and ought to be weak with hunger, for of course no commissariat could cope with such a case; but they are steady and cheerful, and wherever they arrive make straight for the proper authority to report themselves and seek news of their regiment. Apparently every division was in action.

German Losses "Colossal"

"Certain things about the fighting seem clear. One is the colossal character of the German losses. I confess that when I read daily in the official bulletins in Paris of how much greater the German losses were than those of the Allies I was not much impressed. Much contemplation of Eastern warfare, where each side claims to have annihilated the other, has made me over-skeptical in such matters, but three days among the combatants has convinced me of the truth of the story in this case.

"It is clear that although the French General Staff knew that their eastern frontier defenses had been so perfected as to force Germany to turn to the flanks to find a weak spot, and although they knew also that not for nothing did Germany antagonize England and outrage international opinion by violating the neutrality of Belgium, nevertheless they underestimated the force of the German blow through Belgium. All estimates of the number of the German army corps in Belgium will need revision, and behind the screen in Alsace and Lorraine there were probably far fewer than was supposed, else perhaps Mülhausen would not have had to be retaken twice.

"The German commanders in the north advance their men as if they had an inexhaustible supply. Of the bravery of the men it is not necessary to speak. They advance in deep sections so slightly extended as to be almost in close order, with little regard for cover, rushing forward as soon as their own artillery has opened fire.

Mowing Down German Ranks.

"On our position our artillery mows long lanes down the centres of sections, so frequently there is nothing left but the outsides, but no sooner is this done than more men double up, rushing over heaps of dead, and remake the section.

"Last week so great was their superiority in numbers that they could no more be stopped than the waves of the sea.

"Their shrapnel is markedly bad, though their gunners are excellent at finding the range. On the other hand their machine guns are of the most deadly efficacy and are very numerous. Their rifle shooting is described as not first-class, but their numbers bring on the infantry till frequently they and the allied troops meet finally in bayonet tussles.

"The superiority of numbers in men and guns, especially in machine guns, the most successfully organized system of scouting by aeroplanes and Zeppelins, the motors carrying machine guns, cavalry and extreme mobility are elements to their present success.

"To sum up, the first great German effort has succeeded. The British expeditionary force has won imperishable glory. The investment of Paris cannot be banished from the field of possibility. I saw rolling stock being hurriedly moved today. We want reinforcements, and we want them now.

"Whether the chief of the German staff, after reckoning up his losses, will find he has enough men left to attempt further assault with any hope of success is more than doubtful. His army has made a colossal effort and moved with extraordinary speed, but it is possible that its limits have been reached."

By the next day, once the Dispatch had appeared in cold print, the Government began to have severe doubts about the wisdom of allowing it to be published in anything like its original form. Both the Prime Minister, Mr. Asquith, and the Lord Chancellor described the Dispatch as 'regrettable'. Mr. F. E. Smith, the Government minister responsible for censorship, attempted to distance himself from the decision to publish by claiming pressure of work, the work having had to be carried out on a Saturday night. Other newspapers attacked *The Times* for a lack of patriotism, saying that the Dispatch had inflicted 'needless agonies' on the public mind. *The Times* stood by its decision to publish, as of course it had to, the article having gone through all the proper channels, and all details of units involved and all place names having been excised, although it would have been extremely unlikely that Arthur Moore, experienced journalist that he was, would have included place names and individual units in his original dispatch.

The War Office was sufficiently alarmed by the impact on public opinion of Arthur Moore's Dispatch, and its possible adverse effect on recruiting, that it issued a Communiqué at 3.40 p.m., the same day as the publication of *The Times* Special Edition, through the Press Bureau, giving a far more hopeful and satisfactory account of the battles at the frontiers; for good measure a post-script was added warning the public to accept 'with extreme caution' such dispatches as had just been published. It did not mention in this post-script that the Amiens Dispatch had been edited and approved by the Censor for publication and that the Press Bureau itself had urged, even begged, the Editor of *The Times* to publish it in its entirety, as edited by the Censor. It was a shameful piece of back-sliding in response to what was hardly a defeatist article, in fact an article that praised the courage and spirit of the BEF. But it showed that the Government was badly rattled by the events on the ground over the period 23-27th August, although a victory at sea on the 28^{th,} when three German cruisers were sunk with no British losses, had temporarily restored Government morale. The Government had got wind of Field Marshal French's desire to take his whole Force south-west, out of the line of advance of the German 1st Army, for a period of rest and recuperation; this had greatly alarmed the War Cabinet, alerted by the increasingly pessimistic and alarmist tone of his reports to the War Department. The political implications of a British withdrawal from the line were unthinkable. The time was approaching for Kitchener to don his finest uniform and go out to stiffen the sinews of the hapless Sir John French.

The contrast between Moore's Dispatch and the official communiqués was what was particularly shocking to the public. Never before had the public read words like 'broken bits of regiments', although the thrust of the article, that the initial German effort had succeeded but 'it is possible its limits have been reached' was a remarkable piece of military analysis and astonishingly accurate, given that Mr. Moore wrote the article before General Lanrezac went into battle at Guise against the German Second Army on the 29th and before the BEF was able to recover on the 28th, a day when there was no contact with von Kluck's Army at all, von Kluck's divisions not having recovered their forward momentum after the shock they had received west of Le Cateau on the 26th. Not even Field-Marshal Joffre could know on the 27/28th that the allied armies would launch the battle of the Marne on 5th September, the battle that saved Paris and pushed the German invader back to the Aisne. But by the end of August the people of the British Isles, Home Counties gentlefolk and Scottish crofters alike, knew that the BEF had been in a desperate fight with a whole German Army, that it had given a good account of itself, but they must brace themselves for further grave news.

As it happened, the German action that Moore witnessed at Amiens was the furthest west that their armies were to penetrate until April 1918, nearly four years later, in what the Germans were to call the Battle of

Amiens, where they were halted by Allied troops at Villers-Bretonneux. Moore rejoined the BEF in the advance to the Aisne, was briefly captured and released and went on to serve - in uniform- in Gallipoli. He ranks alongside Ashmead-Bartlett, Murdoch and Gibbs as one of the greatest correspondents of the War.

On 27/28th August, Von Kluck was a deluded man; his timetable for the advance on Paris already upset, his losses mounting, his lines of communication lengthening, his troops as exhausted as the British, his horses losing their shoes, his cavalry rapidly becoming a spent force, yet he still believed that Paris lay within his grasp. On the 28th he was to receive his order from von Moltke to march on Paris at the same time as the French Government was preparing to move south to Bordeaux and trenches were being dug on the outskirts of the capital. By the 29th, although his advance troops were reporting back signs of a British collapse, he knew in his heart that the Kaiser's order was issued with a desperate urgency that had more to do with wish fulfilment than operational reality. The scales were dropping from his eyes. He said to his ADC, Oberleutnant von Keppel,

'I tell you Keppel, this is not like 1870, when the French abandoned everything in their haste to get out. I know what an army in pell-mell retreat leaves behind: everything, not just its unwashed laundry. What have the English left behind? Some surplus equipment, some uneaten rations. So my troops are eating some British beef? That does not a victory betoken. The English are now blowing bridges every time they cross a river; an army in desperate straits with no discipline does not do that. Where are the lines of prisoners, the men who will no longer obey their officers? You show them to me and I will show you a beaten army.'

Von Keppel made no answer. On the 30th, Joffre announced that 'The British Army by its devoted exertions has saved France'. By the 31st August, von Kluck's 1st Army was marching south-east, away from Paris, and his cavalry brigades, ranging out to the west, were recalled to rejoin the main army; the German High Command had lost their nerve and the war. The BEF actions at Mons and Le Cateau had given Joffre just enough time to reinforce his left flank, which the Schlieffen Plan had threatened to outflank.

Von Kluck in effect acknowledged the remarkable achievement of Second Corps in keeping its cohesion in the face of two all-out attacks by forces three times their number over the period 23-26th August. He could have blamed his cavalry, with their Jaeger infantry, and von der Marwitz in particular, for failing to exploit their numbers and their mobility in what was an opportunity, never to occur again, to encircle and trap a force that should have been theirs to defeat on the 26th. But to blame his cavalry would have been to blame himself because their failure was his failure.

Lieutenant Montgomery got his stragglers, or what he liked to call his Commando, back to Ham, from where they were taken by lorry to recuperate in the base hospital at Le Mans. They had been seventy-two hours on their journey back to British lines, getting into friendly territory on the 29th, having had to spend long hours laying up in woods as German patrols went past them. His men ate their carrots in Ham. The farm wagon with the five Warwickshire soldiers came safely through to St. Quentin on the 27th. Lieutenant Montgomery was badly wounded at First Ypres, recovered and served on the staff of General Plumer's Second Army. In 1940 he was to lead another retreat, as a Major-General commanding 3rd Division.

Lieutenant Penfold made a recovery from his partial collapse and from Le Mans he was able to return Major Haddow's wedding ring to the barracks at Warwick, from where it was sent to his widow, who was not to learn of

his death for many months. He was not the same man who had marched out from Le Cateau station in the early morning of 23rd August 1914. Gone was the sense of wonderment and keenness, although his attachment to duty remained. He was killed at Second Ypres; his body was never recovered and he remained 'Missing, believed killed' for the duration of the war, giving his parents untold agony. A diary bearing his name and the address of the Vicarage, Petworth, much mud-stained, was found in a dug-out in the Salient in 1919 by a German soldier engaged in battle-field clearance and was returned to the Vicarage. Extracts from the diary were published in the Petworth Parish Magazine in 1995.
Lieutenant Watkins was badly wounded at First Ypres while serving as an acting Company Commander and was invalided out of the Army.

The parish priest of Haucourt was shot by the Germans for 'giving aid and comfort to the enemy'.

Lieutenant-Colonel Elkington went off to join the French Foreign Legion where he redeemed himself, and eventually rejoined the British Army. The Lieutenant-Colonel of the RDF disappeared from history. His name was Mainwaring.

Captain Johnson survived the war, rising to the rank of Brigadier. He was awarded the DSO in 1917 for an act of selfless bravery outside Arras, an act that gave him his fourth wound. He married Phoebe Brett in 1919, who had served as a nurse in the Nursing Yeomanry. They hung Simon Brett's sword above the mantel-piece in their house in Worcestershire. Corporal Grant had managed to find an ASC wagon near Caudry going south on which he placed the sword, which miraculously was reunited with the Brett family.

Lieutenant de Salis survived the War, became a Company Commander with the 3rd Worcesters and then went to Gallipoli with the 9th (Service) Battalion of the Worcester Regiment, where he was wounded near Krithia. He spent the rest of the war in the Middle East with the 9th Battalion, ending the war as its Lieutenant-Colonel.

Captain Altham survived the war, serving on the staff of 3rd Division throughout and rising to the rank of Colonel. He went back to Winchester College after the War and became a housemaster. He taught Latin to the junior boys and cricket to the College First XI ('Lords').

Private Frank Edwards has the almost unique distinction of serving throughout the war as a Private and at the same time escaping serious injury. He served from 1916-18 as a signaller with his Battalion. He became a friend of Captain Robert Graves after the War, who helped him with his memoir. For his reunion with Suzanne, see next chapter.

Buffy, Private Bough, was badly wounded on the Somme in September 1916 and was invalided out of the Army.

Lieutenant Bosanquet, 'Four Eyes', was wounded at First Ypres and served on the staff of 5th Division when he returned to duty in the autumn of 1915. He was a Brigade-Major at the Armistice.

Major Bridges survived the war, was Mentioned in Despatches seven times, wounded three times and promoted to Major-General of 19th Division. In 1917 he served as head of the British Military Mission in Washington. He was the nephew of the Poet Laureate, Robert Bridges.

Lieutenant-General Sir Horace Smith-Dorrien was sacked by Sir John French in May 1915, ostensibly for defeatism, and spent the rest of the war as Military Governor of Gibralter. He was replaced by Lieutenant-

General Plumer.

General von Kluck was wounded by shell-fire in the spring of 1915 and took no further part in the war.
Captain Bowley stayed as ADC to Smith-Dorrien until May 1915 and then left to become a Company Commander in the 1st Sherwood Foresters. He was wounded near Arras in 1917 but survived the war, ending up as Lieutenant-Colonel of the Battalion.

Sir John French was sacked in December 1915 and replaced by Sir Douglas Haig. He became Commander-in-Chief Home Forces. As Sir Douglas Haig became based further from the Front, he became more eager to push on towards more ambitious objectives, in contrast to his pusillanimous behaviour of August 1914. Sir John wrote his memoir even before the end of hostilities, which were little more than a sustained and largely mendacious attack on Lieutenant-General Sir Horace Smith-Dorrien.

Brigadier Forrestier-Walker served throughout the war as a staff officer, apart from a brief spell commanding 48th Division in Italy in 1918.

Brigadier de Lisle was sent to Gallipoli in August 1915, where he commanded the 29th Division, succeeding General Hunter Weston.

Major 'CAL' Yate of the KOYLI, who led a last charge against the Germans and was awarded the VC, was taken, wounded, into captivity. He later escaped but was murdered in mysterious circumstances while evading re-capture.

Arthur Moore was captured by the Germans in September but released after a few days. He later donned uniform and served in Gallipoli.

Second Corps became Second Army, first under Lieutenant-General Smith-Dorrien and then under Lieutenant-General Plumer.

Major-General Sir Henry Wilson was murdered by the IRA in 1921.

St. Quentin became the fulcrum of the war on the Western Front, the Germans hanging on to it when they withdrew from the Somme battlefield to form the Hindenburg line in the winter of 1916/1917. It was from here that the Germans launched their last great offensive of the war, in March 1918, portrayed in microcosm by R.C. Sherriff in *Journey's End*. It was here that the 46th Division crossed the St. Quentin Canal in September 1918 in the final hundred days, the first British troops to breach the Hindenburg Line.

Twelve hundred men and officers lie buried to the west of Le Cateau, killed on 26th August, and thrown into mass burial pits by the Germans. More men and officers succumbed over the next few days to wounds received on the 26th. All those with no known grave, the great majority of those who were killed on the Retreat, nearly four thousand men and officers, are commemorated at the Commonwealth War Graves monument at La Ferté-sous-Jouarre, sixty-six miles to the east of Paris, the point taken to be that at which the BEF turned on their enemy and became the pursuer, as well as on the memorials in their home towns and villages.

The official figure for BEF casualties on the retreat from Mons, including the Battle of Mons itself, is 15,000. Half of these casualties were incurred at the Battle of Le Cateau on the 26th. The Retreat ended on the 5th September when the BEF, much to their joy, turned east to march toward the enemy, who had already turned away from Paris. The Battle of the Marne which ensued was the largest battle fought in the history of warfare, having approximately two million combatants on both sides, although the British contribution was less than glorious. The Germans were driven back to the Aisne where they dug in on the high ground and where they were to remain for the next four years. The Fighting Retreat of the BEF, mostly conducted by Lieutenant-General Smith-Dorrien's Second Corps, was instrumental in the eastward turn of the right wing of the German armies on August 31st, of that there can be no doubt. It was this eastward turn which signalled the abandonment of the Schlieffen Plan and the subsequent course of the war, with four years of attritional warfare and so many false dawns of hope of a return to the mobile warfare of the first two weeks of the war. It was mobile warfare that the BEF had been trained and equipped to fight and to which their generals so stubbornly wished to return, athough perhaps ironically it was Field-Marshal Sir John French who was among the first to appreciate the new reality of trench warfare.

Chapter 29

November 1918: Aulnoye and Le Cateau

Aulnoye lies twenty-seven miles due south of Mons, just to the east of the Forest of Mormal and twenty miles north-east of Le Cateau. An undistinguished town on the river Sambre of less than 10,000 inhabitants, it fell into German hands without a fight on the 25th August 1914, after Haig's divisions passed through on their retreat from Bavai. On the 10th November 1918 it was liberated by the 38th Division (The 'Welsh Division') of the BEF, of which 2nd Royal Welch Fusiliers formed a part, being one of the four battalions in 115th Brigade. Private Frank Edwards was now a signaller in this battalion, the same battalion in which he had gone to war in August 1914, and one of only a handful of 1914 men left in its ranks, a chance of survival he reckoned as twenty thousand to one, the survival chances of a signaller being only marginally better than that of an infantryman. He was lucky however one calculates the odds; if it can be counted lucky to have endured more than four years of trench warfare in the first place and to have seen the brains of his mates ooze out from skulls sliced open by flying metal; if it could be counted lucky to have stood by men in the trenches whose life was blotted out by snipers when his own was spared. The very word 'luck', although it has many meanings, is an inadequate word to describe his being still alive. Kismet, a Persian word, would be a more appropriate word to describe his continued life, the word, in the sense of 'Fate', being actually inscribed on the grave-stone of a soldier in the Commonwealth War Grave at Mons. Kismet can be taken to encompass both life and death. Frank Edwards had no desire to find the burial places of men killed in that far-off battle of 26th August 1914; he had witnessed more than enough death and burials to want to revisit old ones.

Frank's luck didn't extend to the card table where on the night of the Armistice he lost his entire back-pay, together with his war booty of German automatic pistols and field glasses, in a six hour game of Pontoon, the banker being his platoon sergeant. He did however end the war sober; the retreating Germans had cleared out every bottle in the town and what they had not drunk had taken back to Germany. Otherwise, the Armistice was marked in Aulnoye by a Service of Thanksgiving, held in the cinema, at which a *Te Deum* was sung by a scratch choir of French schoolchildren and their teachers. *Last Post* was played by a trumpeter in the Welch Fusiliers, standing on the steps of the church, the church itself too bomb-damaged to be used. Allied flags appeared with astonishing rapidity in the streets and a brass band set up in the square. The Welshmen burst into song with

The bells are ringing
For me and my girl.
The birds are singing
For me and my girl.

And like most songs of the war, this popular favourite soon got changed to 'The bells of hell go ting-a-ling-a-ling……for you and not for me'.

As Frank said to his new mate Tich, a six-foot Lewis-gunner,

'I shall leave France at the end of this fucking war with the same amount of money as when I came in: SFA. And we must be the only sober men in France.'

After which he went to bed and slept for ten solid hours, something he could not remember doing since his last leave.

Frank himself was not filled with untrammelled joy at the prospect of peace. It was also the case that he would get his discharge papers only if he had been a miner, that rigid peace-time discipline was being restored, which meant in effect that socialising with sergeants and corporals was now off-limits, and that for all his years of War Service the only things he now had physically to show for it were rheumatism and haemorhroids, neither of which would gain him a disability pension, his wound of 1914 having long since healed. On the 12th November he was ordered, like the rest of his Battalion, to burnish his helmet to a gleaming shine and on the 13th to have it repainted in the paint-shop to camouflage brown. On the 14th he learnt that he would be going to Cologne with the Army of Occupation and that Tich would be going back to Blighty, having put down his occupation as 'miner', which was not strictly true, considering that he had only worked in the office of a coal-mine as a supplies clerk. On the 15th Frank applied for Compassionate Leave. As their officers pointed out, an Armistice was not the Peace; the blockade of Germany was still in force and there was to be no fraternising with German soldiers, who were still to be treated as the enemy, although a defeated enemy who had laid down their arms. But he felt more than justified in his view that he should take priority in matters of leave over men who had only been out a short time. Edwards had been recalled as a Reservist back in August 1914 'for the duration' and he considered that the 'duration' was now at an end for him, whatever the officers said about an Armistice not being a Peace. If peace was to be left to the politicians there was no telling how long that might take.

His Battalion had fought its way to the Forest of Mormal on the 4th of November, the Germans shelling them remorselessly, as if in a hurry to use up the last of their ammunition, perhaps knowing that the end of the war was imminent. The German infantry wanted to leave all the fighting to their gunners and were quick to surrender when their gunners hitched up the guns to their horses and went back - although some stubborn Germans had to be dealt with by bayonet in the villages, and with Mills bombs thrown down cellars. Frank was surprised to see a couple of German machine-gunners being led back, surprised to see them alive rather than bayoneted. The fighting was very different to that of 1914, with aeroplanes, mortars and machine-guns in profusion on the battlefield. Almost all the men of the Welsh Division were New Army men, put into uniform since conscription was introduced in 1916, and although the old regulars, what was left of them, the volunteers of the early years and the later conscripts all rubbed along together, it was not the same Army that Edwards had known in 1914, the old Army of spit and polish. That it could not be, if only for the simple reason that three quarters of a million British soldiers had been killed on the Western Front since the Retreat from Mons and the old BEF had been destroyed at Ypres and on the Somme. It was now a citizen Army created by conscription, that most un-English thing. The young officers who were coming out now were often immature bullies, trying to hide their insecurity, not being born to lead like the officers in the early years. At least old Four Eyes was not a bully even though he might have been a bit wet behind the ears. And would today's lot manage what we did in August '14, march from the canal to the Marne, fighting and marching for a hundred miles in ten days? Let's just say that we did that in the old BEF, and leave it at that.

They had passed just to the north of Le Cateau at the end of October, leaving the 66th Division, part of 4th Army, to liberate the town. As they crossed the Montay Spur, the dead from the fighting were being interred in a cemetery that had been created for the dead from 1914, the cemetery blown apart by the shelling and exposing the previous occupants. Frank's memory of his brief encounter with Suzanne was alive again, but the image of her throat and face and red-brown hair was dimmed by the passage of four years, an image crowded out by images of men killed over the years since the Retreat of 1914, killed in every conceivable way, by bullet, bomb, shell and gas. As the song went, *he'd seen 'em, he'd seen 'em, hanging on the old barbed wire.*

The Battalion passed through the Forest of Mormal on roads made by

British prisoners, and then crossed the Sambre Canal on a temporary bridge recently made by the Engineers, following the Manchester battalion which had done all the hard fighting, the very same battalion that had fought alongside Frank in August 1914. In the forest they captured a young German soldier who had been hiding for three days, a deserter from a Bavarian regiment, in the last stages of malnutrition. He was fed and handed over to the orderlies. The man was half-blind, having lost his spectacles in the Forest. He was not an impressive specimen of German youth. He was stripped of anything of value for sale to the base-wallahs but treated with kindness.

Frank had met a young French woman in the Forest, the mother of a four-year-old son, who was collecting bits of shell-splintered wood for her kitchen stove, even though there was still sporadic shell-fire. Frank was laying out telephone cable with Tich, and the shelling had stopped for a while. The son was helping his mother as best he could. Frank could now converse after a fashion in French. He learnt that the woman's husband had been called to the colours as soon as the war broke out and that the son was born soon after the husband went away. She was hoping to hear news of him now that communication was being restored with the French Government. Three days later, on the 13th November, he met the woman again, near the church in Aulnoye. She was distraught, clutching the child to her bosom. Frank could guess the reason for her state; she had received an official letter from the French War Department notifying her of her husband's death. The letter was dated August 19th 1914.

The cffect of this small human tragedy concentrated his mind on Suzanne. It even crossed his mind that Suzanne could have borne a child by him. He had to know if she was still there in Le Cateau. She could have gone back with the retreating Germans like so many of the French had done, afraid of the Allied bombs and shells that were about to rain down on them, or perhaps afraid of reprisals for collaboration. She could have formed some sort of liaison with a German during the long years of occupation. She could have been killed in the final battle to liberate the town, perhaps by British troops indiscriminately throwing bombs down into the cellars of houses. And always there lurked in his mind's eye the things that Uhlans did with French girls who were at their mercy. Only yesterday he was a witness to an incident which brought home to him the severity of the German occupation. Two women were walking on the pavement, by the church, in his direction. When they came near him they stepped off the pavement to let him pass and bowed low to him. It came to him that this is what they must have been made to do by the conquering Hun. *Once a Hun, always a Hun*. It put Frank in mind of Hindoos in India and the way they would salaam the British. And everyone, the inhabitants emerging from their years of cruel occupation as well as the captured fritzes, bore the unmistakeable signs of hunger, the vacant expressions, the loose-fitting clothes. As Frank said to Tich,

'If the soldiers have been going hungry, just think what it must have been like for the poor fuckers living here.'

Frank and Tich were billeted in the house of an old widow, in the room once occupied by her son, killed in 1914 on the Sambre. They slept on a paillasse, the original mattress of horse-hair having been requisitioned by the Germans as long ago as 1916. Her copper cooking pots were encrusted with grime; the old lady told them that she had buried them in her garden in August 1914. Frank and Tich spent two hours bringing them up to a nice shine, a job they thoroughly enjoyed.

On the 15th, Frank went up before the Colonel concerning his application for Compassionate Leave. Frank had spruced himself up as well as he could and threw up an impressive salute. He was told to stand easy. The Colonel, a Peer of the Realm, knew Frank well, Frank having served at Battalion HQ as a Signaller for the past two years. The Colonel had Frank's service record in front of him; the Adjutant sat alongside him, together with the padre, a Welsh-speaking Methodist from Brechfa.

Frank had thought a good deal about his application. His last period of home leave had been over six months ago, when he had spent a week at Shrewsbury. His mother seemed to have aged, which saddened him, and there was nothing he could say about life at the front that would have made any sense to her. At the time, the Battalion had been about to go back to the front after a prolonged period in Reserve, following their disastrous losses at Mametz Wood on the Somme, the time when Haig had made his insulting remark about the Welsh Division failing to advance with determination, or some such bollocks. The men had never forgiven him, what with losses at 5,000 in the Division in the attack. How could Frank have described to his mother the blasted stumps of trees in the wood, how the Germans had used the cover to hide their machine-guns, how the shelling was without mercy and how Buffy, along with half his platoon, had got hit by machine gun fire in the advance up to the wood? The Manor had been shrouded in gloom, the furniture covered with dust sheets, the curtains drawn all day, after the death of the Squire's son at Gommecourt, fighting with one of the Service Battalions of the King's Royal Rifle Corps. It had been almost a relief from the seven days of stultifying boredom of it all to go back to his Battalion. Frank now had no desire to hurry back to Shrewsbury and no-one apart from his mother he could claim as a close relative. But the Squire had been most concerned at his safety, telling him to watch out for the whiz-bangs.

But at the same time he could hardly put in a request for Compassionate Leave to visit a woman, a teacher, with whom he had spent a total of three hours over four years ago. So Frank elaborated on a story that was half-true. He told the Peer and the Welsh padre about his step-father who was grieving for his own son, killed on the Somme, how his step-father had brought him up as his own son and how he had just heard that Spanish 'flu had broken out in the village and how Frank was so worried about his mother who was losing her sight that he must get back there to be with them should the worst happen, as it now looked that it might. The 'step-father' was of course the Squire, who had given him

Charles Kingsley's *Water Babies* to read as a child and had shown him the maps of the world, with the Empire coloured in pink, and had taught him to speak in a correct manner. He then added a bit about his step-father being an avid church-goer, remembering that the old boy had his own pew in the village church, and thinking that this might go down well with the padre. So it was all half-true, although Frank had no intention of going back there, at least not for the moment. The Colonel, the padre and the Adjutant listened in silence to his application, given out by Edwards in his 'posh' voice, and then the Adjutant asked him a question.

'Why doesn't your step-father appear on your family details in your Service Record? Your own father is listed as 'Deceased, 1903'. Is that correct?'

At this point Frank knew that he had won and that he would get his Leave; it was all a question of what was or wasn't on his sheet, just form-filling stuff. He had no trouble fielding that one, muttering about how he must have forgotten to mention his mother's remarriage, didn't know it mattered, etc.

'And what does you step-father do for a living, Edwards?'

'He works on the land, Sir, and I can help with the pigs, they could do with a hand', which was true if you considered all the time the old boy spent with his agent and the farm-workers at harvest-time and at Harvest Festival and of how he knew the names of everyone in his cottages. Frank could tell the Peer was impressed with his eagerness to work on the farm, the Peer having a farm of his own and believing in the manly virtue of work on the soil of Old England.

After that it was 'One week's leave granted, with consideration for your long service', the Adjutant signed the docket and told Edwards to get a Travel Warrant from the Guard Room. Edwards said 'Thank you Sir,' saluted and about-turned and he nearly shouted out loud with joy. La Guerre Finie and he was going to go down the road to see Suzanne with the proper papers in his pocket and there was nothing the Red Caps could do about it. Twenty-thousand to one that he was here just down the road from his teacher after all these years of war, all his mates gone west or with Blighty ones if they were lucky, and his only problem now was that he hadn't got a sou to his name after that sergeant had cleaned him out at Pontoon.

His leave started at dawn on the 16th November and Frank had no trouble getting a lift into Le Cateau in a lorry going to Boulogne with spare uniforms from the stores, not needed now that so many ex-miners had been given their discharge papers, the need for coal for the coming winter being paramount. He could have stayed on the lorry all the way to Boulogne, but hopped off in the square at Le Cateau, and couldn't resist saying to the driver 'Thanks, mate. I know my way around. I was here in August '14 when you were still in short trousers'. He was travelling light, no rifle, just a haversack and with two francs he had borrowed off Tich. Two francs would buy a meal for two, he reckoned, with a bit left over, and after that, well, he would just have to see how things worked out. His 1914 ribbon was on his tunic under his great-coat.

He had a look around. The church was still there, just, with all its glass blown out and the tower which had provided such a useful vantage point for the German observer and the machine-gunner in August '14 was still standing, although with a large chunk out of it. Amazingly the Town Hall, French's old HQ, was still standing as well, now serving as the HQ of 66th Division. Both had somehow survived the British bombardment at the end of October and the German counter-barrage, fired more out of spite than anything else, after they had retreated from the town. Edwards could remember all too well the scorched earth tactics the fritzes had employed on the Somme in the winter of 1916/17 in their retreat to the Hindenburg Line, but there was no evidence of similar destruction here. Perhaps they hadn't had time to lay the charges, it was unlike them to leave much behind when they abandoned a position. And there were the water troughs which had provided water to man and beast in that hot

August.

There were three batteries of 18-pounders, eighteen guns in all, neatly lined up at the bottom of the square, the horses quietly munching in their nose-bags, gunners fussing over their equipment now that they had time on their hands. Ever since he had watched with fascinated horror the gunners on Suffolk Hill feeding the shells into the breeches while the fritz shells came screaming down he had admired them as fighting men. His scorn was reserved for the rear-echelon fuckers who had turned up at Battalion HQ once in a blue moon and wanted a souvenir like a German helmet to take back home to show that they had been up there. But his real hatred was reserved for the workers in the arms factories back in Blighty who had gone on strike for more pay. A column of German prisoners came past, carrying duck-boards on their heads, and he realised that if it was a choice between putting them or the strikers at home in front of a firing squad he would volunteer to shoot the strikers every time.

He was now eager to get down the hill to Suzanne's house. It was still only mid-morning, a Wednesday morning. Where would she be, if she was here at all? Might as well start with the house. He didn't even know her last name. Why hadn't he thought to ask? But how many teachers with reddish hair called Suzanne could there be in this town? He was now in a state of nerves. He had fought the Germans for four years from the Mons Canal to the Somme and the Marne, he had been in the water-logged trenches of the Salient, he had stormed a pill-box and stuffed live bombs in the firing-slits, he had been to Mametz Wood where almost no-one came back alive and in one piece, but he was nervous of a girl in Le Cateau. Fucking daft.

He walked down the hill towards the station and the river Selle, the Selle valley which the Germans had used to such good effect in August 1914. He passed the Café de Paris where he had met Suzanne; it looked more or less empty now but no doubt it would fill up later with British troops or Americans if there were any around, they always had more money to spend and it still looked like a soldier's place rather than an officer's. Opposite the Café was a large building he had not noticed before, a hospital by the look of it, with Red Cross ambulances drawn up in the fore-court. Shell damage was more extensive here, with prisoners engaged in clearing-up work, shovelling debris into piles, obviously under orders to keep the reusable bricks and putting them to one side. A Service Corps Private soldier was keeping an eye on them. Edwards thought of all the shell-blasted villages and towns he had been through in the last four years; we could put every fritz to work for the next five years and we still couldn't get the job of putting it all back together done.

He was now at her street. Some houses with their insides cruelly exposed by high explosive. Should he be bringing her something? If she was anything like the other thin women he was seeing all over the place she could do with a nice tin of bully. What a fool I am not to bring something in the way of food. This must be the house. Keeps a nice clean step. Brass knocker, all scrubbed up. Curtains drawn. The window-pane cracked but intact. What the fuck am I going to say?

She came to the door. Red-brown hair in a bob. Traces of grey hair. Apron-dress. A look, not startled but questioning, not alarmed but alert for what was happening. Not smiling but not particularly worried. Thin, gaunt even, but that was to be expected. Wooden shoes. And very much alive after more than four years, one thousand five hundred and twenty-three days to be exact. Couldn't hope for more than that; even that is a miracle.

'I have come back, Suzanne, but I have brought nothing.'

'Well that is not very good, Frank. But you are alive.'

'I am alive and so are you.'

'Voilà quelque chose.'

'I have a leave-pass.'

'Then you have something. So do I, because of the Armistice.'

They both stood there for a while, Frank on the pavement outside her house and Suzanne in the doorway, their eyes on the same level. Frank realised that he had not looked into the eyes of a woman, a fine woman, a good woman, for as long as he could remember. Blue-grey eyes. You don't look into the eyes of the girls in the knocking shops of Peronne; you do the business and hand over money. And the girls in the estaminets, the daughters of the old folk who were the owners, they would flirt and slap his hand and say 'Ooh la-la', but they wouldn't look into his eyes.

'Will you promenade with me, Suzanne?' He liked saying her name.

'You know French now, Frank.'

'We could go across the river and go where I was before.'

'I will fetch my manteau.'

They set off down to the bridge on to the Cambrai road. Debris everywhere, prisoners in forage caps listlessly shovelling broken bits of wood, glass, tiles and stone into carts, thin horses standing in the traces. They had a fire going, made from bits of broken window-frame and the ASC Private watching over the prisoners was enjoying its warmth. His rifle was slung and he was holding his hands toward the fire. Frank and Suzanne walked on down the cutting.

'They shot my friend Christian. Against the wall of the Mairie, because he had some pigeons. The boche accused him of using the pigeons for sending messages to the British.'

Frank didn't know what to say. Perhaps Christian had been her lover.

'I was a nurse in their hospital, when the school was closed. You were fighting them and I was nursing them. So many died. And so many called out for their mothers.'

'British soldiers do the same.'

'One day I will tell you things. But not now. Now we will promenade.'

He took her arm, emboldened. She didn't mind.

'My parents are dead. Of the TB'. She said it 'tay-bay' so that at first

Frank didn't understand.

They were in the lane leading up to the hill, with banks on both sides. It was here that the forward company of the Suffolks had been overwhelmed, early in the day on the 26th August 1914. All those farming lads taken prisoner on that day, well they were the lucky ones, giving up over four years of their lives for the near-certainty of death or wounds. Not a bad exchange. Suzanne had been a prisoner of a sort too. I had my liberty but what sort of liberty was that? A cold wind blew off the hill. A limber with a broken axle lay stuck in the lane.

'Shall we go and eat? I have two francs.'

'Frank, you are rich. You are alive, you have a pass, and you have money. But we will not use your money. For two years I have been hiding in a cache two things; some food from the American Red Cross and some liquor I have made from cherries and nettles. We will return to my house and eat and celebrate.'

Her house was much as he remembered it, the gas lights, the Virgin over the mantel, the settee. He hadn't seen the kitchen before, where Suzanne now busied herself getting some sort of ham out of a can that had been made somewhere in the American mid-west. She gave him the bottle to open, which was full of a dark red liquid, looking like the cough mixture Frank's mother might have given him. But when he stuck his nose in the top of the bottle it smelt of the country and the orchards of home.

'Christian helped me make it. The boche took everything from us but they didn't look under the floor in the vestibule, they just looked in the cellar.'

Again this Christian wallah, well, the poor fucker's dead. He should have eaten his pigeons instead of giving the fritzes a chance to shoot him.

They sat on the settee and ate the ham, which was like bully only made from American pigs. Frank supposed that it was also given to the Yankee troops. He had been fighting alongside them in early October back on the Hindenburg line and they had wanted to get to Berlin in a hurry. Big lads. One of them, a boy of no more than eighteen, had called him 'Sir', not realising that he was a Private. This was in an estaminet and the lad had bought him beer, which was about the only time in the war that Frank had left an estaminet with as much money as when he came in.

They drank some of the red liquor. It was sweet and strong and warmed them. They drank a toast to the victory. She said that she could boil water and make a drink from roasted acorns but he would not like it. He said that he would get some tea from the soldiers in the town. They knew that in time they would talk about the things that had happened but that time was not now. She said that she did not want to eat nettles again, except maybe if they were served au buerre, but butter was a thing scarcely to be dreamt of for four years. And the bread was made of oats and straw.

'I used to dream about *Jambon.*'

'I thought of you when I was in the trenches.'

'And I thought of you sometimes, Frank. Once an English airman was shot down over the Forest and he was brought through the square in a motor and I wanted to go up to him and ask him if he knew a soldier called Frank Edwards, I knew it was a question completely stupide and of course I could not, but later he was brought to the 'opital because he was wounded in the arm but he had a guard and I could not approach. And at other times wounded English soldiers were brought in but they never knew your name. I knew your regiment was Welsh but that is all that I knew. We knew when there was hard fighting because then there would be a whole train of wounded coming to the station, mostly German but sometimes English, but of course it was forbidden to show fraternitė. We knew nothing of the war, until we heard the guns coming closer and the planes coming over to drop bombs on the station and then the shells fell on us and I went back to the cave, how do you say, cellar, for a week.'

Frank wanted to hold this girl, this girl who had never been far from his thoughts for more than four years. She was sitting just a foot away from him on the settee, with her stockinged feet tucked up under her smock-dress, her wooden shoes on the floor, next to his great-coat. Frank reached out and touched the nearest part of her, which was a bit of her right foot, protruding from underneath her dress. She let his hand rest there. She put her own right hand over his. She let it rest there for several minutes. He removed his hand and touched her cheek. She was crying.

'Four years ago when I had to go off and fight I wanted to take you with me.'

'Now we 'ave more time. You will come to my bed. You must take off those 'orrible boots and this time you will take off your socks.'

He followed her up the stairs and into her bedroom. It must be the larger of the two bedrooms, and Frank guessed it must have been her parents' room. A double bed with a hand-made quilt, a bedside table covered with a lace cloth, on which was a stub of candle in a wooden candle-holder and a framed photograph of an elderly couple standing outside a cathedral. A wash-stand with a pitcher and bowl, a chair with a quilted cover, done in the same style as the bed-cover, were the only other pieces of furniture. He looked at the cover of the book on the mantel, *Madame Bovary*, whoever she might be. No photos of any dead pigeon-man. She was as quick to take off her smock and under-clothes as she had been before all the years ago. And as unashamed. While he was sitting on the chair unwinding his puttees, his boots already on the floor, she stood briefly naked before him before turning back the quilt and getting in to the bed, facing away from the door and toward the wash-stand. The dark-red hair in a perfect triangle between her legs, the belly-button pronounced, the breasts small with the pale nipples erect, but again he noticed the grey-blue eyes with the eye-lashes darker than the rest of her hair and the taut throat-muscles.

She did not watch him take off his clothes but remained on her side so that when he got in beside her he lay alongside her and pushed his cock between her buttocks. She arched her back. He let his cock remain between her legs not wanting to move too fast. Her back was cold against his chest but her breasts were warm to his fingers and the nipples still erect. He could feel her heartbeat.

'Ça va mieux, mon Frank. Reste là quelque moments. Ça fait du bien. On a le temps.'

After a while she turned over and she held his cock and put it between her legs but held it there, not letting him push any further. He kissed her eyes and tasted the salt and then with his hands drew back her head so that he could kiss her throat and then tasted the cherry-orchard on her tongue.

She then got on her knees and straddled him and took hold of his cock again and put it in her and he lay back and she smiled at him, a full smile and dimples appeared which he had never seen before and he marvelled at this. She moved but kept him inside her and he knew he was going to come and she knew this and he thrust upwards and he kept looking at her and her dimples and she continued to smile. And then he said,

'J'y suis. J'y reste. La Guerre Finie.'

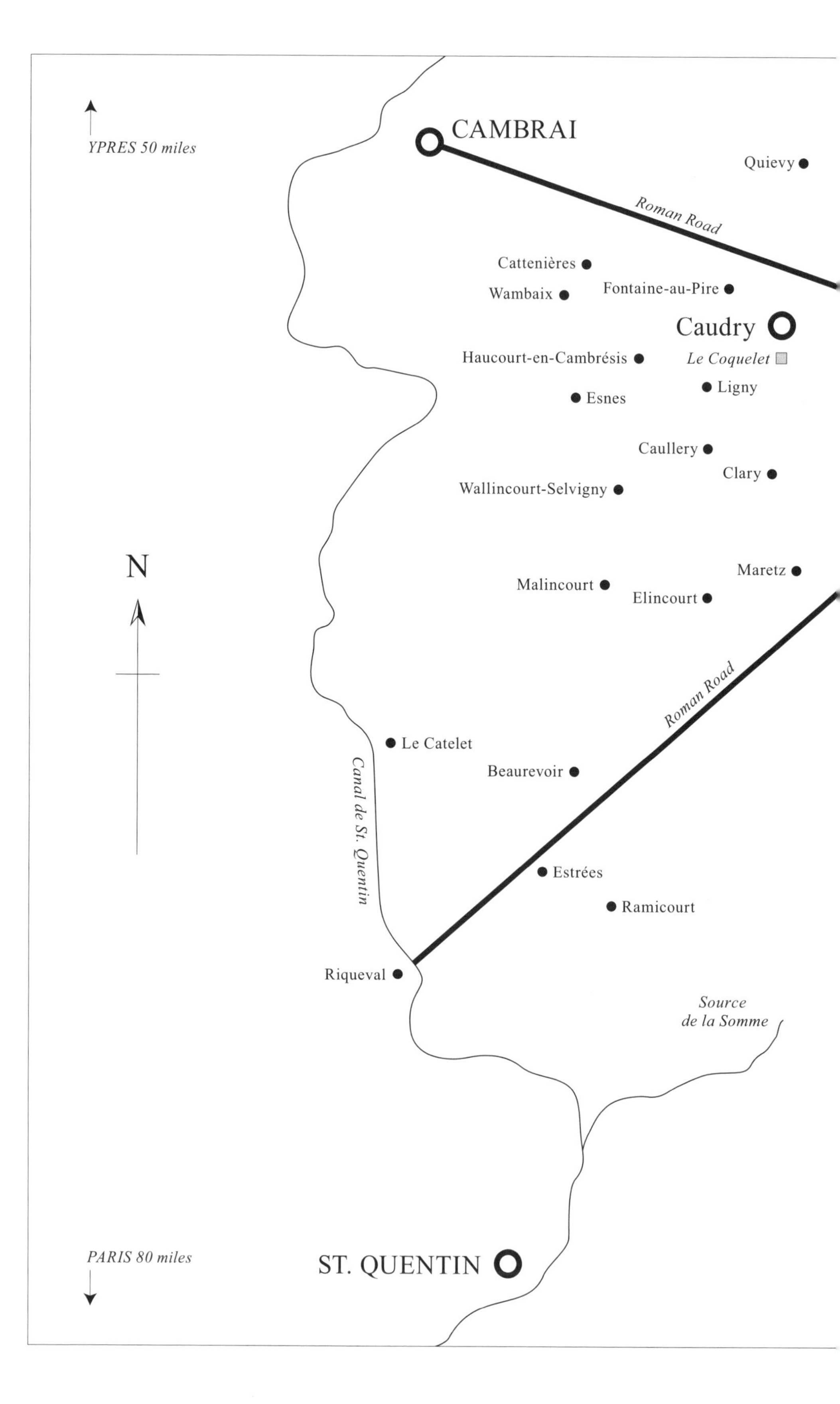

YPRES 50 miles
CAMBRAI
Quievy
Roman Road
Cattenières
Wambaix
Fontaine-au-Pire
Caudry
Haucourt-en-Cambrésis
Le Coquelet
Ligny
Esnes
Caullery
Clary
Wallincourt-Selvigny
N
Maretz
Malincourt
Elincourt
Roman Road
Le Catelet
Canal de St. Quentin
Beaurevoir
Estrées
Ramicourt
Riqueval
Source
de la Somme
PARIS 80 miles
ST. QUENTIN

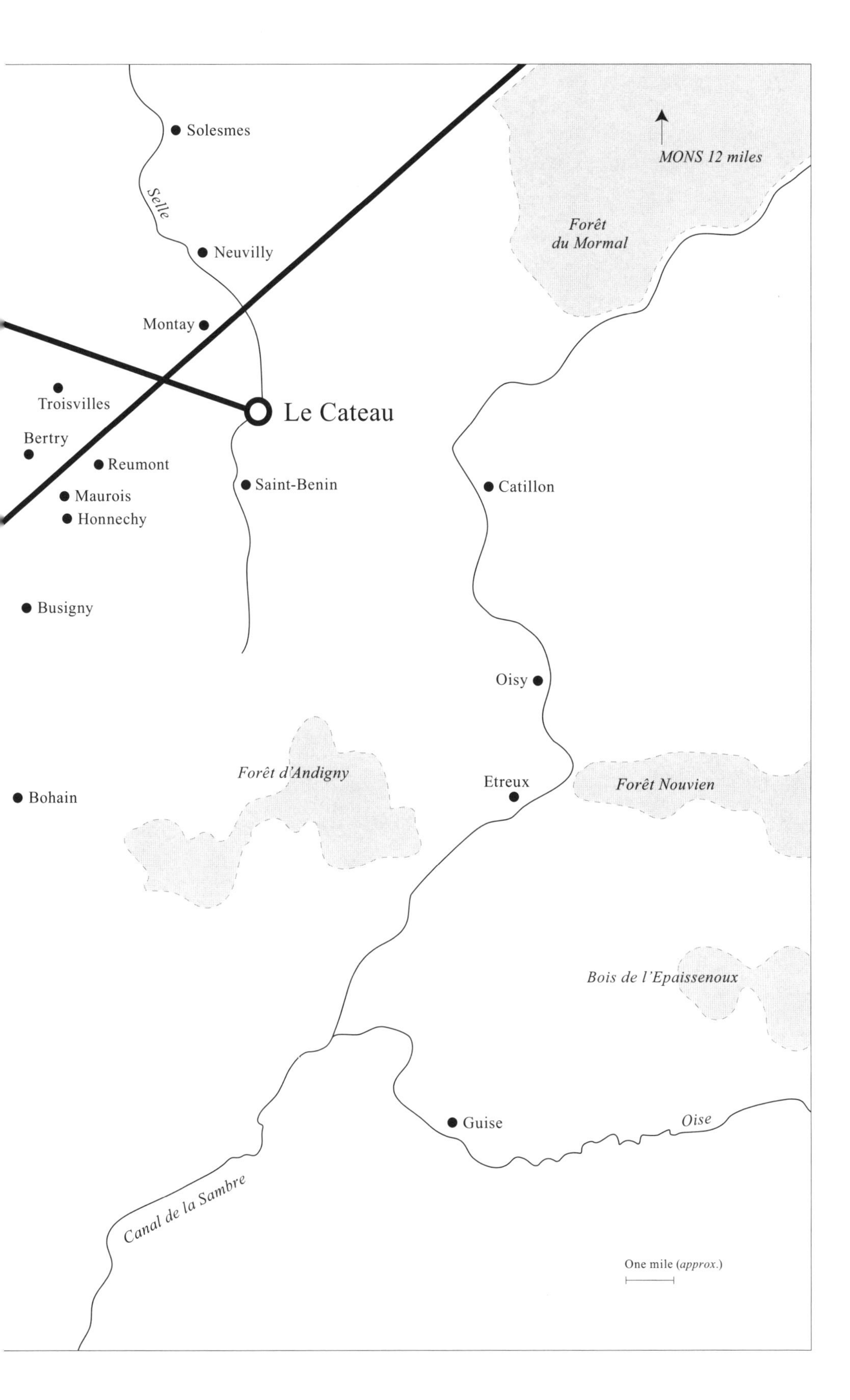
Solesmes
MONS 12 miles
Selle
Forêt
du Mormal
Neuvilly
Montay
Troisvilles
Le Cateau
Bertry
Reumont
Saint-Benin
Catillon
Maurois
Honnechy
Busigny
Oisy
Forêt d'Andigny
Etreux
Forêt Nouvien
Bohain
Bois de l'Epaissenoux
Guise
Oise
Canal de la Sambre
One mile (approx.)